RIGHT TO INFORMATION LAW

TRANSPARENCY & ACCOUNTABILITY

RIGHT TO INFORMATION LAW

TRANSPARENCY & ACCOUNTABILITY

Shikher Deep Aggarwal
Associate Partner
L&L Partners Law Offices

Kush Kalra
BA LL.B, LL.M

SATYAM LAW
INTERNATIONAL

ISBN: 978-93-91345-76-1

Published by : Satyam Law International, 2/13, Ansari Road, Daryaganj,
New Delhi-110002, India

Phones : 0091-11-40391920, 23242686, 23245698

Email : satyambooks@hotmail.com
satyamlawi@gmail.com

Web : www.satyam-books.com

Printed in India

PREFACE

Introduction

'Right to Information' is the right to acquire information from any public authority by way of:

(i) "inspection, taking of extracts and notes ;

(ii) certified copies of any records of such public authority ;

(iii) diskettes, floppies or in any other electronic mode."

Information in this backdrop indicates any material in any form concerning the administration or verdict of a public authority.

As per RTI Act, 2005 it is the duty for making information held by executive agencies of the State available to the public except it comes within any one of the explicit categories of matters exempt from public disclosure. Further as per RTI Act, 2005 nearly all branches of the executive department of the Government are mandated by the RTI Act to issue regulations to put into operation the provisions of the Act.

These regulations notify the public from where certain types of information may be conveniently obtained, however, other information may be obtained on request. Also the internal system of approaching appellate authority is available if a member of the public is refused the requested information by Public Information officer (PIO).

To avert misuse of discretionary power of the Governmental agencies Right to Information Act, 2005 is enacted requiring them to make public certain information about their functioning.

Right to Information or right to know is an essential part and basic rule of the freedom of speech and expression which is a fundamental right[1] provided under Article 19(1)(a)[2] of the Constitution. It also flows from Article 21 of Indian

---

[1] Fundamental Rights are the basic rights contained in Part III under Article 12 to 35 of Constitution of India. It guarantees civil liberties such that all citizens can lead their lives in peace and harmony as citizens of India.

[2] Article 19 in The Constitution Of India 1949

19. Protection of certain rights regarding freedom of speech etc

(1) All citizens shall have the right

(a) to freedom of speech and expression

Constitution[3] as pronounced by the Supreme Court in the case of "*Reliance Petrochemicals Ltd. v. Proprietors of Indian Express Newspapers Bombay Pvt Ltd. and Ors.*"[4]. The Apex Court dealing with the subject of freedom of press and administration of justice, held that "we must keep in mind that the public has a right to know in order to to take part in democracy. Right to know is an essential right which people of a state look for in the broader view of the right to live in this era under Article 21 of Constitution. That right has attained new proportions and importance. That right puts larger answerability upon those who take upon themselves the liability to inform".

However, the citizens have a guaranteed 'Right to Know', the performance of the State and its instrumentalities under the cover of darkness leave the citizens uninformed about the basis of any decision taken by the authorities or any policy made and the implications thereof

The function and purpose of the RTI Act, 2005 is not only to supply information but to keep a check on corruption, and for that matter bestow a right upon the citizens to have the necessary information, so that suitable action may be initiated against the erring officers and also against the arbitrary and unlawful orders.

The preamble of the Right to Information Act, 2005 emphasize that democratic state requires a knowledgeable citizenry and lucidity of information which are necessary to its performance and also to minimize corruption and to put the administration answerable to the governed. In order to support transparency and answerability in the operation of every government department, the setting up of a Central Information Commission (CIC) and State Information Commissions (SIC) and for matters connected thereto the RTI Act, 2005 has been passed.

The Delhi High Court in the case of *Secretary General, Supreme Court of India v. Subhash Chandra Agarwal*[5] observed that "the right to information is an essential element of the freedom of speech and is subject to limitations that can be enforced upon that right under Constitution of India by article 19(2)."

A person, who desires to obtain any information under the RTI Act, 2005 as

---

[3] Article 21 in The Constitution Of India 1949

"21. Protection of life and personal liberty No person shall be deprived of his life or personal liberty except according to procedure established by law"

[4] AIR1989SC190

[5] AIR 2010 Del 159.

per Section 6(1)[6] of the RTI Act, 2005 shall make a demand in writing or through mail (soft copy) denoting the details of the information sought by him/her. Section 6 Sub-Section (2) of RTI Act, 2005 provides that a citizen filing for request for information shall not be compelled to give any ground for asking the information and no personal information apart from those that may be required for contacting him can be asked from him.

It is thus obvious that while allowing RTI application made under RTI Act, 2005 the intention of the applicant cannot be inquired by the Public Information officer (PIO) and PIO is supposed to supply every information sought by applicant except what has been exempted under Section 8[7] of RTI Act, 2005.

---

[6] Section 6 in The Right To Information Act, 2005

6. Request for obtaining information.—

(1) A person, who desires to obtain any information under this Act, shall make a request in writing or through electronic means in English or Hindi in the official language of the area in which the application is being made, accompanying such fee as may be prescribed, to—

(a) the Central Public Information Officer or State Public Information Officer, as the case may be, of the concerned public authority;

(b) the Central Assistant Public Information Officer or State Assistant Public Information Officer, as the case may be, specifying the particulars of the information sought by him or her: Provided that where such request cannot be made in writing, the Central Public Information Officer or State Public Information Officer, as the case may be, shall render all reasonable assistance to the person making the request orally to reduce the same in writing.

(2) An applicant making request for information shall not be required to give any reason for requesting the information or any other personal details except those that may be necessary for contacting him.

(3) Where an application is made to a public authority requesting for an information,—

(i) which is held by another public authority; or

(ii) the subject matter of which is more closely connected with the functions of another public authority, the public authority, to which such application is made, shall transfer the application or such part of it as may be appropriate to that other public authority and inform the applicant immediately about such transfer: Provided that the transfer of an application pursuant to this sub-section shall be made as soon as practicable but in no case later than five days from the date of receipt of the application.

[7] Section 8 in The Right To Information Act, 2005

8 Exemption from disclosure of information.—

(1) Notwithstanding anything contained in this Act, there shall be no obligation to give any citizen,—

(a) information, disclosure of which would prejudicially affect the sovereignty and integrity of India, the security, strategic, scientific or economic interests of the State, relation with foreign State or lead to incitement of an offence;

(b) information which has been expressly forbidden to be published by any court of law or tribunal or the disclosure of which may constitute contempt of court;

(c) information, the disclosure of which would cause a breach of privilege of Parliament or the State Legislature;

Some of the information's requested by the applicant under RTI Act, 2005 will be problematic to the persons to whom it relates and therefore, every attempt would be made for the non-disclosure of such Information by public official by taking protection under the provisions of Sections 8 and 9[8] of the RTI Act, 2005 which are the exemption clauses.

Section 8 of the Right to Information Act, 2005 provides certain kinds of exemptions, where the Government has no responsibility to provide information to any citizen. Generally all information should be given to the citizens but there are certain information's which have been protected from revelation. It means this is an effort to harmonize the public interest with the individual's right to information.

Right to Information in Cases of Life and Liberty

The free course of information is necessary for a democratic society *in personam* because it assist in the growth of society. Information guarantees transparency and answerability in governance and thus becomes a lively constituent of effective democracy. Further, the fundamental right to speech and expression under Article 19(1) of the Constitution of India can never be implemented until and unless the information regarding public matters is being dispersed. This makes Right to Information Act, 2005 (**'the Act'**) a very significant legislation.

The RTI Act, 2005 clearly permit the common man to access the information from any public office and the Central Public Information Officer (CPIO) of all government offices are duty bound to provide the information sought. According to Section 7(1) of the RTI Act, 2005 information sought by means of RTI application

---

(d) information including commercial confidence, trade secrets or intellectual property, the disclosure of which would harm the competitive position of a third party, unless the competent authority is satisfied that larger public interest warrants the disclosure of such information;

(e) information available to a person in his fiduciary relationship, unless the competent authority is satisfied that the larger public interest warrants the disclosure of such information;

(f) information received in confidence from foreign government;

(g) information, the disclosure of which would endanger the life or physical safety of any person or identify the source of information or assistance given in confidence for law enforcement or security purposes

[8] Section 9 in The Right To Information Act, 2005

9. Grounds for rejection to access in certain cases.—Without prejudice to the provisions of section 8, a Central Public Information Officer or State Public Information Officer, as the case may be may reject a request for information where such a request for providing access would involve an infringement of copyright subsisting in a person other than the State.

should be given within 30 days from the demand. The exception to the 30 day rule is when the information required by applicant is related to the 'life and liberty of a person', in that particular case the information should be provided within 48 hours.

Ordinarily the government machinery is not planned in a way that responds to all RTI applications within 48 hours, the question of 'life and liberty of a person' has to be carefully examined.

It is rational to suppose that when the life or liberty of a person is at stake, the information which might save/help the person should be revealed as fast as it can be. But what are life and liberty? Life and liberty are two of the most significant features of our survival. Right to life means the right to lead significant, absolute and distinguished life. It is something more than existing or animal survival. Liberty is the protection from random exercise of authority. It has also been defined as freedom of choice, enjoyment of rights which belong to us as individuals.

However, the term 'life or liberty of a person' has not been clearly defined in the RTI Act, 2005. Therefore, one can take reference Article 21[9] of the Constitution which assurane that '*no person shall be deprived of his life or personal liberty except according to procedure established by law*'. In a catena of cases for many years, the Supreme Court has interpreted and widened the extent of the right to life and liberty to include -

Right to live with human dignity, free from exploitation	*Bandhua Mukti Morcha v. Union of India*, [1984] 3 SCC 161
Right to livelihood	*Olga Tellis v. Bombay Municipal Corporation*, 1985 SCC (3) 545
Right to speedy trial	*Hussainaira Khatoon v. State of Bihar*, [1979] 3 SCR 169
The right against solitary confinement	*Sunil Batra v. Delhi Administration*, [1978] 4 SCC 494
The right against bar fetters	*Charles Sobraj v. Superintendent, Tihar Jail*, 1979 SCR (1) 512
The right to legal aid	*Madhav Hayawadanrao Hoskot v. State of Maharashtra*, 1979 SCR (1) 192
The right against delayed execution	*T.V. Vatheeswaran v. State of Tamil Nadu*, AIR 1983 SC 361

[9] Article 21 in The Constitution Of India
21. Protection of life and personal liberty No person shall be deprived of his life or personal liberty except according to procedure established by law

Unless and until an imminent risk or danger to life and liberty is made out, Section 7(1) of RTI Act, 2005 cannot be cited and only when revelation of information would have a result of saving the applicant from that danger, such information should be given in 48 hours.

In the case of *N.N. Kalia v. University of Delhi*,[10] the Central Information Commission (CIC) observed that section 7(1) of RTI Act, 2005 proviso has to be applied only in outstanding circumstances. Whether the information required by applicant is related to the life or liberty of a person has to be cautiously scrutinized and only in limited number of cases this ground can be relied upon. The government departments working does not happen in a way in India that responses to every RTI Applications can be given within forty-eight hours. The life or liberty provision can be used by applicant only in circumstances where there is an imminent danger to the life and liberty of a person.

In the case of *Mr. J.K. Mittal v. Gnctd*,[11] the CIC held that "the purpose of provision of RTI Act particularly Section 7(1) proviso that life and liberty related information shall be given in 48 hours is to inculcate responsive attitude in the Police Authority. It is pitiable to note that Home Department did not exhibit any concern and remained unresponsive. They simply passed on the back to the Police Authority."

The proviso to Section 7(1) of the RTI Act has to be used only in exceptional circumstances. Whether the information required is related to the life or liberty of a person has to be carefully examined and only in a very limited number of cases this argument can be relied upon.

Also it is necessary that while providing information by Public Information Officer the priority should be given to cases of life and liberty issues because Article 21 of the Constitution itself contains provision regarding right to life and personal liberty.

If the information is not within the meaning of Life and Liberty there is no necessity to be provided in 48 hours as held by CIC in the case of *Ashok Randhawa v. Lok Nayak Hospital, Govt. of NCT of Delhi*,[12] information was sought regarding the child Shanno, who breathed her last due to alleged punishment/thrashing given by the teacher of her school. The Appellant had sought the medical

---

[10] CIC/SG/C/2009/001169/4696

[11] CIC/SA/C/2015/000030

[12] CIC/SG/C/2009/000453

history of the child, cause of death, the status of the child when taken to casualty, treatment given to her, and findings of C.T. scan within 48 hours, terming it as an issue of 'life and liberty'. The Central Information Commission accepted the contention of the PIO that the 'life and liberty' (the child) in this case is dead, hence there was no imminent danger to life and liberty.

Right to Information in Cases of Police FIR's

Life and personal liberty are the most esteemed belongings of an individual. The internal urge for freedom is an ordinary fact for each human being. Respect for life, liberty and property is not simply a standard or a policy of the State but a necessary obligation of any enlightened society.

About a century ago, the Patna High Court in *Dhanpat v. Emperor* [13] laid down as follows:

"It is vitally necessary that an accused person should be granted a copy of the FIR at the earliest possible in order that he may get benefit of the legal advice."

The Scheme of Criminal Procedure Code does not provide for providing copy of the FIR to the accused at any previous stage than by a Magistrate on beginning of the proceeding under Section 207 of the Cr.P.C. Section 173 of the Cr.P.C. however provides that "Officer in charge of the police station shall forward to the Magistrate a report stating the details as mentioned in Section 173(2)".

Section 173(6) also authorizes the police officer to point out by attaching a note requesting the Magistrate not to provide a part of the statement to the accused by giving reasons. When the FIR is registered against a person, the police has to begin investigation under Section 157[14] of the Cr.P.C. If from an information

---

[13] AIR 1917 Pat 625

[14] Section 157 in The Code Of Criminal Procedure, 1973

157. Procedure for investigation preliminary inquiry.

(1) If, from information received or otherwise, an officer in charge of a police station has reason to suspect the commission of an offence which he is empowered under section 156 to investigate, he shall forthwith send a report of the same to a Magistrate empowered to take cognizance of such offence upon a police report and shall proceed in person, or shall depute one of his subordinate officers not being below such rank as the State Government may, by general or special order, prescribe in this behalf, to proceed, to the spot, to investigate the facts and circumstances of the case, and, if necessary, to take measures for the discovery and arrest of the offender; Provided that-

(a) when information as to the commission of any such offence is given against any person by name and the case is not of a serious nature, the officer in charge of a police station

received or otherwise an officer in charge of a police station has basis to believe the commission of an offence which he is empowered under Section 156[15] to examine, he shall forthwith send a report to a Magistrate empowered to take cognizance upon such offence on a police report. The Code (Cr.PC) also empowers the police officer to arrest the accused. Section 438 of the Cr.P.C. provides that where a person who has basis to believe that he may be arrested on charge of having committed a non-bailable offence he may apply to the High Court or the Court of Session for a direction.

For meaningful exercise of the right given to the accused under Section 438 of the Cr.P.C., attaining copy of the FIR is pertinent and essential. A person who is accused of a congnizable offence by registration of the FIR at the police station cannot be deprived of the right to know the contents of the FIR to allow him to defend himself and take such steps as provided under law.

The Division Bench[16] of the Allahabad High Court in *Shyam Lal v. State of U.P. and Others*[17] elaborately considered the question as to whether an accused is entitled for copy of the FIR and he can obtain it either from the police station or the office of the Superintendent of Police or from the Magistrate. In paragraphs 10.4 and 10.5 the following was stated:

"10.4 Court hold that the accused is entitled to know what was said in the

---

need not proceed in person or depute a subordinate officer to make an investigation on the spot;

(b) if it appears to the officer in charge of a police station that there is no sufficient ground for entering on an investigation, he shall not investigate the case.

(2) In each of the cases mentioned in clauses (a) and (b) of the proviso to sub- section (1), the officer in charge of the police station shall state in his report his reasons for not fully complying with the requirements of that sub- section, and, in the case mentioned in clause (b) of the said proviso, the officer shall also forthwith notify to the informant, if any, in such manner as may be prescribed by the State Government, the fact that he will not investigate the case or cause it to be investigated.

15 CrPC 158: Section 158 of the Criminal Procedure Code

Report how submitted

1. Every report sent to a Magistrate under section 157 shall, if the State Government so directs, be submitted through such superior officer of police as the Stale Government, by general or special order, appoints in that behalf.
2. Such superior officer may give such instructions to the officer in charge of the police station as he thinks fit, and shall, after recording such instructions on such report, transmit the same without delay to the Magistrate.

16 A Division Bench is a term in judicial system in India in which a case is heard and judged by *at least* two judges. However, if the bench during the hearing of any matter feels that the matter needs to be considered by a larger bench, such a matter is referred to a larger bench.

17 1998 Crl. L.J. 2879

first information report to connect with the offence so that he may be in a position to protect his interest. He is therefore, entitled to a copy thereof. He can have it from (i) the police station, or (ii) the office of Superintendent of Police, or (iii) C.J.M./Magistrate, Incharge/Special Judge as the case may be and as per his desire. Ours is a welfare democratic State. It is a Government by the people, of the people and for the people, as said by Abraham Lincoln. It is common knowledge that the office of the Superintendent of Police or for the matter of that the Courts are situated invariably at a distance far from the Police Stations. Imagine the plight of such a person who is required to cover a great distance for having a certified copy of the F.I.R. to know its contents so that he could defend himself.

10.5. Accordingly, there is no manner of doubt that an accused person or any person who suspects that his name figures in a first information report can file an application or get an application filed through his pairwikar (representative/ agent) for supplying certified copy of the first information report either before the S.O./S.H.O. of police Station or the office of Superintendent of Police or the C.J.M. or the Special Judge before whom the first information report is kept or forwarded by the Police Station concerned."

When Section 438Cr.P.C. is held to be a means to secure persons liberty, all means to secure the said liberty has to be held to be available to the accused to fulfill the object which clearly reinforces the right of the accused to get copy of the FIR. Therefore, court hold that the accused is allowed for copy of the FIR. The accused can make an application to the police station concerned or office of the Superintendent of Police or the Court of concerned Magistrate which is obligatory to be provided to him straight away within forty eight (48) hours.

The RTI Act, 2005 Act has statutorily recognised the right of information of all citizens. Request for copy of the FIR can also be presented by any person under the RTI Act, 2005. If police authorities are asserting exemption under Section 8(1) of the 2005 RTI Act it is a issue which has to be resolved by the police authorities by taking appropriate decision by the competent authority. In event no such result is taken to claim exemption under Section 8 of the 2005 Act, the police authorities are obliged to supply copy of the FIR on an application under the RTI Act, 2005.

Emerging Trends in Right to Information

The execution of the Right to Information Act, 2005 has taken place in the whole country, however, the pace and growth of execution of the RTI Act varies from region to region in India. The RTI Act has brought in a 'drastic' change in the way the government and bureaucracy function. Now it is no more a period of closed, mysterious unreachable, administration. The common public has also started using their right in progressive numbers. Citizens have progressively become aware of the huge potential of right to know/information in their general empowerment. The government functionaries have started performing in a more accountable as well as open manner. The Act has come as a great rescue and virtue for all the upright and honest officers who want to do their job as per the norms without any interference from any quarter whatsoever. The pro-active disclosure by various public authorities, though not in the preferred quantity, has also reduced the information gap of the citizens.[18]

The RTI Act, 2005 has loopholes and lacunas. Many information seekers are either not informed properly of their rights or are often not provided the required information due to the insensitive approach of the public authorities attached. Poor quality of information and lack of a uniform official structure for providing information across departments in different states adds to the anguish of the applicants for information.

The Patna High Court has observed that the Right to Information Act, 2005 has been put into effect with the chief purpose of open governance, transparency and a participatory government which only shall fulfill the needs of the people as provided under the Constitution of India.[19]

The Allahabad High Court has observed that from the scrutiny of the objects and reasons for passing Right to Information Act, 2005 it is obvious that the Government desired to establish a realistic rule of right to information for citizens to have access to information under the control of public authorities.[20]

The Right to Information Act, 2005, is a special Act. It prevails over the other provisions of laws in India. As per the provisions of section 23, the purpose of the RTI Act is to:

"i. provide information to the applicants from the area of public authority without the cost of litigation

---

18 "Abhishek Jain, "RTI Implementation at the District level: Issues and Challenges.", The Indian Journal of Public Administration, Vol. 55, No. 3, July-September 2009, pp. 346-363, at p. 347."

19 Bihar Public Service Commission v. State of Bihar (2009) 75 AIC 507 (Pat.).

20 Dhara Singh Girls High School v. State of UP, AIR 2008 All. 92.

ii. Avoid postponement and relief available under the Act is available in a better manner without resorting to the complex process of civil courts."

According to section 23 of the Right to Information Act, 2005, no court shall allow any proceeding in respect of any order made under RTI Act and. In other terms, it means all civil courts are disqualified from entertaining any suit, or proceedings in respect of any order made under RTI Act.

The general feeling is that the RTI Act is used only to obtain information from public authorities. What is hardly recognized is that, in some circumstances, it can also be used to get information from private bodies.[21]

In *Celso Pinto v. Goa State Information Commission*[22] the Hon'ble High Court of Bombay (Panji Goa Bench) held that "the definition of information cannot include answers to the question 'why' as that would be asking for a explanation and justification. The public information authorities cannot be expected to correspond to the citizen the reason why a certain thing was done."

In *Shama Parveen, Bijnor v. National Human Rights Commission*[23] the Commission (CIC) permitted the information free of cost to the applicant belonging to Below Poverty Line (BPL) Category, however, it was directed that the PIO shall ensure that the applicant was indisputably BPL and no one should be allowed to misuse the precise advantage allowed to a particular category."

Conclusion

The right to information is a valued right. Right to information is intended to be formidable tools in the hands of accountable citizens to fight dishonesty and corruption and to bring in answerability. The provisions of RTI Act should be enforced firmly.

The objective of provision of RTI Act particularly Section 7(1) proviso is that life and liberty connected information shall be provided in 48 hours. This is done to instill responsive attitude in the Police Authority and to protect the fundamental rights of citizens of India as enshrined in Constitution.

---

21 https://timesofindia.indiatimes.com/india/ngos-private-bodies-getting-government-funds-fall-within-rti-act-supreme-court/articleshow/71176295.cms, retrieved on 31st May, 2020

22 (2008) 24 CLA-BL Supp (snr) 7:2008 (2) ID 386 (Bom. HC).

23 CIC/OK/A/2006/00717 dated 18th April, 2007

It is rational to anticipate that when the life or liberty of a person is at risk, the information which might save/help the person should be revealed as quick as it can be. As Life and liberty are two of the most key aspect of our survival. Right to life means the right to lead meaningful, complete and dignified life. It is something more than surviving or animal subsistence. Liberty is the resistance from random implementation of authority. It has also been defined as freedom of choice, pleasure of rights which belong to us as individuals and as per Law of Land.

Further, request for information for copy of the FIR can also be put forward by any person under the RTI Act, 2005. If police authorities are asserting exemption under Section 8(1) of the 2005 RTI Act it is a question which has to be determined by the police authorities by taking suitable decision by the competent authority in police department as per RTI Act, 2005. In event no such decision is taken to declare immunity under Section 8 of the 2005 Act, the police authorities are obliged to supply copy of the FIR on a request of Information under the RTI Act, 2005. Many citizens who have been falsely implicated by police authorities in cases have obtained copy of FIR and proved themselves innocent in court of law.

Therefore, it can be seen that Right to information has proved to be a bane for common man struggling to receive information in cases of violation of human rights and cases of corruption and also it has helped common man to obtain FIR copies through RTI. Thus, wherever an applicant files an RTI application for revelation of information related to Life and Liberty the public authority takes protection under the provisions relating to exemption clauses under RTI Act, 2005, the Commission (CIC) or the constitutional courts must see that no citizens fundamental right to life with dignity is infringed and suitable information must be provided to information seeker so that his/her Life and Liberty can be protected as provided under constitution of India. In a way the simple procedure of filing RTI without any complex procedure has made RTI very effective in instances of information related to Police FIR's and Life and Liberty matters.

CONTENTS

Chapter - 1

DEATH OF FORMER PRIME MINISTER LATE SHRI LAL BAHADUR SHASTRI AND RIGHT TO INFORMATION[1]

Facts in Nutshell

The complainant sought information relating to death of former Prime Minister Late Shri Lal Bahadur Shastri through two points:

"1. If dead body of Late Prime Minister was brought to India or was he cremated there in Russia?

2. In case his body was brought to India, please supply me certified copy of postmortem conducted on his body".

The Home Ministry has forwarded this RTI request to the National Archives of India (NAI) on 05.08.2017. The NAI could not give any information as they had no answers to these questions in their records. Since no information was received in 30 days, applicant filed complaint against deemed refusal, before the Commission.

The real purport of the RTI request is to know about the mysterious death of India's second Prime Minister late Lal Bahadur Shastri. RTI request was an effort of a citizen to know information regarding the 'truth' behind the death of Lal Bahadur Shastri that cannot be brushed aside.

While representing, the CPIO of the National Archives of India, and other officer claimed that they were not liable in this complaint because they have no possession of the record as the concerned public authorities such as PMO, MEA and MHA did not share any with them.

---

[1] Navdeep Gupta vs. PIO, National Archives of India (11.05.2018 - CIC) : MANU/CI/0335/2018
Hon'ble Judges/Coram:
M. Sridhar Acharyulu, Central Information Commissioner

Decision by CPIO, NAI

The CPIO of National Archives of India stated that they had no specific information about this in their files, and that this RTI was first filed with Ministry of Home Affairs and then it was transferred to National Archives of India. The officer submitted that as late Lal Bahadur Shastri died in Tashkent, the information sought might be with the Ministry of External Affairs or Indian Embassy in Russia or Ministry of Home or some other authority. They said that they have again checked their records and database, which yielded no results. The CPIO stated that except information of some news clippings they do not have any authentic document on Late PM's death or post-mortem.

Doubts about Death of Shri Lal Bahadur Shastri

Several concerns were raised by family members of Shastri, eminent writers and journalists continuously since the death to recent times. Former British High Commissioner and veteran Journalist Mr. Kuldip Nayar's book Beyond The Lines (Nayar, Kuldip, Beyond The Lines, Lotus Collection, Roli Books, page Nos. 198 to 202)[2] contains a detailed account of the incident, as the writer was present in Tashkent as PM's media advisor. The BBC Journalist Mr. Soutik Biswas, referred to Mr. Kuldip Nayar in his out-of-print book "India, the Critical years" and wrote in his August 2009 blog[3]. The write up of Mr. Anoop Bose, Advocate, Supreme Court of India, in Law Z magazine dated 7.12.2016 also offers many interesting facts about the incident[4]. He gave certain details saying that the mystery about Netaji Subhash Chandra Bose has something to do with sudden death of Lal Bahadur Shastri. The doubts raised by Mr. Sidharth Nath Singh, the late prime minister's grandson and a senior member of Bharatiya Janata Party were critically analyzed by Mr. Soutik Biswas. He also highlighted the demand of Late Prime Minister's Shastri's son Mr. Anil Shastri for probe into circumstances leading to his father's death[5]. All these factors increase curiosity about the mystery.

---

[2] (https://www.outlookindia.com/magazine/story/the-night-shastri-died-and-other-stories/281456)

[3] (http://www.bbc.co.uk/blogs/thereporters/soutikbiswas/2009/08)

[4] (http://lawzmag.com/2016/12/07/the-tragic-death-of-lal-bahadur-shastri-and-the-mystifying-netaji-subhas-chandra-bose-angle/)

[5] (https://timesofindia.indiatimes.com/india/Lal-Bahadur-Shastris-death-was-not-natural-claims-his-family/articleshow/49116369.cms).

Senior Journalist Mr. Anuj Dhar revealed some more relevant points regarding the death of Shastri[6]. In these articles, inter alia, he posed four questions: a) The KGB suspected poisoning, b) Shastri's relatives see a needle of suspicion pointing towards an insider's hand, c) rejection of family member's demand to conduct post mortem on his body, and d) earlier RTI responses saying that there were no records[7].

The news magazine Outlook published an article by Mr. Saba Naqui on 16th July 2012, "National History: Shastri's Death: Tashkent Whodunit: An Enduring Tale", referred to another important aspect among other things, that "all records of the post-emergency Raj Narain inquiry committee report on death of Shastri, have vanished; there is not a trace even in Parliament's exalted library". It was stated: "Particularly as the first inquiry was conducted only after the Emergency when the Janata government was in power. Called the Raj Narain Inquiry, it never came up with any conclusions but began the process. However, no record of this can be found in the Parliament library-by itself not a sinister event as lots of vital documents have disappeared often due to carelessness. But there is an even more curious series of events linked to the inquiry. Two witnesses were scheduled to depose before this parliamentary body in 1977. One was R.N. Chugh, Shastri's doctor who accompanied him to Tashkent. The second was Ram Nath, his personal servant, who was also present on the day of his death. Chugh was travelling to Delhi by road to testify before the committee and was hit by a truck and died. Ram Nath came to Delhi and visited Shastri's widow before the deposition. According to family members, he told her, "Bahut din ka bojh tha, amma. Aaj sab bata denge (I have been carrying this burden too long. I will shed it today)." Ram Nath left the 1, Motilal Nehru, residence to make his way to Parliament. He was hit by a moving vehicle, his legs crushed (eventually amputated) and he lost his memory".[8] In view of such incidents reported in media, the absence of record about Raj Narain inquiry commission that probed into the

---

6 available at the links https://www.dailyo.in/politics/lal-bahadur-shastri-son-anil-shastri-west-bengal-netaji-files-subhas-chandra-bose-mamata-banerjee-moscow-tn-kaul-kgb/story/1/6462.html https://www.dailyo.in/politics/lal-bahadur-shastri-tashkent-kgb-russia-rti-congress-pmo-mea-tn-kaul/story/1/8393.html

7 (https://www.dailyo.in/politics/lal-bahadur-shastri-tashkent-kgb-russia-rti-congress-pmo-mea-tn-kaul/story/1/8393.html)

8 https://www.outlookindia.com/magazine/story/tashkent-whodunit-an-enduring-tale/281537.

circumstances leading to death of our late Prime Minister, if true, assumes importance. Whether Raj Narain inquiry reached any conclusion, if so where is the record? This has to be clarified by Ministry of Home Affairs, because commission of inquiry into such affairs would form part of its activity. Mr. Saba Naqui expressed surprise that even the library of Rajya Sabha does not have it.

Right to Information

The Right to information is now a fundamental right, being an intrinsic part of Article 19(1)(a) of Indian Constitution.

Not being an absolute right, there are limitations on the grounds listed under Article 19(2) which are also reflected in the restrictions on right to information under Section 8(1) of RTI Act. Article 19(2) says:

(2) Nothing in sub clause (a) of clause (1) shall affect the operation of any existing law, or prevent the State from making any law, in so far as such law imposes reasonable restrictions on the exercise of the right conferred by the said sub clause in the interests of the sovereignty and integrity of India, the security of the State, friendly relations with foreign States, public order, decency or morality or in relation to contempt of court, defamation or incitement to an offence.

Similarly Section 8(1)(a) of the Right to Information Act, 2005 prescribed exemptions to RTI:

8(1) Notwithstanding anything contained in this Act, there shall be no obligation to give any citizen,- (a) information, disclosure of which would prejudicially affect the sovereignty and integrity of India, the security, strategic, scientific or economic interests of the State, relation with foreign State or lead to incitement of an offence;

There are several judicial precedents before and after passing of Right to Information Act 2005 holding that RTI is intrinsic part of Freedom of Speech and Expression under Article 19(1)(a).

Issue before Central Information Commission (CIC)

Whether information was available with any public authority, and if so whether that could be disclosed under RTI Act, or will that attract any restriction under Section 8 or 9.

Decision of CIC

Commission directed the CPIOs of the PMO, the Ministry of Home Affairs or Ministry of External Affairs to provide information/documents about the referred subject to the applicant. In case the CPIOs of PMO, MEA and MHA consider that any record of part of it was hit by Section 8(1)(a) or any other clause on the ground that were classified, they are required to explain the same and as per section 18(4) of the RTI Act, they are directed to produce in sealed cover the relevant record or part thereof for the examination by the Commission to decide the question of disclosability of the information sought. If any document is claimed to have been classified they have to inform the period of withholding of such information because of such classification, when it will be accessible, or is there any possibility of declassification of records as demanded by eminent citizens and family members of Lal Bahadur Sastri, etc. The Commission considered that these offices especially that of MHA require to make a fresh effort to trace the details about Raj Narain inquiry report or related documents and tell the nation what was inquired and found. Offices were also directed to explain whether they have transferred or transferring any records relating to the death of Lal Bahadur Shastri to the National Archives of India facilitating access to public in general and to requesters in particular, under RTI Act.

As per Section 4(1)(b) clause (iv), the public authority is under an obligation to disclose on its own "a statement of the categories of documents that are held by it or under its control". The Commission directed the PMO, MEA and MHA to publish the statement of categories of documents regarding the death of Late Shri Lal Bahadur Shastri that are available with them.

The Commission recommended the CPIO of Parliament Secretariat to search in their library whether any records regarding the Raj Narain inquiry commission could be retrieved? If they discover any, they are required to share with the appellant, and the National Archives of India.

The Commission directed the CPIO of NAI to explain their efforts to secure records from different public authorities on this subject.

The public authorities have a constitutional duty to inform and the people have legitimate expectation to know the truth behind the death of their beloved leader. More so, it is the primary responsibility of the PMO to inform the people what happened to Late Lal Bahadur Shastri, who once was its head.

Chapter - 2

DENIAL TO PROVIDE INFORMATION RELATING TO DEATH OF FORMER PRIME MINISTER LATE SHRI LAL BAHADUR SHASTRI[9]

Facts in Nutshell

The complainant sought information relating to death of former Prime Minister Late Shri Lal Bahadur Shastri (Shastri): "1. If dead body of Late Prime Minister was brought to India or was he cremated there in Russia? 2. In case his body was brought to India, please supply me certified copy of post-mortem conducted on his body". The Home Ministry forwarded RTI request to the National Archives of India (NAI). The NAI could not give any information. Applicant filed complaint before Central Information Commissio (CIC).

Reply by CPIO (Chief Public Information Officer)

Shri V.K. Rajan, CPIO, Ministry of Home Affairs and Shri Ved Prakash Singh, CPIO, Ministry of External Affairs jointly filed information in regard to questions: "As per record, a statement was made by the then Minister of External Affairs in Lok Sabha/Rajya Sabha on 16.2.1966, on the circumstances under which Shri Lal Bahadur Shastriji occurred because of an acute attack of 'INFARKTMIOCARDA'.

Medical Report on Shastri's Death

During the days of his stay in Tashkent, as well as on the evening of 10th January 1966, the Prime Minister of India, Lal Bahadur Shastri, felt well. He never complained about his health. On the evening of 10th January 1966, the

---

[9] Navdeep Gupta vs. PIO, National Archives of India (24.09.2018 - CIC) : MANU/CI/0671/2018
Hon'ble Judges/Coram:
M. Sridhar Acharyulu, Central Information Commissioner

Prime Minister of India, Lal Bahadur Shastri, was healthy and cheerful while he was attending a reception given by the Chairman of the Council of Ministers of USSR, A.N. Kosygin. According to Dr. R.N. Chugh, the doctor-attendant on the Prime Minister, who used to be always present at his side and thus had attended the reception, after return from the reception to his residence, Lal bahadur Shastri was in normal health and was in a good mood and spoke over the telephone with his relatives in Delhi. He went to bed at about 12.30 midnight. On the 11th of January, at about 1.20 in the morning, Messrs. Shay, Kapur and Sharma approached the Premier's doctor who was in the room next to him and told him that the Prime Minister is feeling unwell. Dr. R.N. Chugh at once approached the Prime Minister and found that the Prime Minister was sitting on his bed, coughing and was complaining of lack of breath. He was holding his chest with his hands and was looking pale. The doctor found the pulse to be very fast and weak. Blood pressure was not registered. The heart beats were hardly audible. The doctor put the Prime Minister in a reclining position, gave him intra-muscular injection of MEPTHENTIH SULPHATE one ml (15 milligrams) and 1 ml of MICCRENA. Within the next 3 minutes, Prime Minister L.B. Shastri lost consciousness, the pulse disappeared, breathing stopped and the heart beats could not be heard. Death occurred at 1.32 on the morning of 11th January 1966. Doctor R.N. Chugh had already begun revival treatment by the methods of indirect massage of the heart and artificial respiration through the mouth by means of the air tube. The Soviet doctor E.G. YEREMENKO who had come there immediately on a call from Dr. R.N. Chug also took part in the treatment by revival procedures. She found Prime Minister L.B. Shastri dead when she arrived: The pulse had stopped, the heart was silent, there was no breath and no corneal reflexes. The revival treatment was continued further with the help of the anti-shock group of doctors which had arrived immediately on call. Indirect massage of the heart was done; in the left cavity under the heart at an interval of 15 minutes was twice introduced a mixture of Potassium Chloride with Adrenalin and glucose. Artificial respiration by means of the machine with the help of "Intubation tube" was also attempted. However, these measures yielded no results.

Doctors Observation about Death

Taking into account the fact that Prime Minister L.B. Shastri had suffered even in the past from INFARKTMIOCARDA and the fact that during the night from 10th to 11th of January 1966 there was an acute attack of the same disease it can be considered that death occurred because of an acute attack of INFARKTMIOCARDA.

No Records with Rajya Sabha

On 24.05.2018, Mr. Devashish Sen, Under Secretary, Rajya Sabha, Secretariat in his note-sheet bearing reference No. RS/5(3)/2018-RTI stated that "no record related to Raj Narain Commission of Inquiry is available with this Section" and demarcated it to the RTI Cell. Mr. K. Sudhakaran, Director, RTI Cell on 25.05.2018 in his note-sheet explained that neither the report of Raj Narain Inquiry Commission nor the date of laying of the report on the Table of the Rajya Sabha is available with them. As Parliament Library comes under the jurisdiction of the Lok Sabha Secretariat, the requisite information may be ascertained from that Secretariat and subsequently this note-sheet was further put up to Shri Arun Sharma, Director (Q) and CPIO, who in turn wrote a letter to Shri J.M. Baisakh, Director & CPIO, Lok Sabha Secretariat on 28.05.2018 stating that the subject matter of this interim order also concerns Lok Sabha Secretariat. Afterwards, Mr. Rosey Sailo Damodaran, Additional Director, LARRDIS (Publications an Who's Who Unit) in his note-sheet stated that the requisite information is not available with them and also suggested that the query may be transferred to the parliament Library, Lok Sabha Secretariat as it is repository of books, reports etc.

The Rajya Sabha Secretariat submitted that they do not have any information relating to this subject matter neither in their table office nor legislative branch nor library. Dr. Keshab Chandra Jana, National Archives of India stated that there are no details available with them and the Ministry of Home Affairs have unnecessarily forwarded the RTI application to NAI and also pleaded before the Commission to direct the concerned Ministry to check in their registry/records before transferring to NAI.

Issues Emerging Out of Facts & Circumstances

In February, 1966, the issue of Shastri's death was raised for the first time in the Indian Parliament. In April, 1970, Shastri's childhood friend Tribhuvan Narain Singh, demanded a comprehensive enquiry into his death as he had not been autopsied. The maiden inquiry into Shastri's death was conducted by the Raj Narain Inquiry Committee in 1977 which proved to be utterly abortive and not a trace of the inquiry survives even in the archives of Parliament House.

Answers to questions: The body of Shastri was brought from Tashkent and was cremated in India. No post mortem was conducted on his body (Unofficial answer). Though the questions could be answered either in 'yes' or 'no', the real purport of the RTI request is to know about the mysterious death of India's second Prime Minister Shastri. Serious doubts were raised by family members of Shastri, eminent writers and journalists continuously. Former British High Commissioner and veteran Journalist Mr. Kuldip Nayar's book Beyond The Lines[10] contains a detailed account of the incident, as the writer was present in Tashkent as PM's media advisor. It was a matter of great concern that our late Prime Minister met with sudden death on Russian dacha on January 11, 1966. Journalist Mr. Nayar has posed the question—was Shastri poisoned?

The Outlook published excerpts from this book and wrote after contacting the members of the family: "As we pieced together the strange circumstances of Shastri's death through family accounts and on the basis of RTI applications, we can only conclude that the mystery deepens and some answers must be found. His family has always maintained that he was poisoned and his death hushed up". The magazine listed some 'certainly unanswered questions':

(a) Press reports of the incident show that the authorities in Tashkent immediately arrested a Russian cook. He was released after five hours of questioning. However, in spite of the initial suspicion of poisoning, no post-mortem was done, either in Russia or in India. His late wife kept trying to raise questions about his death, but nothing was ever investigated.

---

[10] (Nayar, Kuldip, Beyond The Lines, Lotus Collection, Roli Books, page Nos. 198 to 202) (https://www.outlookindia.com/magazine/story/the-night-shastri-died-and-other-stories/281456)

(b) The couple had six children, of whom only two, Anil and Sunil Shastri, survive. Both are members of the Congress, although the latter had joined the BJP briefly. Grandson Siddhartha Nath Singh (son of Shastri's late daughter Suman) is in the BJP. But regardless of political affiliations, there is a unanimity within the family that Shastri was poisoned and the case was never investigated.

(c) In 2009, the PMO had replied that it had only one document relating to Shastri's death but refused to declassify it under a clause that would "prejudicially affect the sovereignty and integrity of the country, the security, strategic, scientific or economic interests of the state, relation with foreign state or lead to incitement of an offence".

(d) "I'm willing to believe my grandfather died of a heart attack. But at least declassify the documents" says Siddhartha Singh: "I'm willing to believe my grandfather died of a heart attack. But please share the information with us as our family has never got closure on this issue. Please just declassify the information." He recounts something that was an obsession with his late mother who was the last family member to speak to Shastri. She was on the phone with her father, as her husband, V.N. Singh, an employee of the State Trading Corporation, was travelling to Cairo on work where Shastri too was headed. Shastri therefore told his daughter to ensure that her husband carried Indian newspapers to Cairo. His last words to her were—"I'm going to have a glass of milk and sleep." The line got disconnected and Suman tried again. However, when she got through 15 minutes later, she was told her father was dead.

(e) The first inquiry was conducted only after the Emergency when the Janata government was in power-called the Raj Narain Inquiry-it never came up with any conclusions but began the process. However, no record of this can be found in the Parliament library by itself not a sinister event as lots of vital documents have disappeared often due to carelessness.

(f) Two witnesses were scheduled to depose before this parliamentary body in 1977. One was R.N. Chugh, Shastri's doctor who accompanied him to Tashkent. The second was Ram Nath, his personal servant, who was also present on the day of his death. Chugh was travelling to Delhi by road to testify before the committee and was hit by a truck and died. Ram Nath came to Delhi and visited Shastri's widow before the deposition. According to family members, he told her, "Bahut din ka bojh tha, amma. Aaj sab bata denge (I have been carrying this burden too long. I will shed it today)." Ram Nath left the 1, Motilal Nehru, residence to make his way to Parliament. He was hit by a moving vehicle, his legs crushed (eventually amputated) and he lost his memory.[11]

Shastri's Last Moments: Kuldip Nayar's Account

a. When I returned from Tashkent, Lalita Shastri asked me why Shastri's body had turned blue. I replied: 'I am told that when bodies are embalmed, they turn blue.' She then inquired about 'certain cuts' on Shastri's body. I did not know about those because I had not seen the body. Even so, her remark that no postmortem had been conducted either at Tashkent or Delhi startled me. It was indeed unusual.

b. Apparently, she and others in the family suspected foul play. A few days later I heard that Lalita Shastri was angry with the two personal assistants, who had accompanied Shastri, because they had refused to sign a statement which alleged that Shastri did not die a natural death.

c. As days passed, the Shastri family became increasingly convinced that he had been poisoned. In 1970, on 2nd October (Shastri's birthday), Lalita Shastri asked for a probe into her husband's death. The family seemed to be upset that Jan Mohammed, T.N. Kaul's cook at the time, had cooked the food, not Ram Nath his personal servant. This was strange as the same Jan Mohammed had prepared food for Shastri when he visited Moscow in 1965.

d. Following newspaper reports, the old guard Congress party supported the demand for a probe into Shastri's death. I asked Morarji Desai towards the end of October 1970 whether he really believed that Shastri did not die a natural death. Desai said: 'That is all politics. I am sure there was no foul play. He died of a heart attack. I have checked with

[11] https://www.outlookindia.com/magazine/story/tashkent-whodunit-an-enduring-tale/281537

the doctor and his secretary, C.P. Srivastava, who accompanied him to Tashkent.'[12]

The BBC Journalist, Mr. Soutik Biswas, analysed the narration by Kuldip Nayar and said it leads to an inference of possible heart attack as the cause of death.

Mr. Biswas, asked for bringing out the truth to end controversy once and for all. Late PM's son Mr. Anil Shastry on 26th September 2015 urged the Prime Minister that documents related to Shastri's death should be declassified. In an interview to news channel CNN-IBN, said that his father's death did not look natural. He said:

"When my father's body came to the Delhi airport, the Palam airport as it was called then, and when it was taken out of the aircraft, that came as a shock because his body had turned blue. His face had turned blue and there were white spots on the temple.... It is "unbelievable" that the Prime Minister's room in the capital of then Soviet Uzbekistan had "no call bell, no telephone, no caretaker in his room and no first aid. He had to walk up to the door himself."

He alleged that the death was due to fault done by the Indian embassy and termed it as "height of negligence".

"His death was badly handled by the Indian government. It hurts me to a great extent, ...Post-mortem could have been done in Tashkent if there was a request from the Indian government or a request from the Indian doctors.....some close associates feel that suspicion revolves around an Indian hand or a foreign power".

He claimed that his father had come to know about a scam involving a shipping tycoon Dharam Teja and cited an article by eminent journalist Khushwant Singh that Teja was in Tashkent at the time of his father's death. Shri Anil Shastri further said:

"...Lal Bahadur Shastri had suddenly gained a lot of power, when he retaliated with full force against Pakistan. Whether it was America, China or any

[12] (Nayar, Kuldip, Beyond The Lines, Lotus Collection, Roli Books, page Nos. 198 to 202)

third country... I cannot name any country but the truth is Lal Bahadur Shastri was becoming very strong in the region."

He raised several other issues like: the sudden death of Dr. R.N. Chugh, the personal physician accompanying the Prime Minister, who died in an accident with his family; his father's personal assistant too met with an accident, was crippled and lost his memory; his father's red personal diary, in which he made daily notings was missing. He says his father may have even written about the Tashkent agreement and the pressures he was under... It is not a bad idea to have an inquiry into his death, question all remaining witnesses and clear all speculation and at least establish the negligence."[13]

In 2009, the Indian Ministry of External Affairs revealed that no 'postmortem was conducted by the authorities of the former USSR'. The solitary record available is the report of the joint medical investigation conducted by Dr. Chugh and some Russian doctors attributing Shastri's death to 'an acute attack of INFARKTMIOCARDIA'. Mr. Bose wrote: "Shastri's Russian butler Akhmed Sattarov was arrested, subjected to an excruciating interrogation and eventually let off the hook by the dreaded KGB. It is not known whether Jan Mohammed, who joined the Rashtrapati Bhavan staff in Delhi subsequent to Kaul becoming India's Foreign Secretary, was also interrogated". He pointed out that apart from mother and wife of Lal Bahadur, the Union Law Minister in Shastri's cabinet Mr. Asoke Sen also noticed blue patches on Shastri's body much to his consternation.

Mr. Anoop Bose in his article titled - Tragic Death of Lal Bahadur Sashtri and the Mystifying Netaji (Subhas Chandra Bose) Angle, raised another question linking Shastri's death with mystery of Netaji's disappearance. He wrote:

"Shastri was an indefatigable champion of Netaji. Jagdish Kodesia, a former Delhi Congress chief and a confidante of Shastri, appeared before the Khosla Commission in March, 1971 as a witness. He deposed that Shastri did not believe in Netaji's death in a plane crash and went on to assert, 'When he became Home

[13] https://timesofindia.indiat imes.com/india/Lal-Bahadur-Shastris-death-was-not-natural-claims-his-family/articleshow/49116369.cms

Minister, he wanted to know the truth whether Subhas Bose was alive or not.' Shastri also showed a deep interest in the antecedents of Gumnami Baba of Faizabad who was rumoured to be Netaji. It is widely believed that Netaji was present at Pandit Jawaharlal Nehru's funeral on 27th May, 1964 at Teen Murti Bhavan dressed as a monk. According to Capt. Ajit Vadakayil, the well known blogger, Netaji came in a taxi and sent an envelope to Shastri whereupon Shastri came running out to meet him. Then Shastri and Netaji went inside Teen Murti Bhavan. Netaji took out a package, stood beside Nehru's body and offered a giant garland of roses with an attached note saying 'Another name of Jawaharlal Nehru is courage. Let us confront the crisis of our nation for the future of India'. The note was undersigned as 'Subhas Chandra Bose'. After Shastri became the Prime Minister, 80 Members of Parliament visited him and proclaimed that the monk was none other than Netaji without any shadow of doubt Shastri wanted to set up a second inquiry commission to investigate the mystery behind Netaji's death.....In 1965, Shastri was invited to unveil Netaji's statue on the occasion of his birth anniversary on 23rd January, 1966 at Mayo Road in Kolkata. For some inexplicable reason, Shastri preponed the ceremony and unveiled the statue in December, 1965, three weeks prior to his Tashkent visit. Netaji's nephew Amiya Nath Bose, the eminent lawyer and parliamentarian, who happened to be at the ceremony requested Shastri to probe into the circumstances relating to Netaji's death whereupon Shastri assured him that he would personally pursue the matter in Russia. Bose was extremely close to our family. After my father retired from government service in 1966 shortly after Shastri's death, we stayed with him for a few months at his 10, South Avenue flat. During those days, he used to regale us with his personal reminiscences of the intense relationship that existed between Shastri and Netaji and was never tired of telling us about the Mayo Road ceremony. In 1976, I joined the legal profession and became a member of the Bar Library Club within the majestic confines of the Calcutta High Court in 1991. Bose, who used to come infrequently to the High Court, most graciously allowed me to sit on his hand crafted Elizabethan chair in the Library which fortuitously happened to be right next to the chair of Asoke Sen. After his death, the chair was permanently allotted to me prompting Sen to remark in a jocular vein, 'The chair moves from Bose to Bose'. I continue to occupy that chair to this day with a sense of immense pride. On 12th December, 2015, the Times of India divulged that a forensic face-mapping report submitted by a British expert Neil Miller had found a strong resemblance between Netaji and a man photographed in Tashkent. According to Miller, the face mapping of the mystery man seen in Tashkent 'lends support leaning on strong support to the contention that the person seen in the picture and Subhas Chandra Bose are one and the same person.' Shastri had made a call before his death to his family members. In a moment of helpless nostalgia, Sanjay, who was standing right beside the telephone, vividly recalled, 'Amma first spoke to Babuji but could hardly hear his voice. Then Hari Mama (Shastri's eldest son) exchanged a few words with him. Lastly, Ramji (his father Vijay Nath Singh) spoke to Babuji who asked him about the reaction in India to the Declaration. When Ramji told him that certain prominent opposition leaders were planning to hold a black flag demonstration against him for having returned Haji Pir Pass, Babuji clearly told him that he would bring forth such a thing that would make his countrymen forget about the return of the Pass and any criticism about the Declaration. He was alluding to Netaji. Within a fraction of minutes, we got a call saying Babuji had taken ill. This was followed by another call after 10 minutes announcing his death...On 16th August, 2015, Sunil disclosed on Zee 24 Ghanta that his father told him shortly before his death about a 'special person' he was going to meet. Was this 'special person' Netaji? Was Shastri planning to present Netaji before his countrymen on 23rd January, 1966? Did he intend to invite Netaji as the Chief Guest to the Republic Day parade on 26th January, 1966? Was he going to abdicate in favour of Netaji? These questions will perhaps remain inscrutable forever.[14]"

Anuj Dhar, Author of "What happened to Netaji?"

In 2009 Mr. Anuj Dhar, author of "What happened to Netaji?", "CIA's Eye on South Asia", and moderator of a transparency website, seeking the correspondence between the Indian embassy in Moscow and the external affairs ministry and between the two countries after the Shastri's death and on the demand of Shastri's family to declassify 1966 correspondence between MEA and Indian embassy. He claimed the PMO replied that only one document relating to Shastri's death was available but refused to declassify as it would "prejudicially affect the

[14] http://lawzmag.com/2016/12/07/the-tragic-death-of-lal-bahadur-shastri-and-the-mystifying-netaji-subhas-chandra-bose-angle/

sovereignty and integrity of the country, the security, strategic, scientific or economic interests of the state, relation with foreign state or lead to incitement of an offence". Mr. Dhar wrote: "The ministry of external affairs (MEA) informed me on July 1, 2009 that the division concerned had no information on the subject. It was quite strange because the sudden death of the prime minister must have thrown the Indian embassy in Moscow and the ministry in New Delhi into a tizzy. The correspondence between the MEA and the Indian embassy in Moscow too remain classified. Under ordinary circumstances, there should have been several reports from the embassy on the incident. They should have included an assessment by the Indian ambassador, T.N. Kaul at that time. Surely these should be ordinary routine documents, not dark secrets of state". In their response dated 25th September 2009, the MEA, rejected information on points 1 to 4 and 6 of Anuj Dhar's application and regarding point 5, stated: "No records with the Embassy of India, Moscow, relating the demise of Prime Minister Shri Lal Bahadur Shastry in Tashkent on 11.01.66, or subsequent events, have either been destroyed or lost".

Mr Anuj, who wrote extensively on mystery of Netaji's death, in one of his articles stated '4 reasons Lal Bahadur Shatri's death was suspicious"[15]:

(i) The KGB suspected poisoning: At 4am, Ahmed Sattarov, the Russian butler attached to Shastri, was rudely woken up by an officer of the Ninth Directorate of the KGB (responsible for the safety of VIPs). In Sattarov's own words, the KGB officer "said that they suspected the Indian prime minister had been poisoned. Sattarov was handcuffed and, along with three junior butlers, was rounded off to a location 30km away. Their harsh interrogation commenced in a dungeon. After some time, Jan Mohammad was brought in. In Sattarov's words again: "We thought that it must have been that man who poisoned Shastri."

(ii) Shastri's near and dear ones see a needle of suspicion pointing towards an insider's hand: His mother screamed that someone had poisoned her son. "Mere bitwa ko jahar de diya!" Shastri's sons Anil and Sunil Shastri (one in Congress, another in BJP) and grandsons Sanjay and Siddharth

[15] (https://www.dailyo.in/politics/lal-bahadur-shastri-tashkent-kgb-russia-rti-congress-pmo-mea-tn-kaul/story/1/8393.html)

Nath Singh have often spoken about their ongoing anguish and pain about what happened so long ago. Shastri's wife Lalita died thinking that her husband had been poisoned. Other family members and near and dear ones, like childhood friend TN Singh and close follower Jagdish Kodesia, were not able to make sense of the cut marks on Shastri's stomach and back of the neck. The cut on his neck was pouring blood and the sheets, pillows and clothes used by him were all soaked in blood. A grandson of Shastri told me that he still has his nanaji's blood-soaked cap". Dr Chugh, his wife and two sons were run over by a truck in 1977. Only his daughter survived, but was crippled.

(iii) No post mortem was carried out on Shastri's body: Family demanded postmortem, but was not accepted.

(iv) RTI responses muddied the water further, by saying that MEA have no records.

Law of Access to Records and Official Secrets

As the ambiguity, secrecy and mystery shrouded sudden demise of Lal Bahadur Shastry, the issues assumes of high significance and high larger public interest. Whether people have right to information and express about the death of their second prime minister? Supreme Court, before and after passing of Right to Information Act 2005, held that RTI was intrinsic part of Freedom of Speech and Expression under Article 19(1)(a), which says:

19. Protection of certain rights regarding freedom of speech etc, (1) All citizens shall have the right...(a) to freedom of speech and expression; Not being an absolute right, there are limitations on the grounds listed under

Article 19(2) which will straight away apply as restrictions on right to information too.

(2) Nothing in sub clause (a) of clause (1) shall affect the operation of any existing law, or prevent the State from making any law, in so far as such law imposes reasonable restrictions on the exercise of the right conferred by the said sub clause in the interests of the sovereignty and integrity of India, the security of the State, friendly relations with foreign

States, public order, decency or morality or in relation to contempt of court, defamation or incitement to an offence.

Similarly the Right to Information Act, 2005 in Section 8(1)(a) prescribed exemptions to RTI:

8(1) Notwithstanding anything contained in this Act, there shall be no obligation to give any citizen,—

(a) information, disclosure of which would prejudicially affect the sovereignty and integrity of India, the security, strategic, scientific or economic interests of the State, relation with foreign State or lead to incitement of an offence;

US Secrets and Security; Pentagon Papers

Can fundamental right of the people be denied on this excuse? The US Executive resisted publication of articles in Newspapers about Pentagon Papers, on similar grounds. But they failed. In 1967 Secretary of Defense Robert S. McNamara commissioned a "massive top-secret history of the United States role in Indochina". It's report of the office of the Secretary of Defense Vietnam Task Force, was popularly known as Pentagon Papers. Daniel Ellsberg, who had helped to produce the report, leaked 43 volumes of the 47-volume, 7,000-page report to reporter Neil Sheehan of The New York Times in March 1971 and the Newspaper began publishing articles outlining the findings revealing that the Johnson Administration "systematically lied, not only to the public but also to Congress". [Sheehan, Neil (1971-06-13). "Vietnam Archive: Pentagon Study Traces 3 Decades of Growing U.S. Involvement" (PDF) The New York Times] This article explained how clandestinely the US enlarged scope of Vietnam War with bombings of nearby Cambodia and Laos, coastal raids on North Vietnam and Marine Corps attacks, none which were reported in the mainstream media. [Frum, David (2000). How We Got Here: The '70s. New York: Basic Books. p. 43] The US charged the journalist with conspiracy, espionage and theft of government property, which were later dismissed by prosecutors. Ellsberg discussed the study with The New York Times reporter Neil Sheehan and gave 43 volumes to him. Times started publishing reports on June 13, 1971. [Correll,

John T. "The Pentagon Papers" Air Force Magazine, February 2007] Nixon Administration obtained a federal court injunction forcing the New York Times to cease publication after three articles. Then the Times approached the Supreme Court. Meanwhile The Washington Post began publishing articles based on the Pantagon Papers given by Ellsberg.

President Nixon had claimed executive authority to force the Times to suspend publication of classified information in its possession. The question before the court was whether the constitutional freedom of the press, guaranteed by the First Amendment, was subordinate to a claimed need of the executive branch of government to maintain the secrecy of information. District court declined to give injunction, refusing to concede the contention of the state that security of nation was threatened, saying "the security of the Nation is not at the ramparts alone. Security also lies in the value of our free institutions. A cantankerous press, an obstinate press, a ubiquitous press must be suffered by those in authority to preserve the even greater values of freedom of expression and the right of the people to know"[16]. The Government approached the Supreme Court which combined case with New York Times Co. vs. US [403 U.S. 713] case. Fifteen more newspapers also started publishing the reports. In Dennis v. United States, [341 U.S. 494 (1951)], state contended that certain message will likely to cause 'grave and irreparable danger to the American public when expressed, then the message's prior restraint could be considered an acceptable infringement of civil liberties. On June 30, 1971 the Supreme Court of US decided 6-3, that the government failed to meet the heavy burden of proof required for prior restraint injunction. The US SC concurred with the decisions of the two lower courts. Justice Black wrote:

"...To find that the President has 'inherent power' to halt the publication of news...would wipe out the First Amendment and destroy the fundamental liberty and security of the very people the Government hopes to make 'secure.'... The word 'security' is a broad, vague generality whose contours should not be invoked to abrogate the fundamental law embodied in the First Amendment. The guarding of military and diplomatic secrets at the expense of informed representative government provides no real security.... The Framers of the First Amendment,

[16] [United States v. N.Y. Times Co., 328 F. Supp. 324, 331 (S.D.N.Y. 1971)]

fully aware of both the need to defend a new nation and the abuses of the English and Colonial governments, sought to give this new society strength and security by providing that freedom of speech, press, religion, and assembly should not be abridged.... Only a free and unrestrained press can effectively expose deception in government. And paramount among the responsibilities of a free press is the duty to prevent any part of the government from deceiving the people and sending them off to distant lands to die of foreign fevers and foreign shot and shell". [17]

Justices Potter Stewart and Byron R. White agreed that it is the responsibility of the Executive to ensure national security through the protection of its information. However, in areas of national defense and international affairs, the President possesses great constitutional independence that is virtually unchecked by the Legislative and Judicial branch. "In absence of governmental checks and balances", wrote Justice Stewart, "the only effective restraint upon executive policy and power in [these two areas] may lie in an enlightened citizenry - in an informed and critical public opinion which alone can here protect the values of democratic government".[18]

Justice Thurgood Marshall argued that the term "national security" was too broad to legitimize prior restraint, and also argued that it is not the Court's job to create laws where the Congress had not spoken.[19]

Is there a clear and present danger?

In the 1919 case Schenck v. United States, [249 U.S. 47 (1919)] Justice Oliver Wendell Holmes, Jr. introduced the clear and present danger test, which would become an important concept in First Amendment law. "The question in every case is whether the words used are used in such circumstances and are of such a nature as to create a clear and present danger that they will bring about the substantive evils that the United States Congress has a right to prevent. It is a question of proximity and degree. When a nation is at war, many things that might be said in time of peace are such a hindrance to its effort that their utterance

17 (New York Times Co. v. United States, 403 U.S. at 714-20)
18 (New York Times Co. v. United States, 403 U.S. at 727-30.)
19 (New York Times Co. v. United States, 403 U.S. at 740-48)

will not be endured so long as men fight, and that no Court could regard them as protected by any constitutional right". Brandeis and Holmes, JJ again promoted the clear and present danger test, this time in a concurring opinion in 1927's Whitney v. California decision [(274 U.S. 357 (1927), & Dunlap, William V., "National Security and Freedom of Speech", in Finkelman (vol 1), pp 1072-1074)]. The clear and present danger test was invoked by the majority in the 1940 Thornhill v. Alabama [310 U.S. 88 (1940)] decision in which a state antipicketing law was invalidated. Following Schenck v. United States, "clear and present danger" became both a public metaphor for First Amendment speech [Derrick, Geoffrey J. (2007). "Why the Judiciary Should Protect First Amendment Political Speech During Wartime: The Case for Deliberative Democracy". Lethbridge Undergraduate Research Journal, 2(1)] [Tsai, Robert L. (2004). "Fire, Metaphor, and Constitutional Myth-Making". Georgetown Law Journal. 93: 181-239] and a standard test in cases before the Court where a United States law limits a citizen's First Amendment rights; the law is deemed to be constitutional if it can be shown that the language it prohibits poses a "clear and present danger".

The publication of Pentagon papers that analysed the defense defects of US in Vietnam War (1945 to 1967), could not have posing any clear and present danger to the security of nation in 1971 when it was published. The US government has ultimately, declassified all of the Pentagon files in June 2011. The National Archives and Records Administration released to the Richard Nixon Presidential Library and Museum in Yorba Linda, California, which means anybody can have the benefit of that critical analysis, as that cannot have any imminent danger to the security of nation.

Official Secrets Act and RTI

People centric governance could be ushered in if the Right to Information is used as key to strengthen the participatory democracy. The RTI is basic necessity of good governance. With reference to OSA (official secrets act), the RTI Act has a non-obstante clause:

"Sec. 8(2): Notwithstanding anything in the Official Secrets Act, 1923 nor any of the exemptions permissible in accordance with sub-section (1), a public authority may allow access to information, if public interest in disclosure outweighs the harm to the protected interests".

The provisions of the Act which allow disclosure of information even where there is a clash with the exemption provisions of Sec. 8(1) enjoy a general immunity from other Acts and instruments by virtue of Sec. 22 of the Act:

"Sec. 22 The provisions of this Act shall have effect notwithstanding anything inconsistent therewith contained in the Official Secrets Act, 1923, and any other law for the time being in force or any instrument having effect by virtue of any law other than this Act".

Though OSA (official secrets act) does not come in the way of disclosure generally the OSA along with other rules and instructions may impinge on the regime of freedom of information as they historically nurtured a culture of secrecy and nondisclosure, which is against the spirit of the Right to Information Act Section 5 of OSA is the catch all provision, which says:

Any person having information about a prohibited place, or such information which may help an enemy state, or which has been entrusted to him in confidence, or which he has obtained owing to his official position, commits an offence if (s)he communicates it to an unauthorised person, uses it in a manner prejudicial to the interests of the State, retains it when (s)he has no right to do so, or fails to take reasonable care of such information.

Any kind of information is covered by this Section if it is classified as 'secret'. Most interesting part of this OSA is that the word "secret" or the phrase "official secrets" has not been defined anywhere. Whatever a Babu says that could be 'secret', and its leak could be a serious offence. The information which does not have a bearing on national security cannot be disclosed if the public servant obtained or has access to it by virtue of holding office as per this Act. Such illiberal and draconian provisions clearly bred a culture of secrecy. Though the RTI Act now overrides these provisions in relation to matters not exempted by the Act itself from disclosure, the fact remains that OSA in its current form in the statute books is an anachronism.[20]

---

20 (Comment in 2.2.5 ARC II, https://darpg.gov.in/sites/default/files/rti_masterkey1.pdf)

The public servants should never forget that the people are sovereign in democracy and they are functionaries of elected government. That means they are people's servants. They have duty to inform the masters. Transparency should be the norm in all matters of governance. The Official Secrets Act, 1923 (OSA), enacted during the colonial era, governs all matters of secrecy and confidentiality in governance. Given the colonial climate of mistrust of people and the primacy of public officials in dealing with the citizens, OSA created a culture of secrecy. Confidentiality became the norm and disclosure the exception. The Administrative Reforms Commission II report observed: While Section 5 of OSA was obviously intended to deal with potential breaches of national security, the wording of the law and the colonial times in which it was implemented made it into a catch-all legal provision converting practically every issue of governance into a confidential matter. This tendency was buttressed by the Civil Service Conduct Rules, 1964 which prohibit communication of an official document to anyone without authorization. Not surprisingly, Section 123 of the Indian Evidence Act, enacted in 1872, prohibits the giving of evidence from unpublished official records without the permission of the Head of the Department, who has abundant discretion in the matter. Needless to say even the instructions issued for classification of documents for security purposes and the official procedures displayed this tendency of holding back information. (ARC II Para 2.1.2)

Undefined Powers and Abuse

What are "official secrets"? The Official Secrets Act did not define it. This law is unique as there are no provisions for rules and regulations. Thus it is totally left to the individual discretion of the officers without any guidance from anywhere. If an officer declares any file as prohibited, the possession of that document would attract severe penalty without looking into intention or purpose of the possession. Supreme Court restricted meaning of the term 'official secret' to "secret code or password mentioned in Section 3(c) of OSA'.[21] Similarly the clause like sketches, maps, plans and documents used in OSA cannot be considered as "official secrets"? The OSA does not require all kinds of government-held information to be classified as "official secrets". That is why the MoDSI is not part of OSA.

---

[21] [Sama Allana Abdulla vs. State of Gujarat, MANU/SC/0143/1996 : AIR 1996 SC 569, para 7]

Most of documents are not connected to OSA at all. Why the Government not make MoDSI public? Thus the power to classify documents, irrespective of OSA is huge, undefined and also unguided. Even the routine matters are classified. There should be a file with filenotings and reasons for classification of documents by appropriate designated officer. A mere labeling or typing 'top secret' on the top of document make it 'top secret'. Is it appropriate? The OSA without definition of 'secrecy' leaving huge discretion with public servant, is not only threatening the freedom of press and people's right to information, but also essential civil liberties of the people. Recent example of misuse is the judgment of Supreme Court in case of Nambi Narayanan, ISRO Scientist who was victim of abuse of OSA & discretionary power of Police. For fifty days of wrongful imprisonment of the scientist, the SC ordered Rs. 50 lakh compensation. What documents were classified, who classified, who leaked it, and what was illegal consideration? There was no trace of evidence on these questions at all. Over 24 years after Nambi Narayanan's career got "smothered" in the infamous ISRO (Indian Space Research Organisation) spy scandal case, a three-judge Bench led by Chief Justice of India Dipak Misra, on Sept 14, 2018, found him a victim of trumped-up allegations of espionage by the Kerala police. Bench agreed with contention that prosecution launched by the Kerala police had a "catastrophic effect" on his career and personal life besides setting back the technological advancement in space research. Bench said: "The criminal law was set in motion without any basis... His liberty and dignity, basic to his human rights, were jeopardised... Despite all the glory of the past, he was compelled to face cynical abhorrence," Chief Justice Misra wrote. Based on 'confessions' of two arrested foreigners, Kerala Police registered a case in 1994 under Section 3 and 4 of Official Secrets Act, 1923 alleging leak of secrets of ISRO by scientists. CJM Ernakulam found allegations false. Siby Mathew, head of SIT, was found by CBI to have surrendered his duties to IB and ordered indiscriminate arrest of scientist under OSA though no incriminating ISRO documents could be recovered, and no monies paid. They specifically stated "Shri Siby Mathew and his team miserably failed..." No document was recovered, no secrecy and no classification was proved, yet a scientist was arrested and tortured for 50 days. Apex court's decision proved how the state was left with absolute powers that were abused, in the hands of the police under OSA. While Nambi Narayanan was struggling for justice for several decades, the Kerala Government refused to take any action against the police team for this gross abuse, instead, appointed their head as the Chief Information Commissioner of Kerala.[22]

The Law Commission in its 43rd Report (1971), summarized the difficulties encountered with the all inclusive nature of Section 5 of OSA, in the absence of a clear and concise definition of 'official secret', in the following words:

"7.6.1 The wide language of section 5(1) may lead to some controversy. It penalizes not only the communication of information useful to the enemy or any information which is vital to national security, but also includes the act of communicating in any unauthorized manner any kind of secret information which a Government servant has obtained by virtue of his office. Thus, every noting in the Secretariat file to which an officer of the Secretariat has access is intended to be kept secret. But it is notorious that such information is generally communicated not only to other Government servants but even to some of the non-official public in an unauthorized manner. Every such information will not necessarily be useful to the enemy or prejudicial to national security. A question arises whether the wide scope of section 5(1) should be narrowed down to unauthorized communication only of that class of information which is either useful to the enemy or which may prejudicially affect the national security leaving unauthorized communication of other classes of secret information to be a mere breach of departmental rules justifying disciplinary action. It may, however, be urged that all secret information accessible to a Government servant may have some connection with national security because the maintenance of secrecy in Government functions is essentially for the security of the State. In this view, it may be useful to retain the wide language of this section, leaving it to the Government not to sanction prosecution where leakage of such information is of a comparatively trivial nature not materially affecting the interests of the State.

7.6.3 The language of sub-section (1) of section 5 is cumbersome and lacks clarity. Hence without any change in substance, we recommend the adoption of a drafting device separately defining "official secret" as including the enumerated classes of documents and information."

---

[22] (https://www.thehindu.com/news/national/sc-appoints-panel-to-look-into-harrowing-torture-of-nambi-narayanan/article24943213.ece).

The Shourie Committee Commented about OSA

"It is the Official Secrets Act that has been regarded in many quarters as being primarily responsible for the excessive secrecy in government. Its "Catch-all" nature has invited sustained criticism and demand for its amendment. Section 5 of this Act provides for punishment for unauthorized disclosure of Official secrets but omit to define secrets". The Shourie Committee recommended a comprehensive amendment of Section 5(1) to make the penal provisions of OSA applicable only to violations affecting national security.

Administrative Reforms Commission II has Ultimately Recommended

"OSA, in its present form is an obstacle for creation of a regime of freedom of information, and to that extent the provisions of OSA need to be amended. The Commission, on careful consideration agrees with the amendment proposed by the Shourie Committee, as it reconciles harmoniously the need for transparency and the imperatives of national security without in anyway compromising the latter. These can be incorporated in the proposed new chapter in the NSA relating to Official Secrets".

The MoDSI at 172 Defines Classified Documents as Follows

"172. Definition of Classified Documents

(I) Top Secret: This grading is reserved for papers containing information of such a vital nature that, for reasons of national security, it must not be disclosed to anyone for whom it is not essential to have knowledge of it for the proper performance of his duty. Such papers include references to current or future military operations, intending movements or disposition of armed forces, shaping of secret methods, of war, matters of high international and internal political policy, ciphers and reports derived from secret sources of intelligence. The distribution of papers having "Top Secret" classification must be limited to the minimum of persons concerned and in such cases it will be safer to err on the side of security.

(II) Secret: This marking is reserved for papers which are of a nature that their disclosure to persons other than those whose duty is to have knowledge of them would cause administrative embarrassment or difficulty or internal breach of peace and amity or injury to the interest and prestige of the Government or would be of advantage to a foreign nation or enemy. NOTE: This is the highest classification ordinarily used for very important matters.

(III) Confidential: This marking is reserved for papers containing information, the unauthorized disclosure of which, while not endangering national security, would be prejudicial to the interests of the nation, any government activity or individuals, or would cause administrative embarrassment or difficulty or be of an advantage to a foreign nation. NOTE: Most matters will, on proper analysis, be classified higher than Confidential".

(IV) Personal - Not for Publication: This is reserved for communications to members of the public when it is desired to make it clear that these communications or the information contained therein should not be published. The words 'Not for publication' are generally added.

Nothing in this Office Manual tells us about the grade/rank of the officer who can classify documents in this manner. The only guideline given is that the officer must be authorized to handle documents of such sensitivity in order to be able to grade them. However, downgrading must be done by an officer of at least the same rank or higher.

Decision by Central Information Commission (CIC)

CIC directed that government has a duty to justify that release of documents (shastri ji's death) prejudicially affect the security sovereignty and integrity of India and relation with foreign state and even after half a century, they should remain restricted. Compared to Pentagon Papers, can the papers of Lal Bahadur Shastry's death be considered as threat to security or integrity of the nation or friendly relations with neighbours, as claimed?

The Government has taken a historical decision to declassify 33 of Nethaji related files on 4th December 2015, thereafter 37 and 25 files and made 100 files digitally available on 23rd January 2016 to meet the long standing public demand to access these files. NAI has released 75 declassified copies of Nethaji. Fourth batch of 25 files of 1968-2008 was launched on 27th May 2016.[23] When

---

[23] http://www.netajipapers.gov.in/.

Pentagon papers in US and Nethaji papers in India could be declassified why not Shastri papers also?

People's right to know the 'truth' behind the death of Shastri cannot be brushed aside on the ground of Section 8(1)(a) en bloc. In view of the startling incidents that followed the mysterious death, such as killing of his personal doctor and assistant in two separate 'accidents', disappearance of records of Rajya Sabha Committee's probe, and various significant points raised by Journalists Kuldip Nayar, Anuj Dhar, Soutik Biswas, Advocate Anoop Bose, Shastri's wife Mrs Lalitha, other family members, the Commission was of opinion that the Union Government has a duty to explain the nation why and how Lal Bahadur Shastri died in Tashkent. The Government representatives have not come up with any justification for continuing these documents 'secret' for unlimited period of time. They did not produce documents earlier claimed as 'classified' before the Commission, in spite of specific direction, to facilitate the Commission considering the claim of classification in terms of S. 8(1)(a) of RTI Act and OSA.

Except a medical report, nothing was disclosed, and mystery was being allowed to persist. In view of the law of Official Secrets Act, Manual of Departmental Security Instructions, reply given to Lok Sabha referred in Paragraphs 41-42 following information-questions emerge, which need to be answered by the concerned Ministries of the Government of India in response to RTI of appellant, family members of Shastri and the people;

(a) As records are not being classified under OSA, and it is being done by individual ministry, which Ministry has classified the documents of Shastri?

(b) Whether Shastri's death related papers are classified as 'top secret', 'secret' or 'confidential', on what basis?

(c) Which part of 8(1)(a) of RTI Act is invoked to deny and what is the justification for such invocation?

(d) What is the normal period for such classification? Whether any norms are guidelines prescribed? If yes, same shall be furnished.

(e) What is the period prescribed for classification of Shastri documents?

(f) Whether any ministry is considering declassification, if so what is the status?

(g) As per Section 10 of RTI Act, using doctrine of severability, the portion of document classified could be blocked or deleted. As the MoDSI cannot override RTI Act, and RTI overrides the MoDSI, the ministry which classified has a duty to provide such portion of information which his not hit by S. 8-9 of RTI Act. Whether concerned Ministry would be disclosing that part of the information, which is not hit by Section 8(1)(a)?

For these doubts, serious questions, deaths and disappearance of records, the Commission directed the CPIOs of PMO, Ministry of External Affairs and Ministry of Home Affairs to place all those so-called 'classified papers' before the Honourable Prime Minister and the Home Minister, who are recommended to consider the fundamental right to know and demand of the people, family members of Lal Bahadur Shastri and opinion of legendary senior journalists like Late Kuldip Nayar, to declassify either through an expert Committee or by any other process to get the mystery probed and resolved. Even if they can prove that Shastri died by heart attack, that can answer the doubts of the people.

All the CPIOs and seniors of PMO, MEA and MHA have a duty to resolve this mystery and to provide to complete answer these frequent RTI requests to pay due respect to the most honest former Prime Minister of India, and the people who admire him.

However the Commission found it very difficult to get convinced about claim that there were no records with Rajya Sabha pertaining to probe by Raj Narain Committee into the death of Shastri initiated during Janata Government. The Parliament is known for meticulous maintenance of documents. Every word uttered in Parliament is recorded and kept in public domain, a humongous task the office is perfectly performing. Then how such a significant record disappeared? It may not be justified to hold the present or past CPIO liable for the absence of this record. But it is certainly worrying factor and the Rajya Sabha and Parliament as a whole should worry about. The Commission recommends the constitutional authorities in the Parliament to look into this matter and initiate measures including probing or finding means to secure those records, to prevent such loss of documents in future, and to reinforce the credibility of the institution.

Chapter - 3

SARDAR BHAGAT SINGH AND THE GRANT OF STATUS OF SHAHEED[24]

Facts in Nutshell

The appellant questioned if "Sardar Bhagat Singh, who was sentenced to death on 23rd March, 1931 was given the status of Shaheed (Swatantrata Senani)? Whether The Government of India gave him status of Shaheed (Swatantrata Senani)? If the answer is no, what must have been legal limitations on according Shaheed status to Bhagat Singh. How to accord him Shaheed status? According to Government requirements and regulations, how Bhagat Singh could be considered as Shaheed or Swatantrata Senani?" He wanted detailed information in Hindi. This RTI application was originally addressed to CPIO of Rashtrapathi Bhavan, which transferred it to CPIO of Home Ministry. The Home Ministry dispatched it to National Archives of India. The CPIO of NAI on 13.03.2018 wrote that from the records available with them, it is difficult to answer the questions raised without doing a deep research, which a CPIO cannot do. However, the CPIO has rightly offered inspection of records to the appellant any time during working hours on working days saying that in the absence of records, inspection would serve no purpose. Being dissatisfied, the appellant approached Central Information Commission (CIC).

Bhagat Singh laid down life for the liberty of the motherland, which is an established fact as he was sentenced by British India rulers and was executed on proof of charge called 'Lahore Conspiracy', which is a significant part of Indian Independence struggle. It was a great sacrifice and none can deny that he was a true Shaheed.

---

[24] Amit Kumar vs. CPIO, National Archives of India (31.10.2018 - CIC) : MANU/CI/0713/2018
Hon'ble Judges/Coram:
M. Sridhar Acharyulu, Central Information Commissioner.

A demand to declare Bhagat Singh, Rajguru and Sukhdev as martyrs is made every year during their birth and death anniversaries. Punjab government had declared Sarabjit Singh as a 'national martyr', who died in Kot Lakhpat jail, but Bhagat Singh and others were ignored.

Status of Martyr

On 20th May 2018 newspapers reported that Punjab & Haryana High Court in Chandigarh held that status of martyr could not be conferred on these three martyrs because there was no statutory basis. Punjab government also claimed that no official recognition could be given to anybody as a "martyr" as Article 18 of the Constitution does not permit conferring of any title by the state. The letter from the superintendent, general administration department (freedom fighters branch) of the state has also mentioned that the state government gives due respect to all martyrs, and tributes are paid to martyrs at state-level functions. Many memorials to martyrs have also been raised but there is provision to declare it as holiday. The Punjab government has also referred to a book "Dictionary of Martyrs - India's Freedom Struggle (1857-1947)" published by "Indian Council of Historical Research, New Delhi, and suggested that a reference could be made to the book.

Former Prime Minister Views

The then Prime Minister Manmohan Singh asserted that the "fact" that late freedom fighter was a martyr is not dependent on any official records. He said: "That Shaheed Bhagat Singh was a martyr in the supreme national cause of independence is a fact. It is not dependent on the presumed presence or absence of official records. His role in our freedom struggle is an inalienable part of the discourse of our independence. He is a part of our proud national legacy. The nation will always be grateful to Shaheed Bhagat Singh and other freedom fighters who laid down their lives for a better future for India," he said.

The Grand nephew of Bhagat Singh, Yadavendra Singh also has approached the government pleading for declaration of three martyrs officially as Shaheeds[25].

[25] https://www.indiatoday.in/india/north/story/pm-says-bhagat-singhs-martyr-status-doesnt-dependon-records-174149-2013-08-18.

Government Scheme for Freedom Fighters

The Government of India has a scheme of felicitating Swatantra Sainiks Freedom Fighters with Swatantra Sainik Samman. They were given initially a copper plate (Tamra Patr) and thereafter the Freedom fighters and their spouses were being given pension. The pension amount has now increased to beyond Rs. 25,000. In some cases dependents also get a part of pension. But martyrs like Bhagat Singh were not declared 'shaheed' or 'freedom fighters' or eligible for pension. Bhagat Singh was not married, hence pension to spouse did not arise. His dependents also were not given any pension. Everyone regards Bhagat Singh and similar other martyrs as Shaheed, but is there any official or governmental recognition? If not Bharat Ratna or Padma stream of awards, why the martyrs like Bhagat Singh were not recognized by any other nomenclature of national status? Top level political personalities are generally given Bharat Ratna, martyrs of war and heroic personalities in army get Veer chakra awards, meritorious persons from different civilian services get recognized with Padma awards. At a different level, the nation expressed gratitude to the freedom fighters and their families by tamra patra and pension. But surprisingly great heroes like Bhagat Singh, members of Indian National Army under leadership of Netaji Subhash Chandra Bose and those faced turbulent times and worst state oppression as they were charged under various British laws for such as Lahore Conspiracy case their patriotic deeds writing the history, were totally ignored by both Congress and non-Congress Governments. It's unthinkable that any Indian Government is not ready to accord appropriate recognition to these martyrs except offering flowers and paying tributes from tip of mouth.

Decision by CIC

Commission recommended the NDA Government and the Home Ministry to consider appeal of appellant, whether Shaheed Bhagat Singh and others could be officially recognized as Shaheed, and if they feel it could not be done so, the Government may have to explain the reasons for the same.

The Home Ministry should not have transferred many of such RTI applications routinely without application of mind to NAI, who cannot say anything on such a significant policy matter that could have been decided only by the Home Ministry or the Union Cabinet. How NAI decide what Home Ministry cannot? The Commission recorded its displeasure at such wasteful transfer of RTI applications by Home Ministry. The CPIO should have placed the matter before the Minister and conveyed the response instead of making a futile transfer. Hence, the Commission directed the CPIO of Home Ministry to place the matter before the Home Minister for a decision.

Chapter 4

INFORMATION REGARDING SUPERSEDING SENIORITY OF A JUDGE[26]

Facts in Nutshell

By an application of 23.1.09 received by the CPIO on 27.1.09 Shri Subhash Chandra Agrawal sought the following information from the CPIO, Supreme Court of India Shri Raj Pal Arora:

Kindly arrange to send me copy of complete file/s (only as available in Supreme Court) inclusive of copies of complete correspondence exchanged between concerned constitutional authorities with file nothings relating to said appointment of Mr. Justice HL Dattu, Mr. Justice A. K. Ganguly and Mr. Justice RM Lodha superseding seniority of Mr. Justice AP Shah, Mr. Justice AK Patnaik and Mr. Justice VK Gupta as allegedly objected to Prime Minister's Office (PMO) also. Please do not invoke Section 6(3) on this RTI petition, as I need copy of the file on the issue only as available at Supreme Court. Kindly attached file nothings on movement of this RTI petition also. Postal order number 77E 255672 for rupees ten is enclosed herewith towards RTI fees.

To this Shri Subhash Chandra Agrawal received a response on 25.2.2009 from CPIO Shri Arora informing him as follows:

I write to inform you that this Registry does not deal with the matters pertaining to appointment of Hon'ble Judges in the Supreme Court and High Court of India. Appointments of Hon'ble Judges of the Supreme Court and High Courts are made by the President of India as per the procedure

[26] Shri Subhash Chandra Agrawal vs. Supreme Court of India (SCI) (24.11.2009 - CIC) : MANU/CI/0075/2009
Hon'ble Judges/Coram:
Wajahat Habibullah, C.I.C.

prescribed by law and the matters relating thereto are not dealt with and handled by the Registry of the Supreme Court of India. Such information sought by you is neither maintained nor available in the Registry. Hence your request cannot be acceded to under the Right to Information Act, 2005.

Not satisfied Shri Agrawal moved an appeal before Shri M.P. Bhadran, Registrar on 28.2.2009.

But instead of providing copies of sought documents, the learned CPIO tried to explain the procedure of appointment of judges. Appeal was dismissed on 25.3.09 by appellate authority Shri Bhad ran, as follows:

CPIO has informed the appellant that Registry is not dealing with the matters pertaining to appointment of Hon'ble Judges in the Supreme Court of India, that appointment of Hon'ble Judges of the Supreme Court is made by the President of India as per the procedure prescribed by law and the matters relating thereto are not dealt with and handled by the Registry of Supreme Court of India and that such information is neither maintained nor available in the Registry. The information sought by the appellant also does not come within the ambit of Sections 2(f) and (j) of RTI Act. There was no merit in this appeal and same was dismissed.

Second Appeal before Central Information Commission (CIC)

Appellant Shri Subhash Chandra Agrawal's prayer before CIC in his second appeal is as below:

Authorities at Supreme Court may kindly be directed to kindly provide me copy of complete file(s) (copy as available in Supreme Court) inclusive of copies of complete correspondence exchanged between concerned constitutional authorities with file nothings relating to appointment of Mr. Justice HL Dattu, Mr. Justice A. K. Ganguly and Mr. Justice RM Lodha superseding seniority of Mr. Justice AP Shah, Mr. Justice AK Patnaik and Mr. Justice VK Gupta. Any other relief deemed fit in favour of the petitioner may kindly be allowed.

Contention by the Opposition/Respondent Counsel

Learned Counsel for respondents submitted that the information sought by appellant Shri Subhash Chandra Agrawal in the present case falls squarely within the exemption Under Section 8(1)(e) of the RTI Act. He has, in this context, closely examined the meaning of the term 'fiduciary' and in this connection has quoted from the decision of the Supreme Court in Subhash Sharma v. Union of India MANU/SC/0643/1990 : (1991) (Supp) 1-SCC 574 specifically with reference to information held under Article 124 of the Constitution or in discharge of a trust, as follows:

It is a participatory constitutional function. It is, perhaps, inappropriate to refer to any 'power' or 'right' to appoint Judges. It is essentially a discharge of a constitutional trust of which certain constitutional functionaries are collectively repositories.

He has gone on to describe the role of the Chief Justice of India in the appointment process, as below:

It is submitted that the Chief Justice of India whilst performing his functions under Article 124(2) acts in a fiduciary capacity visa a vis other judges and Chief Justices of High court. The information made available with the Chief Justice in pursuance of his functions under Article 124(2) is held in confidence and in trust being the pater families of the Judiciary for the purposes for forming an opinion under Article 124(2).

In the SC Advocates case, the Hon'ble Supreme Court whilst elaborating on the role of chief Justice in the consultation process held that the provisions for consultation with CJI was introduced in the Constitution as he was best equipped to know and assess the worth of the candidate. It was submitted that the 'information' about the candidate available with the Chief Justice is in fiduciary capacity as the pater families of the Judiciary.

Counsel has also quoted from the decision of Justice Verma in Supreme Court Advocates on Record Association v. Union of India MANU/SC/0073/

1994 : (1993) 4 SCC 441, as follows:

"452. This is not surprising if we remember that even in United Kingdom where similar judicial appointments are in the absolute discretion of the executive, these appointments are made by convention on the advice of the Prime Minister after consultation with the Lord Chancellor, who himself consults with senior members of the judiciary before making his choice or consulting with the Prime Minister and the Prime Minister would depart from the recommendations of the Lord Chancellor only in the most exceptional case. (See The Politics of Judiciary-J.A. G. Griffith at pp. 17-18). The Lord Chancellor, Lord Mackay speaking recently on 'The Role of the Judge in a Democracy said:

One of the most important responsibilities of a Lord Chancellor in our democracy is for judicial appointments. It is my duty to ensure that neither political bias, nor personal favouritism, nor animosity play any party in the appointment of judges and that they are selected regardless of sex, ethnic origin or religion on the basis of their fitness to carry out the solemn responsibility of judicial office. I look for those with integrity, professional ability, experience, and standing, a sound temperament and good health. To achieve this I consult widely and regularly with the judges, Law Lords and other members of the legal profession. I naturally attach particular importance to the opinion of the Division of the High Court. Judges therefore have an important role in judicial appointments, albeit informally father than prescribed by statute."

Learned Counsel then gone on to quote extensively from Supreme Court Advocates as below:

"462. The constitutional purpose to be served by these provisions is to select the best from amongst those available for appointment as judges of the superior judiciary, after consultation with those functionaries who are best suited to make the selection. It is obvious that only those persons should be considered fit for appointment as judges of the superior judiciary who combine the attributes essential for making an able, independent and fearless judge. Several attributes together combine to constitute such a personality. Legal expertise, ability to handle cases, proper personal conduct and ethical attributes of a person suitable for appointment as a superior judge. The initial appointment of judges in the High

Courts is made from the Bar and the subordinate judiciary. Appointment to the Supreme Court is mainly from amongst High Court Judges, and on occasions directly from the Bar. The arena of performance of those men are the courts. It is, therefore, obvious that the maximum opportunity for adjudging their ability and traits, is in the Courts and, therefore, the judges are best suited to assess their true worth and fitness for appointment as Judges. This is obviously the reason for introducing the requirement of consultation with the Chief Justice of India in the matter of appointment of all Judges, and with the Chief Justice of the High Court in the case of appointment of a Judge in a High Court. Even the personal traits of the members of the Bar and the Judges are quite often fully known to the Chief Justice of India and the Chief Justice of the High Court who get such information from various sources. There may, however, be some personal trait of an individual lawyer or Judge, which may be better known to the executive and may be unknown to the Chief Justice of India and the Chief Justice of the High Court, and which may be relevant for assessing his potentially to become a good judge. It is for this reason, that the executive is also one of the consultees in the process of appointment. The object of selecting the best men to constitute the superior judiciary is achieved by requiring consultation with not only the judiciary but also the executive to ensure that every relevant particular about the candidate is known and duly weighed as a result of effective consultation between all the consultees before the appointment is made."

He concluded that there is no public interest involved in the present case and that the Hon'ble Supreme Court in the Supreme Court Advocates case has specifically held that public interest lies in keeping appointments and transfers undisclosed.

Contention by the Appellant Counsel

Learned Counsel for appellant Shri Prashant Bhushan cited the decision of the Supreme Court in S.P. Gupta v. Union of India MANU/SC/ 0080/1981 : AIR (1982) SC 149, which he has relied, as follows:

"82. These selfsame reasons must apply equally in negativing the claim for immunity in respect of the correspondence between the Law Minister and the

Chief Justice of India and the relevant nothings made by them in regard to the transfer of a High Court Judge including the Chief Justice of a High Court. These documents are extremely material for deciding whether there was full and effective consultation with the Chief Justice of India before effecting the transfer and the transfer was made in public interest, both of which are, according to the view taken by us, justiciable issues and the non disclosure of these documents would seriously handicap the petitioner in showing that there was no full and effective consultation with the Chief Justice of India or that the transfer was by way of punishment and not in public interest. It would become almost impossible for the petitioner, without the aid of these documents, to establish his case, even if it be true. Moreover, the transfer of a High Court Judge or Chief Justice of a High Court is a very serious matter and if made arbitrarily or capriciously or by way of punishment or without public interest motivation, it would erode the independence of the judiciary which is a basic feature of the Constitution and therefore, when such a charge is made it is in public interest that it should be fully investigated and all relevant documents should be produced before the court so that the full facts may come before the people, who in a democracy are the ultimate arbiters. It would be plainly contrary to public interest to allow the inquiry into such a charge to be baulked or frustrated by a claim for immunity in respect of documents essential to the inquiry. It is also important to note that when the transfer of a High Court Judge or Chief Justice of a High Court is challenged, the burden of showing that there was full and effective consultation with the Chief Justice of India and the transfer was effected in public interest is on the Union of India and it cannot withhold the relevant documents in its possession on a plea of immunity and expect to discharge this burden by a mere statement in an affidavit. Besides, if the reason for excluding these documents is to safeguard the proper functioning of the higher organs of the State including the judiciary, then that reason is wholly inappropriate where what is charged is the grossly improper functioning of those very organs. It is, Court Judge or Chief Justice of a High Court is challenged, no immunity can be claimed in respect of the correspondence exchanged between the Law Minister and the Chief Justice of India and the nothings made by them, since, on the balance, the non-disclosure of these documents would cause greater injury to public interest than what may be caused by their disclosure.

83. But, quite apart from these considerations, we do not understand how the disclosure of the correspondence exchanged between the Law Minister, the Chief Justice of the High Court, the State Government and the Chief Justice of India and the relevant notes made by them in regard to non appointment of an Additional Judge for a further term or transfer of a High Court Judge can be detrimental to public interest. It was argued by the learned Solicitor-General on behalf of the Union of India that if the Chief Justice of the High Court and the Chief Justice of India differ in their views in regard to the suitability of an Additional Judge for further appointment, the disclosure of their views would cause considerable embarrassment because the rival views might be publicly debated and there might be captious and uninformed criticism which might have the effect of undermining the prestige and dignity of one or the other Chief Justice and shaking the confidence of the people in the administration of justice. If the difference in the views expressed by the Chief Justice of the High Court and the Chief Justice of India becomes publicly known, contended the learned Solicitor-General, it might create a difficult situation for the Chief Justice of the High Court vis-à-vis the Chief Justice of India and if despite the adverse opinion of the Chief Justice of the High Court, the Additional Judge is continued for a further term, and the Additional Judge knows that he has been so continued overruling the view of the Chief Justice of the High Court, it might lead to a certain amount of friction which would be detrimental to the proper functioning of the High Court. So also if an Additional Judge is continued for a further term accepting the view expressed by the Chief Justice of the High Court and rejecting the opinion of the Chief Justice of India, it would against create a piquant situation because it would affect the image of the Chief Justice of India in the public eyes. Moreover, a feeling might be created in the mind of the public that a person who was regarded as unsuitable for judicial appointment by one or the other of the two Chief Justices, has been appointed as a Judge and the litigants would be likely to have reservations about him and the confidence of the people in the administration of justice would be affected. The learned Solicitor-General contended that for these reasons it would be injurious to public interest to disclose the correspondence exchanged between the Law Minister, the Chief Justice or the High Court and the Chief Justice of India.

84. We have given our most anxious thought to this argument urged by the leaned Solicitor General, but we do not think we can accept it. We do not see any reason why, if the correspondence between the Law Minister, the Chief Justice of the High Court and the Chief Justice of India and the relevant notes made by them, in regard to discontinuance of an Additional Judge are relevant to the issues arising in a judicial proceeding, they should not be disclosed. There might be difference of views between the Chief Justice of the High Court and the Chief Justice of India but so long as the views are held bona fide by the two Chief Justices, we do not see why they should be worried about the disclosure of their views? Why should they feel embarrassed by public discussion or debate of the views expressed by them when they have acted bona fide with the greatest care and circumspection and after mature deliberation. Do Judges sitting on a Division Bench not differ from each other in assessment of evidence and reach directly contrary conclusions on questions of fact? Do they not express their judicial opinions boldly and fearlessly leaving it to the jurists to decide which of the two differing opinions is correct? If two Judges do not feel any embarrassment in coming to different findings of fact which may be contrary to each other, why should two Chief Justices feel embarrassed if the opinions given by them in regard to the suitability of an Additional Judge for further appointment differ and such differing opinions are made known to the public. Not only tolerance but acceptance of bona fide difference of opinion is a part of judicial discipline and we find it difficult to believe that the disclosure of their differing opinions might create a strain in the relationship between the Chief Justice of the High Court and the Chief Justice of India. We have no doubt that the Chief Justice of the High Court would come to his own independent opinion on the material before him and he would not surrender his judgment to the Chief Justice of India, merely because the Chief Justice of India happens to be head of the judiciary having a large voice in the appointment of Judges on the Supreme Court Bench. Equally we are confident that merely because the Chief Justice of the High Court has come to a different opinion and is not prepared to change that opinion despite the persuasion of the Chief Justice of India, no offence would be taken by the Chief Justice of India and he would not harbour any feeling of resentment against the Chief Justice of the High Court. Both the Chief Justices have trained judicial

minds and both of them would have the humility to recognize that they can be mistaken in their opinions. We do not therefore see any real possibility of estrangement or even embarrassment for the two Chief Justices, if their differing views in regard to the suitability of an Additional Judge for further appointment are disclosed. We also find it difficult to agree that if the differing views of the two Chief Justices become known to the outside world, the public discussion and debate that might ensue might have the effect of lowering the dignity and prestige of one or the other of the two Chief Justices. When the differing views of the two Chief Justices are made public as a result of disclosure, there would certainly be public discussion and debate in regard to those views with some criticizing one view and some criticising the other, but that cannot be helped in a democracy where the right of free speech and expression is a guaranteed right and if the views have been expressed by the two Chief Justices with proper care and deliberation and a full sense of responsibility in discharge of a constitutional duty, there is no reason why the two Chief Justices should worry about public criticism. We fail to see how such public criticism could have the effect of undermining the prestige and dignity of one or the other Chief Justice. So long as the two Chief Justices have acted honestly and bona fide with full consciousness of the heavy responsibility that rests upon them in matters of this kind, we do not think that any amount of public criticism can affect their prestige and dignity. But if either of the two Chief Justices has acted carelessly or improperly or irresponsibly or out of oblique motive, his view would certainly be subjected to public criticism and censure and that might show him in poor light and bring him down in the esteem of the people, but that will be the price which he will have to pay for his remissness in discharge of his constitutional duty. No Chief Justice or Judge should be allowed to hide his improper or irresponsible action under the clock of secrecy. If any Chief Justice or Judge has behaved improperly or irresponsibly or in a manner not befitting the high office he holds, there is no reason why his action should not be exposed to public gaze. We believe in an open government and openness in government does not mean openness merely in the functioning of the executive arm of the State. The same openness must characterize the functioning of the judicial apparatus including judicial appointments and transfer. Today the process of judicial appointments and transfers is shrouded in mystery.

The public does not know how Judges are selected and appointed or transferred and whether any and if so what, principles and norms govern this process. The exercise of the power of appointment and transfer remains a sacred ritual whose mystery is confined only to a handful of high priests, namely the Chief Justice of the High Court, the Chief Minister of the State, the Law Minister of the Central Government and the Chief Justice of India. In case of appointment or non appointment of a High Court Judge and the Law Minister of the Central Government and the Chief Justice of India in case of appointment of a Supreme Court Judge or transfer of a High Court Judge. The mystique of this process is kept secret and confidential between just a few individuals, not more than two or four as the case may be, and the possibility cannot therefore be ruled out that howsoever highly placed may be these individuals, the process may on occasions result in making of wrong appointments and transfers and may also at times, though fortunately very rare, lend itself to nepotism, political as well as personal and even trade off. We do not see any reason why this process of appointment and transfer of Judges should be regarded as so sacrosanct that no one should be able to pry into it and it should not be protected against disclosure at all events and in all circumstances. Where it becomes relevant in a judicial proceeding, why should the Court and the opposite party and through them the people not know what are the reasons for which a particular appointment is made or a particular Additional Judge is discontinued or a particular transfer is affected. We fail to see what harm can be caused by the disclosure of true facts when they become relevant in a judicial proceeding. In fact, the possibility of subsequent disclosure would act as an effective check against carelessness, impetuosity, arbitrariness or mala fides on the part of the Central Government, the Chief Justice of the High Court and the Chief Justice of India and ensure bona fide and correct approach objective and dispassionate consideration, mature thought and deliberation and proper application of mind on their part in discharging their constitutional duty in regard to appointments and transfers of Judges. It is true that if the views expressed by the Chief Justice of the High Court and the Chief Justice of India in regard to the suitability of an Additional Judge for further appointment become known to the public, they might reflect adversely on the competence, character or integrity of the Additional Judge, but the Additional

Judge cannot legitimately complain about it, because it would be at his instance that the disclosure would be ordered and the views of the two Chief Justices made public. If the Additional Judge is appointed for a further term either accepting the opinion expressed by the Chief Justice of the High Court in preference to that of the Chief Justice of India or vice versa, the question of disclosure of differing opinions of the two Chief Justices would not arise, because no one would know that the two Chief Justices were not agreed on continuing the Additional Judge for a further term and therefore, ordinarily, there would be no challenge to the appointment of the Additional Judge. It is only if the Additional Judge is not continued for a further term that he or someone on his behalf may challenge the decision of the Central Government not to continue him and in that event, if he asks for disclosure of the relevant correspondence embodying the views of the two Chief Justices, and if such disclosure is ordered, he has only himself to thank for it and in any event, in such a case there would be no harm done to public interest if the views expressed by the two Chief Justices become known to the public."

Shri Prashant Bhushan further submitted that respondent has not taken the plea of exemption Under Section 8(1)(e) earlier nor the plea that the information sought is not under the control of Chief Justice of India, as a public authority. However, he conceded that in case the information sought contained any information of a personal nature warranting exemption Under Section 8(1)(j), this can be exempted under the severability clause contained in Section 10(1) while making the disclosure.

Decision by CIC

The following kinds of relationships may broadly be categorized as "fiduciary":

- Trustee/beneficiary (Section 88, Indian Trusts Act, 1882)
- Legal guardians / wards (Section 20, Guardians and Wards Act, 1890)
- Lawyer/client;
- Executors and administrators / legatees and heirs
- Board of directors / company

- Liquidator/company
- Receivers, trustees in bankruptcy and assignees in insolvency / creditors
- Doctor/patient
- Parent/child:

The Advanced Law Lexicon, 3rd Edition, 2005, defines fiduciary relationship as

a relationship in which one person is under a duty to act for the benefit of the other on the matters within the scope of the relationship.... Fiduciary relationship usually arise in one of the four situations (1) when one person places trust in the faithful integrity of another, who is a result gains superiority or influence over the first, (2) when one person assumes control and responsibility over another, (3) when one person has a duty to act or give advice to another on matters falling within the scope of the relationship, or (4) when there is specific relationship that has traditionally be recognized as involving fiduciary duties, as with a lawyer and a client, or a stockbroker and a customer

From the above discussion, it may be seen that a fiduciary relationship is one whereby a person places complete confidence in another in regard to a particular transaction or his general affairs or business. The relationship need not be "formally" or "legally" ordained, or established, like in the case of a written trust; but can be one of moral or personal responsibility, due to the better or superior knowledge or training, or superior status of the fiduciary as compared to the one whose affairs he handles. If viewed from this perspective, it is immediately apparent that the CJI cannot be a fiduciary vis-à-vis Judges of the Supreme Court; he cannot be said to have superior knowledge, or be better trained, to aid or control their affairs or conduct. Judges of the Supreme Court hold independent office, and are there is no hierarchy, in their judicial functions, which places them at a different plane than the CJI. In these circumstances, it cannot be held that asset information shared with the CJI, by the judges of the Supreme Court, are held by him in the capacity of a fiduciary, which if directed to be revealed, would result in breach of such duty. So far as the argument that the 1997 Resolution had imposed a confidentiality obligation on the CJI to ensure non-disclosure of the asset declarations, is concerned, the court is of opinion that with the advent of the Act, and the provision in Section 22 - which overrides all other laws, etc. (even overriding the Official Secrets Act) the argument about such a confidentiality condition is on a weak foundation. The mere marking of a document, as "confidential", in this case, does not undermine the overbearing nature of Section 22. Concededly, the confidentiality Clause (in the 1997 Resolution) operated, and many might have bona fide believed that it would ensure immunity from access. Yet the advent of the Act changed all that; all classes of information became its subject matter. Section 8(1) (f) affords protection to one such class, i.e. fiduciaries. The content of such provision may include certain kind of relationships of public officials, such as doctor-patient relations; teacher-pupil relationships, in government schools and colleges; agents of governments; even attorneys and lawyers who appear and advise public authorities covered by the Act. However, it does not cover asset declarations made by Judges of the Supreme Court, and held by the CJI.

The CJI does not hold such declarations in a fiduciary capacity or relationship.

The principles on which the fiduciary relationship can be relied on to seek exemption have been clearly laid down. In the present case excluding personal information, which in any case will be deleted under the severability clause in any disclosure order, the recommendation of appointment of justices is decidedly a public activity conducted in the overriding public interest. Hence the plea of seeking exemption under the definition of fiduciary relationship cannot stand, and even if accepted in technical terms, will not withstand the test of public interest.

Appeal was allowed. The information sought by appellant Shri Subhash Chandra Agrawal will be provided to him. Since the information was not provided within the time specified for the same, it will now be provided free of cost under sub Section (6) of Section 7.

Chapter - 5

DISCLOSURE OF THE ACCOUNTS AND FUNDING OF POLITICAL PARTIES[27]

Facts in Nutshell

Complainant Subhash Chandra Agrawal (Shri S.C. Agrawal) filed Complaint No. CIC/SM/C/2011/001386 and Complainant Shri Anil Bairwal, Complaint No. CIC/SM/C/2011/000838. In both the complaints, the common issue relating to the disclosure of the accounts and funding of Political Parties has been raised.

File No. CIC/SM/C/001386

By his RTI application dated 16.5.2011, complainant S.C. Aggarwal sought the following information from the Presidents/Secretaries of the Indian National Congress (INC/AICC) and the Bhartiya Janata Party (BJP):

1. Copies of Election Menifestoes by BJP for Lok Sabha elections in the years it formed NDA government with Shri Atal Bihari Vajpayee as Prime Minister.
2. Were all the promises made in these election manifestoes fulfilled after BJP having formed government at the Centre.
3. If not, list of promises highlighted in BJP election manifestoes but remained unfulfilled after BJP came to power.
4. Outline of receipts (separately by cash/online/cheque etc) by BJP in last two years separately for each year for which updated account information may be there.

---

[27] Shri Subhash Chandra Aggarwal and Shri Anil Bairwal vs. Indian National Congress/All India Congress Committee and Ors. (03.06.2013 - CIC) : MANU/CI/0068/2013
File No. CIC/SM/C/2011/001386 and File No. CIC/SM/C/2011/000838
Decided On: 03.06.2013
Hon'ble Judges/Coram:
Annapurna Dixit, I.C., M.L. Sharma, I.C. and Satyananda Mishra, C.I.C.

5. Outline of payments (separately by cash/online/cheque etc.) made by BJP in last three years separately for each year for which updated account information may be there.
6. Is it compulsory for every BJP legislature either at Centre or in States or in civic bodies etc to contribute towards party funds?
7. If yes, please provide complete and detailed information including also defaulters in making such contributions to party fund in last three years.
8. Is BJP aware of any of its legislatures (both at Centre and in States)/ civic body member etc. involved in corrupt and other malpractices in last three years?
9. If yes, please provide complete details including action taken by party and others against such persons.
10. Has B.J.P. suggested any proposals to Union government/Election Commission towards electoral reforms?
11. If yes, please provide complete details including reply received from concerned ones if any.
12. Any other related information;
13. File notings on movement of this RTI petition and on all aspects mentioned in this RTI petition.

Shri Moti Lal Vora, Treasurer, AICC, in his letter dated 20th May, 2011, informed the complainant that AICC did not come under the purview of the RTI Act.

Shri Shanti Prasad Aggarwal, Rashtriya Prabhari of BJP, in his letter dated 28th May, 2011, informed the complainant that BJP was not a public authority and, therefore, the Party was not obliged to provide the requisite information.

File No. CIC/SM/C/2011/000838

Complainant Anil Bairwal, in his RTI application dated 29.10.2010 had sought the following information from the under mentioned Political Parties:

- INC/AICC

- BJP
- NCP
- CPI(M)
- CPI
- BSP

1. (a) Sources of the 10 maximum voluntary contributions received by your party from Financial Year 2004-05 to Financial Year 2009-10?
   (b) The modes of these donations (Cheque, cash, DD etc.)?
   (c) The amounts of these donations?
   (d) The Financial Years in which these contributions were made?
2. Sources/Names of all Voluntary Contributors along with their addresses who have made single contributions of more than Rs. 1 lakh to your party from Financial Year 2004-05 to Financial Year 2009-10?

By his letter dated 15th November, 2010, Shri Moti Lal Vora, Treasurer, AICC, had informed the complainant that AICC did not come under the purview of the RTI Act. Shri Chandan Bose, PRO, Nationalist Congress Party, in his letter dated 27th November, 2010, had informed the complainant as under:

It is very important to mention here that NCP is a non-government organization. Hence, we do not have much more resources nor surplus staff to expedite unusual work, which is not in our routine job.

We generate funds from the membership drive and through other resources also, i.e. voluntary contributions from the well-wishers, and followers etc. State units of NCP have major role in membership drive from which we are getting funds in lakhs. State units of NCP at district level, block level and panchayat level organize membership camps frequently and every two years, we file the details regarding our membership and all necessary requisites in Election Commission and other government authorities.

However, I would like to inform you that ours is a National Party duly recognized by Election Commission of India and that from the day of inception of our party, we have been regularly filing our returns to the Income Tax authorities and also to the Election Commission of India along with whatever voluntary contributions received. It is pertinent to mention here that our all obligation towards authorities are up to date.

If you feel like, you may collect all the information you desired, from the above said authorities.

In case you want any clarification, please feel free to contact us.

Shri K.C. Bansal of CPI, in his letter dated 6th November, 2010, had informed the complainant of the sources of ten maximum voluntary contributions received by the Party for the financial years 2004-05 to 2009-10. Importantly, other Political Parties chose not to respond to the RTI application.

Complain before Central Information Commission (CIC)

Shri Subhash Chandra Agrawal filed a complaint dated 6th September, 2011, before CIC in which he had mentioned that All India Congress Committee and Bhartiya Janata Party, being national parties, had got premium land in Delhi/New Delhi at zonal variant institutional rate which was much less than the prevailing market rate and, therefore, it was not correct on their part to plead that they did not fall under the purview of the RTI Act. It was his contention that both AICC/INC and BJP fell under the ambit of section 2(h) of the RTI Act.

Likewise, Shri Anil Bairwal had filed a complaint dated the 14th March, 2011, before the Commission against the responses received from INC/AICC, NCP & CPI, contending therein that the Political Parties, being beneficiaries of the Government, fell under the ambit of Section 2(h) of the RTI Act and, therefore, they were mandated to disclose full and complete information to him.

Written Representation by Shri S.C. Agarwal before CIC

Shri S.C. Agrawal filed a written representation before the Commission in which he has vehemently pleaded for declaring Political Parties as public authorities under section 2(h) of the RTI Act. The salient points made in his representation are enumerated herein-below:-

(i) The Political Parties hold constitutional status and wield constitutional powers under the Tenth Schedule of the Constitution in as much as they have the power to-

(a) disqualify legislators from Parliament and State Assemblies;

(b) bind legislators in their speeches and voting inside the house;

(c) decide what laws are made;

(d) decide whether Government remains in power or which Government should come to power;

(e) decide public policies that affect lives of millions of people.

(ii) As per Article 102(2) of the Constitution, a person can be disqualified from being a member of either House of Parliament under the Tenth Schedule and that a similar provision exists for the State Legislators under Article 191(2) of the Constitution. Furthermore, as per Article 102(2), if a member of a House belonging to a Political Party votes or abstains from voting in the House contrary to the directions issued by the Political Party, he is liable to be disqualified from being a Member of the House.

(iii) The Political Parties have been given statutory status under Section 29A of the Representation of the People Act, 1951.

(iv) Under Section 29A (5) of the Representation of People Act, 1951, the Political Parties are required to bear true faith and allegiance to the Constitution of India as by law established.

(v) The Political Parties give tickets to the candidates and the people vote on party symbols and, thus, the Political Parties are important instrumentalities of democratic governance.

(vi) The Political Parties are substantially financed by the 'appropriate Government' in multiple ways and are exempt from Income Tax.

To canvass his case, Shri Agrawal furnished a copy of letter dated 2.9.2011 of the CPIO of the Land and Development Office(L&DO), Ministry of Urban Development, addressed to him providing information regarding allotment of land by Land and Development Office to various Political Parties. The details of the land allotment to various Political Parties as furnished by the L&DO are extracted below:

S.No	Name of Party	Location, Area & Date of allotment
1.	All India Congress Committee of Indian National Congress	Plot at Dr. Rajinder Prasad Road, New Delhi (also known as Jawahar Bhawan), Area = 9518,42 sq.yds, allotted on 8.9.75, Pocket-9A, Kotla Road, Area = 8092 sq. m. Allotted on 19.11.2007
2.	Rashtriya Janata Dal	Plot Nos. 34, 57, 58 & 59 at Kotla Road, New Delhi Area = 1904 sq. m. allotted on 3,7.2007.
3.	Communist Party of India (Marxist)	Plot Nos. 27, 28 & 29 at Market Road Institutional Area, New Delhi Area = 1197 sq. m. allotted on 24.11.1967 Plot Nos. 10, 11, 12 & 13 at Kotla Road Area = 2535 sq.m. allotted on 11.12.2008.
4,	Samajwadi Party	Plot No. 1, Vasant Kunj Institutional Area, New Delhi Area = 1 acre, Allotted on 21.1.2009.
5.	Communist Party of India	Plot No. 15, Kotla Marg, New Delhi Area = 0.3 acres. Allotted on 2.12.1967
6.	Bharatiya Janata Party (National Level)	Between Dr. Rajendra Prasad Road and Raisina Road, New Delhi. Area = 1.87 acres. Allotted on 8.3.2001.
7.	Janata Dal (United)	Plot No.4, Vasant Vihar Institutional Area, New Delhi Area = 2000 sq. m. allotted on 27.4.2010
8.	Bharatiya Janata Parly (Delhi State)	Alternative allotment at Plot No.4 & 5, Kotla Road, New Delhi Area = 1060.80 sq. m. allotted on 12.5.2010
9.	All India Anna Dravida Munnetra Kazhakham	Plot No. 13 & 25, Pushp Vihar, M.B. Road. Saket, New Delhi, Area = 1008 Sq. m. Allotted on 30.7.2010
10.	Delhi Pradesh Congress Committee	Plot No. 2, Rouse Avenue Institutional Area Area = 1127 sq.yds. Allotted on 15.5.1987
11.	All India Trinamool Congress	Plot Nos. 2 and 3, at DDU Marg, New Delhi Area = 1000 sq.m. allotted on 01.03.2011.

Shri Agrawal also furnished information regarding the allotment of accommodation to various Political Parties on rental basis and the outstanding dues against them, as received by him from the Directorate of Estates vide their letter dated 24.8.2011. The relevant information is extracted below–

S.No.	Name of the Party	Accommodation	Monthly rent charged
1.	Indian National Congress Committee (I)	26, Akbar Road	3015 + Furniture charges
2.	Indian National Congress	24, Akbar Road	42817 + Furniture charges
3.	Indian National Congress	5, Raisina Road	34189 + Furniture charges
4.	Indian National Congress	CII/109, Chanakyapuri	8078
5.	Bhartiya Janata Party	11, Ashoka Road	66896 + Furniture charges
6.	Bharatiya Janata Party	14, Pandit Pant Marg	15077 + Furniture charges
7.	C.P.I.	AB-4, Purana Quila Road	1550
8.	Nationalist Congress Party	10, Dr. B.D. Marg	1320
9.	President Bahujan Samaj Party	4, G.R.G. Road	1320
10.	Samajwadi Party	18, Copernicus Road	12138
11.	Shri Prakash Karat, General Secretary, CPI(M)	8, Teen Murti Lane	1550

Senior Advocate, Shri Prashant Bhushan addressed the Commission on 26th September, 2012 on behalf of complainant Shri S.C. Agrawal. He vehemently contended that the entire political system in India revolved around the Political Parties. They perform a public function and, therefore, warrant to be declared 'public authority' under section 2(h) of the RTI Act. He has advanced the following arguments:-

(i) Tenth Schedule to the Constitution vests tremendous powers with the Political Parties in as much as they can oust an elected member-whether MP or MLA-from out of the Party if he steps out of the party line. The vast power of the Political Parties has been recognised in this Schedule and, therefore, if purposive interpretation of the Tenth Schedule is made, then the Political Parties can be deemed to be covered under Section 2(h) of the RTI Act.

(ii) As per Section 29C of the Representation of People Act, 1951, all donations of and above Rs. 20,000/- made to Political Parties are required to be reported to the Income Tax Department. This obligation cast on the Political Parties points towards their public character.

(iii) By virtue of powers conferred on it under Article 324 of the Constitution read with section 29A of the Representation of People Act, 1951, and Rules 5 and 10 of the Conduct of Election Rules, 1961, and other powers vested in it, the Election Commission of India made and promulgated the Election Symbols (Reservation and Allotment) Order, 1968. Under this Order, Election Commission allots symbols to various Political Parties. The Election Commission is an instrumentality of the State. Allotment of election symbols by the Election Commission to various Political Parties is suggestive of the public character of the Political Parties.

(iv) The Political Parties get huge tax exemptions under section 13A of the Income Tax Act, 1961, which amounts to indirect financing of the Political Parties in terms of Section 2(h)(d)(i) of the RTI Act.

(v) The Central Government and the State Governments have allotted huge plots of land/buildings/other accommodation in prime locations to all Political Parties all over the country either, free of cost, or on hugely concessional rates. This also amounts to indirect financing of the Political Parties.

(vi) Doordarshan of India allots free air time to the Political Parties during the elections. This is another instance of indirect financing of the Political Parties.

(vii) As the Political Parties are the life blood of the entire constitutional scheme in a democratic polity and as they are indirectly financed by the Central Government and the State Governments in various ways, as discussed hereinabove, the Political Parties need to be declared public authority under section 2(h) of the RTI Act.

Written Representation by Shri Anil Bairwal before CIC

Shri Anil Bairwal also filed a detailed representation before this Commission to contend that Political Parties fall in the ambit of section 2(h) of the RTI Act. In his representation, Shri Bairwal has made the following salient points:-

(i) All the Political Parties have been claiming tax exemption under section 13A of the Income Tax Act. As per his representation, various Political Parties claimed Income Tax exemption as given in the following Table[28]:

Party	Tax Payable Exempted in FY 2006-07 (Rs Crores)	Tax payable Exempted in FY 2007-08 (Rs Crores)	Tax payable Exempted in FY 2008-09 (Rs Crores)	Tax payable Exempted in 3 years (Rs Crores)
BJP	26.86	40.68	73.71	141.25
INC	57.00	75.05	168.87	300.92
BSP	15.44	23.60	0.80	39.84
CPI(M)	6.98	4.62	6.53	18.13
CPI	0.01	0.21	0.02	0.24
NCP	0.90	0.68	8.06	9.64

28 (Source: Compilation from copies of Income Tax Returns received from Income Tax Department under RTI Act)

(ii) State has been indirectly financing various Political Parties by way of free air time on All India Radio. As per his calculation, the amount spent by the State on the Political Parties under this Head is as follows[29]:

S.No.	Name of the Party	Time Allotted for Broadcast at the AIR during LS'09 (Min) for Political Parties	Rate Charged by AIR in Time Category-3 for Every 10 Seconds	Amount Spent by the State for AIR (Rs Lakhs)
1.	BJP	140	800	6.72
2.	BSP	70	800	3.36
3.	CPI	50	800	2.40
4.	CPI(M)	70	800	3.36
5.	INC	160	800	7.68
6.	NCP	50	800	2.40
7.	RJD	55	800	2.64
	Total	595	800	28.56

(iii) The complainant has also argued that the State has spent huge amounts on the Political Parties in the matter of free air time on Doordarshan. The table given by him is reproduced below[30] :

S. No.	Name of the Party	Time Allotted for Telecast at the National Network of DD During Lok Sabha'09 (Min)	Rate Charged by National Network of DD at Non Prime Time Every 10 Seconds	Amount Spent by the State for the National Network during LS'09 (Rs. Crores)	Time Allotted for Telecast at the Regional Network during LS'09 (Min.)	Rate Charged by Regional Network at Non Prime Time Every 10 Seconds	Amount Spent by State for the Regional Network during LS'09 (Rs. Crores)	Total Amount Spent by the State on Political Parties for both the National and Regional Network during LS'09 (Rs. Crores)
1	BJP	140	15,000	1.26	215	10,000	1.25	2.51
2	INC	160	15,000	1.44	240	10,000	1.44	2.88
3	BSP	70	15,000	0.63	100	10,000	0.60	1.23
4	CPI	50	15,000	0.45	75	10,000	0.45	0.90
5	CPI(M)	70	15,000	0.63	105	10,000	0.63	1.26
6	NCP	50	15,000	0.45	80	10,000	0.48	0.93
7	RJD	55	15,000	0.49	85	10,000	0.51	1.00
	Total	595		5.35	900		5.40	10.75

29 (Source: Compilation from Spot Buy Rates and Time Allocated to various Political Parties received from All India Radio and Election Commission of India under various RTI applications).

30 (Source: Compilation from Spot Buy Rates and Time Allocated to various Political Parties received from Doordarshan and Election Commission of India under the RTI Act).

(iv) The valuation of the properties allotted by the Government, as estimated by the complainant Shri Bairwal, as given in his representation, is as follows:-

Parly	**Office and Address (With Allotment Dates)**	**Area**	**Area in Sq.fts. (1 sq.m.= 10.76 Sq. fts, 1 sq. yd.= 9 sq.fts., 1 Acre = 4840 sq.yds.)**	**Current Market Value of the Allotteed Plots on Land (based on Real Estate Consulting Reports @ Rs. 60,000 per sq. ft (Rs.in Crores) (C=B*60,000)**	**Current Market Value of these of allotted plots (Party-wise) (Rs. in crores)**
		(A)	(B)		
INC	1. Plot at Dr. Rajinder Prasad Road, New Delhi (Allotted on 08.09.1975)	9518.42 sq. yds.	85665.78	513.99	1036.41
	2. Pocket 9A, Kotla Road, New Delhi (allotted on 19.11.2007	8092 sq. m.	87069.92	522.42	
BJP	1. Between Dr. Rajendra Prasad Road and Raisina Road (allotted on 08.03.2001)	1.87 acres	81457.20	488.74	557.23
	2. Plot No.4 & 5 Kotla Road New Delhi (allotted on 12.05.2010)	1060.80 sq.m	11414.21	68.49	
CPI(M)	Plots No.27, 28 & 29 at Market Road Institutional Area, New Delhi(allotted on 11.04.1967) Plot No. 10, 11, 12 & 13 Kotla Road, New Delhi (allotted on 11.12.2008)	1197 sq.m 2535 sq.m	12879.72 27276.60	77.28 163.66	240.94
CPI	Plot No. 15 Kolla Marg, New Delhi (allotted on 2.12.1967)	.3 acres	13068.00	78.41	78.41
RJD	Plots No. 34, 57, 58 & 59 at Kotla Road, New Delhi(allotted on 03.07.2007)	1904 sq.m	20487.04	122.92	122.92

SP	Plot No.1, Vasant Kunj Institutional Area, New Delhi (Allotted on 21.01.2009)	1 Acre	43560.00	261.36	261.36
JD	Plot No.4, Vasant Vihar Institutional Area, New Delhi (allotted on 24.10.2010)	2000 sq.m	21520.00	129.12	129.12
AIAD MK	Plot Nos.2 and 3 at DDU Marg New Delhi(Allotted on 01.03.2011)	1008 sq.m	846.08	65.08	65.08
AITC	Plot Nos.2 and 3 at DDU Marg, New Delhi (Allotted on 01.03.2011)	1000 sq. m.	10760.00	64.56	64.56
Total of current Market Values of the plots of land allotted to the Political Parties(Rs. In Crores)				2556.02	2556.02

(v) Under Rules 11 and 12 of the Registration of Electors Rules, 1960, two copies of the Electoral Rolls are supplied to the recognized Political Parties, free of cost. This is another instance of indirect financing of the Political Parties by the State.

(vi) The Central Govt. and the State Governments have allotted various houses/buildings/other types of accommodation to various Political Parties either free of cost or at concessional rates. This also amounts to indirect financing of Political Parties by the respective Governments.

(vii) The Political Parties are continuously engaged in the performance of public duty and it is, therefore, important that they become accountable to the public. Transparency in the working and financial operations of the Political Parties is essential in the larger public interest.

Complainants draw the Commission's attention to section 80GGB of the Income Tax Act which provides that contribution made by an individual or Company to a Political Party is deductible from the total income of the assessee. This provision is exclusively applicable to the Political Parties and is suggestive of indirect financing of the Political Parties by the State.

Transparency in the functioning of Political Parties was recommended by the Law Commission of India in their 170th Report on "Reform of Electoral Laws (1999)". The relevant para of the Law Commission's report is given below:-

On the parity of the above reasoning, it must be said that if democracy and accountability constitute the core of our constitutional system, the same concepts must also apply to and bind the Political Parties which are integral to parliamentary democracy. It is the Political Parties that form the Government, man the Parliament and run the governance of the country. It is therefore, necessary to introduce internal democracy, financial transparency and accountability in the working of the Political Parties. A political party which does not respect democratic principles in its internal working cannot be expected to respect those principles in the governance of the country. It cannot be dictatorship internally and democratic in its functioning outside.

Shri Bairwal relied on CIC decision dated 29.04.2008 in File No. CIC/AT/A/2007/01029 & 01263-01270 wherein transparency in the functioning of Political Parties has been underlined. He particularly draws our attention to para 28 of the decision extracted below:-

28. Political Parties are a unique institution of the modern constitutional State. These are essentially civil society institutions and are, therefore, non governmental. Their uniqueness lies in the fact that in spite of being non governmental, Political Parties come to wield or directly or indirectly influence, exercise of governmental power. It is this link between State power and Political Parties that has assumed critical significance in the context of the Right of Information-an Act which has brought into focus the imperatives of transparency in the functioning of State institutions. It would be facetious to argue that transparency is good for all State organs, but not so good for the Political Parties which control the most important of those organs. For example, it will be a fallacy to hold that transparency is good for the bureaucracy but not good enough for the Political Parties which control those bureaucracies through political executives.

The Commission Has Further Observed

38. The laws of the land do not make it mandatory for Political Parties to disclose the sources of their funding, and even less so the manner of expending those funds. In the absence of such laws, the only way a citizen can gain access to the details of funding of Political Parties is through their Income Tax Returns filed annually with Income Tax authorities. This is about the closest the Political Parties get to accounting for the sources and the extent of their funding and their expenditure. There is unmistakable public interest in knowing these funding details which would enable the citizen to make an informed choice about the Political Parties to vote for. The RTI Act emphasizes that "democracy requires an informed citizenry", and that transparency of information is vital to flawless functioning of constitutional democracy. It is nobody's case that while all organs of the State must exhibit maximum transparency, no such obligation attaches to Political Parties. Given that Political Parties influence the exercise of political power, transparency in their organization, functions and, more particularly, their means of funding is a democratic imperative, and, therefore, is in public interest.

Yet another submission of the complainant was that the Political Parties are being indirectly financed by the State in various ways viz. allotment of land, free of cost, or at nominal rates and exemptions from the Income Tax etc. Paras 3.1 to 3.7 of his representation are extracted below:-

3.1 All Political Parties claim to work for the people and in the national interest. Income tax returns of Political Parties obtained by ADR using the RTI Act reveal that on an average only about 20 per cent of the income of Political Parties comes from donations that they disclose to the Election Commission under section 29C of the Representation of People Act. The sources of the remaining 80 per cent of the income are shrouded in mystery. This is what gives rise to all kinds of speculation about the pernicious influence of illegal money.

3.2 After various RTI applications filed to the central agencies, it was discovered that Political Parties enjoy a number of "facilities" provided to them by the government. This is a clear instance of being "financed indirectly by funds provided by the appropriate government" which puts Political Parties squarely under the definition of 'public authority' as provided for in section 2(h)(d)(ii) of the RTI Act.

3.3 In addition to the 100% exemption on income under section 13A of the Income Tax Act, all the major Political Parties have been provided "facilities" for residential and official use by Directorate of Estates (DOE), Government of India, in New Delhi. They have been given offices and residential accommodations at prime locations in New Delhi (Lutyen's Delhi) such as Akbar Road, Raisina Road, Chanakyapuri. The rentals charged are a fraction of the market rent. These facilities are not just provided to them at nominal rates but their maintenance, upgradation, modernization, renovation, etc. are also done at State expense. Similar "facilities" are also provided at various State capitals, details of which are extremely difficult to obtain.

3.4 Money is also spent by Election Commission of India on Political Parties for providing "facilities" to Political Parties such as free electoral rolls, Doordarshan and All India Radio also provide free broadcast facilities to the Political Parties at election time which results in loss of revenue in terms of air time which has a market value.

3.5 If closely monitored and totalled, the total of public funds spent on Political Parties would possibly amount to hundreds of crores.

3.6 There have been several Judicial pronouncements and also decisions by the Central Information Commission that have held that allotment of real estate, rental on subsidized rated, exemption from tax of various types including income tax amount to "indirect financing" in terms of section 2(h)(d)(ii) of the RTI Act. A few of the more useful citations are given below.

3.6.1 Land: The case that is relevant here is Civil Writ Petition No. 16750 of 2010, The Sutlej Club vs. State Information Commission and another decided on 09.05.2011, commonly referred to as CWP No. 19224 of 2006 alongwith 23 connected cases. The Punjab and Haryana High Court held as follows:

72. Now adverting to the financial help of petitioner-Sutlej Club, Ludhiana (at Sr. No. 15) is concerned, the SIC mentioned that as per revenue record, the land owned by the Provincial Government is given to the Club which amounts to substantial financial assistance by the State Government. The fact that the valuable land upon which the Club was constructed, belongs to the Government and no rent/lease is paid by it to the Government shows that there is a substantial financial assistance by the State to the Club. The cost of prime land provided to the club would be much more than its normal revenue expenditure. Apart from land provided for construction of the club building, the Government has also incurred a part of expenditure on its construction.... In my view, the SIC has recorded the correct finding of fact based on the material on record, by virtue of impugned order dated 8.7.2010.

3.6.2 Land and Income Tax concessions: A directly relevant case here, dealing with both, land and income tax, was decided by the Central Information Commission on 11.01.2012. It was Mr. Tilak Raj Tanwar vs. Government of NCT of Delhi, File No.: CIC/AD/A/2011/001699. After considering all aspects of the issue, the Commission decided as follows:

12. The Commission while relying upon the various decisions given hereinabove is convinced that the Mount St. Mary's School may be considered as being "substantially financed" by the appropriate Government, in view of the 5 acres of prime land granted to it at subsidized rates and income tax concessions being enjoyed by the school and that, therefore, it can be declared as a Public authority.

3.6.3 Exemption from Tax: The case that is relevant here is Civil Writ Petition No. 16086 of 2008, Punjab Cricket Association, SAS Nagar (Mohali) vs. State Information Commission, Punjab and another, decided on 09.05.2011, commonly referred to as CWP No. 19224 of 2006 alongwith 23 connected cases. The Punjab and Haryana High Court held as follows:

68. Now adverting to the case of petitioner-PCA (at Sr. No. 12), it is admitted position that it is enjoying tax exemption from entertainment tax which is an direct financial aid by the State to it. Although the SIC has negatived the plea of the complainant-information seeker, but to my mind, the SIC has slipped into deep legal error in this regard because the PCA is saving heavy amount from exemption of entertainment tax which naturally is an incidence of financial aid by the Government.

3.6.4 Tax exemption and nominal rent: Another case relevant here is Board of Control for Cricket India and another vs. Netaji Cricket Club and others [MANU/SC/0019/2005 : AIR 2005 (SC) 5921]. The Supreme Court observed as follows:

80. The Board is a society registered under the Tamil Nadu Societies Registration Act. It enjoys a monopoly status as regard regulation of the sport of cricket in terms of its Memorandum of Association and Articles of Association. It controls the sport of cricket and lays down the law therefor. It, inter alia, enjoys benefits by way of tax exemption and right to use stadia at nominal annual rent.

3.7 While it may well be argued that the above quoted decisions refer to institutions such as schools, clubs which, in some characteristics, are different from Political Parties but these decisions do recognize, accept and establish the principle that exemption from tax and allotment or permission to use land and other real estate is an accepted form of "financing", though it may be considered "indirect" as it is not in the physical form of money. And this principle is one of the factors that makes Political Parties come under the definition of "public authority" as given in section 2(h) of the RTI Act.

More importantly, the complainant contended that Political Parties have constitutional and statutory status. It was his contention that incorporation of Articles 102(2) and 191(2) through the 42nd Amendment and the 10th Schedule to the Constitution has given constitutional status to the Political Parties. According to him, it is a fallacy to say that any individual can form a political party. A body or entity does not become a political party in the legal sense until it is registered by the Election Commission of India under section 29A of the Representation of the People Act, 1951, and this registration lends it the colour of Public Authority.

Complainant also contended that in exercise of its powers, the Election Commission of India under Elections Symbols (Reservation and Allotment) Order, 1968, promulgated under article 324 of the Constitution and Rules 5 & 10 of the Conduct of Election Rules, 1961, grants symbols to various Political Parties for election purposes for the recognition of Political Parties and can suspend or withdraw recognition of recognized Political Parties on their failure to observe model code of conduct or not following the lawful directions and instructions of the Commission. It is indicative of the public character of the Political Parties.

Director of Estates

Allotment of government accommodation to various Political Parties on monthly rental is extracted below:-

S.No.	Name of Parties	Address of Govt. Accommo dation	Allotment Letter	License Deed	Current Monthly Rent Charged From Parties
1.	Indian National Congress Committee	26, Akbar Road	Enclosed		Rs.8,632/- + Furniture charges
2.	Indian National Congress	24, Akbar Road	Enclosed	Enclosed	Rs.68,571/- Furniture charges
3.	Indian National Congress	5, Raisina Road	Enclosed		Rs.47,665/- Furniture charges
4.	Indian National Congress	C-II/109, Chanakya puri	Enclosed		Rs. 15,137/- + Furniture charges
5.	Bhartiya Janata Party	11, Ashoka Road			Rs.86,832/- + Furniture charges
6.	Bhartiya Janata Party	14,Pandit Pant Marg	Inclosed	Enclosed	Rs.24,788/- + Furniture charges
7.	C.P.I.	AB-4, Purana Quila Road			Rs.1,550/-
8.	Nationalist Congress Party	10, Dr.B. D. Marg			Rs.1,320/-
9.	President Bahujan Samaj Party	4, G.R.G. Road	Enclosed	Enclosed	Rs.1,320/-
10.	Samajwadi Party	18, Coper-Nicus Road	Enclosed	Enclosed	Rs.20,352/-
11.	Shri Prakash Karat, Ceneral Secretary, CPI(M)	8. Teen Murti Lane			Rs. 1,550/-

Contention by Counsel for the BSP

Shri Ambeth Rajan filed a counter affidavit dated 31.10.2012 on behalf of Bahujan Samaj Party (BSP) in which he has taken the plea that the Political Parties are not public authorities under section 2(h) of the RTI Act. Taking his argument further, he submitted that BSP is a political party that has not been notified as public authority by means of any Notification of the appropriate government to the effect that BSP is under control of or substantially financed by the appropriate government. He also contended that State funding on the electoral rolls during elections is done merely to meet statutory obligations under the Registration of Electoral Rules, 1960. Similarly, tax exemption under section 13A of the IT Act is subject to the compliance of the provisions of Income Tax Act. Further more, allotment of government/public land to the Political Parties on concessional rates does not cloth the party into a public authority within the meaning of section 2(h) of the RTI Act.

Contention by the Counsel for Nationalist Congress Party (NCP)

Shri Amit Anand Tiwari, counsel for Nationalist Congress Party(NCP), argued at length to canvass that NCP is not a public authority. He filed a detailed representation in this regard. It was his contention that the NCP does not fall within the ambit of section 2(h) of the RTI Act. He has refuted the arguments advanced by the complainants that the Political Parties are substantially financed by the Government. His contention was that free airtime granted to NCP during the election time on national television and national radio is not suggestive of government financing in as much as during elections, it is a popular practice in most of the democracies. He has referred to the case of Canada in this context. Further, according to him, supply of free electoral rolls during elections to NCP, again, is not indicative of financing by the Government. It is his contention that under rule 11(C) of the Registration of Electoral Rolls, 1960, the Registration Officer is mandated to provide two copies of Electoral Rolls, free of cost, to Political Parties registered under section 29A of the Representation of People Act. This is a statutory requirement and cannot be construed as substantially financing. Similarly, allotment of party office to NCP at economical rates cannot be construed as substantial financing in as-much-as the Government makes this facility available not only to Political Parties recognized by the Election Commission but also to other segments of population such as journalists etc. Further more, it was Shri Tiwari's contention that exemption from Income Tax granted under section 13A of the Income Tax Act also does not mean that the NCP is substantially financed by the Government. He has given the example of Income Tax exemption to the farmers but by virtue of this, the farmers cannot be designated as public authority under section 2(h) of the RTI Act.

Advocate Tiwari filed additional submissions dated 1.11.2012 for NCP in which he has made the following salient points:-

(i) The power exercised by the Political Parties under the 10th Schedule of the Constitution cannot be construed to mean that the Political Parties are public authorities under section 2(h) in as much as these powers can be exercised only when an elected Member has voted or abstained from voting against the whip of the political party or he has voluntarily given up the membership of such political party. Even in such cases, the political party cannot disqualify a Member of Legislature. All that it can do is to move an application seeking disqualification of such elected Member before the Chairman/Speaker of the House who has exclusive authority to declare such elected Member to be disqualified or otherwise.

(ii) No doubt, Political Parties have played a significant role in public life but public interest is not the criterion for declaring a body or institution as public authority under section 2(h) of the RTI Act.

(iii) If Political Parties are declared to be public authorities,, then they will be flooded with applications by pseudo information seekers to maliciously engage the party workers only in responding to the RTI applications thereby causing detriment to their political functioning. The law laid down by the High Court in the Indian Olympic Association case, Commonwealth Games Committee case and Sanskriti School case is not applicable to the Political Parties in as much as there was evidence of huge direct financing by the Government to these bodies/entities which is not true in case of Political Parties.

(iv) Public interest argument is not valid in case of Political Parties under section 11 of the RTI Act. If this argument is accepted, then the identities of the contributors would have to be disclosed and the contributors may not like this to happen. Such disclosure may expose them to harassment and threats by other Political Parties.

(v) In decision dated 8.7.2009 of a Single Bench of this Commission in Complaint No. CIC/MISC./2009/0001 & CIC/MISC./2009/0002, it was held that Political Parties are not covered under section 2(h) of the RTI Act.

(vi) In the decision dated 5.2.2010 of Goa State Information Commission (Shri Pandu Ram-Vs-the President, Maharashtrabadi Gomantak Party), it was held that MGP was not established or constituted under any enactment of State Legislature or by any Notification or order by the Government. Nor was it owned or substantially financed by the State Government and, therefore, was not a public authority.

As per counsel if Political Parties are held to be Public Authorities, then the political rivals would maliciously flood their CPIOs with numerous RTI applications at the time of elections thereby wasting their time and energy and, thus, causing detriment to their political functioning.

Registration, Recognition and Functioning of Political Parties in India

- The Political Parties are registered with the Election Commission of India(ECI) under section 29A of the Representation of People Act, 1951.
- For the purposes of R.P. Act and elections, an association/body gets the status of political party only on its registration with the ECI under section 29A.
- Para 16A of the Election Symbols (Reservation & Allotment) Order, 1968, empowers ECI to suspend or withdraw the recognition of a political party if it refuses to follow the lawful directions and instructions of the Commission or if it refuses to observe the provisions of the Model Code of Conduct.
- As per Supreme Court judgment in Common Cause-Vs-Union of India (MANU/SC/0810/1996 : AIR 1996 SC-3081), ECI is empowered

under Article 324 of the Constitution to require the Political Parties to submit details of expenditure incurred by them in connection with elections.

- ECI has directed the Political Parties to submit their accounts within 90 days after general elections in case of Lok Sabha and within 75 days in the case of Assembly elections.
- Under Section 29C of the R.P. Act, a Political Party is required to report to the ECI in respect of contributions received by it in excess of Rs. 20,000/- from any person or Company.
- The contributions made to the Political Parties are exempt from the Income Tax, both for the donor and the donee.
- Recognition of Political Parties is governed by the provisions of Election Symbols (Reservation and Allotment), 1968, which is an order issued by ECI under Article 324 of the Constitution read with Rules 5 & 10 of the Conduct of Election Rules, 1961, to provide for specification, reservation & allotment of symbols and recognition of Political Parties and matters related thereto.

CIC Previous Decisions on Public Authority

In decision dated 22.4.2010 in Amardeep Walia-vs.-Chandigarh Lawn Tennis Association (File No. CIC/LS/C/2009/900377), the Central Information Commission held Chandigarh Lawn Tennis Association to be public authority. Para 19 of the order is extracted below:-

19. The gravamen of the above judgments is that for a private entity to qualify to be a public authority, substantive financing does not mean 'majority' financing. What is important is that the funding by the appropriate Government is achieving a "felt need of a section of the public or to secure larger societal goals." The ratio of the above judgments, particularly of Delhi High Court, applies to the present case on all the fours. A huge property has been placed at the disposal of CLTA by the Chandigarh Administration at a notional rental of Rs. 100/- per annum. Besides, grant of one lakh rupees was also given to CLTA in FY 2008-09. Concededly,

CLTA fulfills the felt need of a section of the society by way of imparting training to the budding tennis players. It is, therefore, held that CLTA is a Public Authority.

In another decision dated 21.1.2011 in Pradeep Bhanot-Vs-Chandigarh Club, Chandigarh (File No. CIC/LS/A/2010/001184), the Central Information Commission held that the Chandigarh Club was a public authority. The broad facts in this case were that a plot of land measuring 3.85 lacs sq. ft. was leased out to the Club at the rent of Rs. 1,08,208/- per month w.e.f. 20.7.2005 to 19.7.2010 with annual increase of 5%. The Finance Department of Chandigarh Administration had submitted before the Commission that the aforesaid rent was not at par with the market rent. Considering the totality of circumstances, the Commission had concluded that Chandigarh Club was public authority under section 2(h).

In Amrit Mehta-Vs-India International Centre (File No. CIC/WB/A/2009/000965/LS) decided on 1.2.2011, the Commission held that India International Centre is a public authority under section 2(h). The broad facts in this case were that 4.69 acres of prime land was given on perpetual lease to IIC against deposition of Rs. 1,68,840/- as per agreement signed on 22.4.1960 between the President of India and IIC. The yearly rent payable by IIC to the Central Government was Rs. 8,442/- which has remained unchanged during the last five decades. In the facts of the case, the Commission had held as follows:-

XVIII. In view of the above discussion, it clearly emerges that a huge chunk of land measuring 4.69 acres was allotted to IIC in 1968 at a premium of Rs. 1,68,840/- only, obviously, at a concessional rate. The agreement between the parties expressly speaks of concessional allotment of land. Further, IIC was required to pay rent of Rs. 8,442/- per year to the Central Government and this amount has remained unchanged during the last 52 years. This is also clearly indicative of the rent being nominal/concessional in nature. These facts clearly establish that the Central Government has indirectly financed IIC. The RTI Act does not define 'substantial financing'. The expression 'substantial financing' has to be interpreted in the context of a specific case. This has been so held by the Punjab and Haryana High

Court in Civil Writ Petition No. 19224/2006(The Hindu Urban Cooperative Bank Ltd.-Vs-State Information Commission, Punjab) extracted above. Considering the fact that a huge chunk of land was allotted to IIC in 1960 in the very heart of the capital city of Delhi at a premium of Rs. 1,68,840/ - only and also considering the fact that IIC is paying rent of only Rs. 8,442/ - per year to the Central Government over all these years, in our opinion, amounts to indirect substantial financing of IIC by the Central Government. In this view of the matter, we hold that IIC is a Public Authority under section 2(h) of the RTI Act.

Decision by Central Information Commission (CIC)

The Political Parties constitute one of the most important institutions in a constitutional democracy. Prof. Harold J Laski in his classic text "Grammar of Politics" has termed them 'natural', though not 'perfect'. According to him, the life of a democratic State is built upon the party system. Without Political Parties, there would be no means available of enlisting the popular decisions in a politically satisfactory manner. To quote him.

The life of the democratic State is built upon the party-system and it is important at the outset to discuss the part played by party in the arrangement of affairs. Briefly, that part may be best described by saying that parties arrange the issues upon which people are to vote. It is obvious that in the confused welter of the modern State, there must be some selection of problems as more urgent than others. It is necessary to select them as urgent and to present solutions of them which may be acceptable to the citizen-body. It is that task of selection, the party undertakes. It acts, in Mr. Lowell's phrase, as the broker of ideas. From the mass of opinions, sentiments, beliefs, by which the electorate moves, it chooses out those it judges most likely to meet with general acceptance. It organizes persons to advocate its own view of their meaning. It states that view as the issue upon which the voter has to make up his mind. Its power enables it to put forward for election candidates who are willing to identity themselves with its view. Since its opponents will do the same, the electorate, thereby, is enabled to vote as a mass and decision that would otherwise be chaotic, assumes some coherency and direction.

What, at least, is certain, is that without parties there would be no means available to us of enlisting the popular decision in such a way as to secure solutions capable of being interpreted as politically satisfactory.

All modern democracies operate on a party system, some with two as in the USA and some others with multiple Political Parties like in India. The Political Parties mobilize public opinion around their ideologies and beliefs and contest elections to form government. No democracy can exist today without Political Parties. An ordinary citizen does not have direct access to the government except through his elected representative and cannot hope to be part of the government without being a member of a Political Party. His membership of a legislature depends on his membership of a Political Party to begin with. It is, thus, through the Political Parties that the citizens of a democracy operationalise the democratic state. This is precisely what Prof Laski has meant when he says that the existence of Political Parties gives the citizens of a country a viable means to give shape to their political aspirations and beliefs by forming a government of their choice. It will, therefore, not be an exaggeration to say that no Political Party, no democracy. In view of this central importance that they enjoy that the Political Parties have been given in our country such enormous powers and benefits, through both constitutional and statutory arrangements so that they can fulfill their just roles in representing their constituents.

The Political Parties, for example, play a critical role in the disqualification of legislators on ground of defection. As per paragraph 02 of the Tenth Schedule, a Member of a House belonging to any Political Party can be disqualified in certain circumstances. Paragraphs 01, 02 & 03 of Article 02 are extracted below:-

2. Disqualification on ground of defection.-

(1) Subject to the provisions of paragraphs 3, 4 and 5, a member of a House belonging to any political party shall be disqualified for being a member of the House-

(a) if he has voluntarily given up his membership of such political party;

or

(b) if he votes or abstains from voting in such House contrary to any direction issued by the political party to which he belongs or by any person or authority authorized by it in this behalf, without obtaining, in either case, the prior permission of such political party, person or authority and such voting or abstention has not been condoned by such political party, person or authority within fifteen days from the date of such voting or abstention.

Explanation-For the purposes of this sub-paragraph,—

(a) an elected member of a House shall be deemed to belong to the political party, if any, by which he was set up as a candidate for election as such member;

(b) a nominated member of a House shall,—

(i) where he is a member of any political party on the date of his nomination as such member, be deemed to belong to such political party;

(ii) in any other case, be deemed to belong to the political party of which he becomes, or, as the case may be, first becomes, a member before the expiry of six months from the date on which he takes his seat after complying with the requirements of article 99 or, as the case may be, article 188.

(2) An elected member of a House who has been elected as such otherwise than as a candidate set up by any political party, shall be disqualified for being a member of the House if he joins any political party after such election.

(3) A nominated member of a House shall be disqualified for being a member of the House if he joins any political party after the expiry of six months from the date on which he takes his seat after complying with the requirements of article 99 or, as the case may be, article 188.

Section 29A of the Representation of People (RP) Act, 1951, empowers the Election Commission of India (ECI) to register Political Parties for the purposes of this Act. In other words, without such registration, a Political Party cannot participate in the electoral process. Sub section (1) of 29-A is extracted below:-

(1) Any association or body of individual citizens of India calling itself a political party and intending to avail itself of the provisions of this Part shall make an application to the Election Commission for its registration as a political party for the purposes of this Act.

Further, in exercise of its powers under Article 324 of the Constitution read with section 29A of the RP Act, 1951, and rules 05 and 10 of the Conduct of Election Rules, 1961, the Election Commission issues the Election Symbols (Reservation & Allotment) Order, 1968. This Order has been issued for the purity of the elections in the Lok Sabha and the Legislative Assemblies of States and in the interest of conduct of such elections in a fair and efficient manner and for "the specification, reservation, choice and allotment of symbols for the recognition of Political Parties". This order lays down conditions for recognition of the National Parties and the State Parties. The Election Commission allots symbols to National and State Political Parties under para 08 of the Order. This order also provides for allotment of symbols to unrecognized Political Parties. Para 16-A of the order empowers the Commission to suspend or withdraw permission of a recognized political party for its failure to observe the model code of conduct or follow lawful directions and instructions of the Commission. Importantly, as per para 07 of the order, the Election Commission can issue Notifications in the Gazette of India publishing therein the list specifying the National Parties/State parties and the symbols respectively reserved for them. It can also issue Gazette Notifications in respect of unrecognized Political Parties and addresses of their Headquarters etc.

Question before CIC

Whether the political parties have the ingredients which would qualify them to be public authorities within the meaning of section 2(h)[31] of the Right to Information (RTI) Act.

---

[31] Section 2(h) of the RTI Act defines 'public authority' as follows:-

(h) "public authority" means any authority or body or institution of self-Government established or constituted,—

(a) by or under the Constitution;

(b) by any other law made by Parliament;

(c) by any other law made by State Legislature;

In CIC View

(A) Legal/General

(a) that the Political Parties are the building blocks of a constitutional democracy;

(b) that under Tenth Schedule of the Constitution, a Political Party can have a Member of the House disqualified in certain circumstances;

(c) that a Political Party is required to be registered by the Election Commission of India under section 29A of the Representation of People Act, 1951;

(d) that under section 29C of the RP Act, 1951, a Political Party is required to submit a report for each Financial Year to the Election Commission of India in respect of contributions received by it in excess of 20,000/- rupees from any person as also contributions in excess of 20,000/- rupees received from non-Government companies;

(e) that in exercise of its powers under Article 324 read with section 29A of the RP Act, 1951, and rules 5 & 10 of the Conduct of Election Rules, 1961, the Election Commission has issued Election Symbols (Reservation & Allotment) Order, 1968, under which election symbols are allotted to various National/State Political Parties;

(f) that Election Commission can suspend or withdraw recognition of a recognized political party in the event of violation of provisions of Election Symbol (Reservation & Allotment) Order, 1968;

(g) that Central Information Commission's order dated 29.4.2008 directing the Political Parties to disclose their Income Tax Returns holds the field and is being complied with.

(B) Financial

(a) that the Land & Development Office of the Ministry of Urban

---

(d) by notification issued or made by the appropriate Government, and includes any-

(i) body owned, controlled or substantially financed;

(ii) non-Government Organisation substantially financed, directly or indirectly by funds provided by the appropriate Government

Development has allotted large tracts of land in Delhi to various Political Parties either free of cost or at concessional rates;

(b) that the Directorate of Estates, Ministry of Urban Development, has allotted accommodation in Delhi to various Political Parties on rental basis at concessional rates;

(c) that Political Parties have been claiming and granted total tax exemption under section 13A of the Income Tax Act for all their income;

(d) that the State has been indirectly financing Political Parties by way of free air time on All India Radio and Doordarshan of India during the elections; &

(e) that recognized Political Parties are issued copies of electoral rolls by the Election Commission, free of cost, at the time of elections.

It is also true that these political parties have not been established or constituted by any specific notification issued or order made by an appropriate government as provided in (d)[32] of this particular section. However, it is pertinent to remember that they have been brought into existence first as political parties and then as national level political parties by the Election Commission of India thereby entitling them to a host of benefits, the principal among them being the right to accept contribution from both individual citizens and private companies and also to get complete income tax exemption on all their incomes. The other important benefit that accrues to these political parties on account of their recognition by the Election Commission of India as national level political parties is the common symbol on which their candidates can contest elections. Thus, if not strictly within the letter of this particular provision (d), but at least, in spirit,

---

[32] Section 2(h) of the RTI Act defines 'public authority' as follows:-

(h) "public authority" means any authority or body or institution of self-Government established or constituted,—

(a) by or under the Constitution;

(b) by any other law made by Parliament;

(c) by any other law made by State Legislature;

(d) by notification issued or made by the appropriate Government, and includes any-

(i) body owned, controlled or substantially financed;

(ii) non-Government Organisation substantially financed, directly or indirectly by funds provided by the appropriate Government.

these political parties can be said to have been constituted by their registration by the Election Commission of India, a fact akin to the establishment or constitution of a body or institution by an appropriate government.

The complainants have submitted that the land and buildings provided to these political parties in the national capital at Delhi and probably elsewhere in the States and the complete income tax exemption provided to them would amount to substantial financing, the political parties themselves have strongly argued that whatever benefits they might have received from the Central Government would hardly amount to any substantial financing. While it is true that the expression "substantial" has not been defined in the Right to Information Act, in a number of decisions, the superior courts have held that "substantial financing" need not be "majority financing". In other words, there must be evidence of state funding which is not "insubstantial" of such non-governmental bodies to bring them within the ambit of this particular provision.

The complainants adduced the following three principal grounds to persuade the Commission to hold that the aforesaid Political Parties are Public Authorities viz.:-

(i) Indirect substantial financing by the Central Government;

(ii) Performance of public duty by the Political Parties; and

(iii) Constitutional/legal provisions vesting Political Parties with rights and liabilities.

Substantial Financing of Political Parties by the Central Govt.

The first and foremost method of indirect financing is allotment of large tracts of land in prime areas of Delhi either, free of cost, or at concessional rates. Even allowing for the margin of error in the estimation of the value of land allotted to various political parties by complainant Shri Bairwal, CIC held that this land has been allotted at hugely concessional rates. Thus, in CIC considered opinion, it amounted to indirect financing and when added to the income tax exemption enjoyed by these political parties, it would amount to substantial financing.

Another method of financing of Political Parties by the Central Government is allotment of houses on rental basis on concessional rates. Of the various benefits that the central government extends to these political parties, the total exemption from payment of income tax on their incomes, very obviously, constitutes the most important benefit. Section 13A of the Income Tax Act reads as follows:

Any income of a political party which is chargeable under the head income from house property or income from other sources or capital gains or any income by way of voluntary contributions received by a political party from any person shall not be included in the total income of the previous year of such political party:

Provided that-

(a) such political party keeps and maintains such books of account and other documents as would enable the assessing officer to properly deduce its income therefrom;

(b) in respect of each such voluntary contribution in excess of Rs. 20,000, such political party keeps and maintains a record of such contribution and the name and address of the person who has made such contribution; and

(c) the accounts of such a political party are audited by an accountant as defined in the explanation below subsection 2 of section 288:

Provided further that if the treasurer of such political party or any other person authorised by that political party in this behalf fails to submit a report under subsection 3 of section 29C of the Representation of the People Act 1951 for the financial year, no exemption under this section shall be available for that political party for such financial year.

Since these political parties have not paid any income tax, the exact quantum of money that the Central Government has forgone in the process has not been worked out specifically. However, since the level of income of all these political parties would place them in the highest slab of income tax, at least 30% of their total income would have been collected as income tax but for the total exemption given to them by law. By a simple calculation, this would show that the Central

Government has bestowed financial benefits on the six political parties to the extent of the amount shown against each as per the following table:

Party	Tax Payable Exempted in FY 2006-07 (Rs. Crores)	Tax Payable Exempted in FY 2007-08 (Rs. Crores)	Tax Payable Exempted in FY 2008-09 (Rs. Crores)	Tax Payable Exempted in 3 years (Rs. Crores)
BJP	26.86	40.68	73.71	141.25
INC	57.00	75.05	168.87	300.92
BSP	15.44	23.60	0.80	39.84
CPI(M)	6.98	4.62	6.53	18.13
CPI	0.01	0.21	0.02	0.24
NCP	0.90	0.68	8.06	9.64

Thirty per cent of their income which these political parties would have otherwise paid by way of income tax has been given up in their favour by the Central Government. No one can dispute that this is substantial financing, though indirectly. Added to this the concessional allotment of land and buildings in prime locations in the national capital and, probably, in several state headquarters, if not at district level also, the total amount of direct and indirect financing/funding of these political parties is considerable. On behalf of the political parties, it has been argued that the income tax exemption cannot be said to be a form of financing. In support of this argument, they have submitted that such concessions and exemptions are routinely extended to many charitable and non-profit non-governmental organisations across the country. Therefore, according to them, if those numerous nongovernmental organisations are not considered to be public authorities, there is no reason why the political parties should be considered so. We cannot accept this argument. There is a great difference between the tax exemption given to charitable and non-profit nongovernmental organisations and that given to the political parties. The exemption given to the former is strictly conditional: full or part exemption is given to these organisations only if they pursue the objectives outlined in their respective charters, be it the memorandum of association and bye-laws in case they are societies or the trust deeds, in case they are private trusts. There are other strict conditions laid down in the Income

Tax Act which the assessee must comply with. In other words, if any of these non-governmental organisations are found not to be pursuing their objectives or spending the tax exempt amount on activities other than what is enshrined in their respective charters or not comply with the conditions, their entire income becomes subject to taxation, sometimes with penalty. On the other hand, the tax exemption given to the political parties is complete, the only condition being that they must report to the Election Commission of India, every year, the details of all the contributors who contribute Rs. 20,000 or more to the political party concerned. Thus, the political parties enjoy an almost unfettered exemption from payment of income tax, a benefit not enjoyed by any other charitable or non-profit non-governmental organisations.

The Income Tax exemptions granted and the free air time at AIR and Doordarshan at the time of elections also has substantially contributed to the financing of the Political Parties by the Central Government. CIC therefore concluded that INC/AICC, BJP, CPI(M), CPI, NCP and BSP have been substantially financed by the Central Government and, therefore, they are held to be public authorities under section 2(h) of the RTI Act.

Performance of Public Duty

The Political Parties are the life blood of our polity. As observed by Laski "The life of the democratic state is built upon the party system". Elections are contested on party basis. The Political Parties select some problems as more urgent than others and present solutions to them which may be acceptable to the citizens. The ruling party draws its development programs on the basis of its political agenda. It is responsible for the growth and development of the society and the nation. Political Parties affect the lives of citizens, directly or indirectly, in every conceivable way and are continuously engaged in performing public duty. It is, therefore, important that they became accountable to the public.

Political Parties are the unique institution of the modern constitutional State. These are essentially political institutions and are non-governmental. Their uniqueness lies in the fact that inspite of being non-governmental, they come to wield or directly or indirectly influence exercise of governmental power. It would be odd to argue that transparency is good for all State organs but not so good for Political Parties, which, in reality, control all the vital organs of the State. The National Commission to Review the Working of the Constitution in its report submitted in March 2002 has recommended that Political Parties as well as individual candidates be made subject to a proper statutory audit of the amounts they spend. In Common Cause (A Registered Society vs. Union of India) (MANU/SC/0810/1996 : AIR 1996 SC 3081), the Supreme Court has dealt with the income and expenditure incurred by the Political Parties and has laid emphasis on transparency on election funding.

The people of India must know the source of expenditure incurred by Political Parties and by the candidates in the process of election. Preamble to the Constitution of India aims at securing to all its citizens: JUSTICE, social, economic and political; LIBERTY of thought, expression, belief, faith and worship; and, EQUALITY of status and of opportunity. Coincidentally, the preamble of RTI Act also aims to promote these principles in the form of transparency and accountability in the working of the every public authority. It also aims to create an 'informed citizenry' and to contain corruption and to hold government and their instrumentalities accountable to the governed. Needless to say, Political Parties are important political institutions and can play a critical role in heralding transparency in public life. Political Parties continuously perform public functions which define parameters of governance and socio-economic development in the country.

In view of the nature of public functions performed by Political Parties (INC, BJP, CPI(M), CPIO, NCP and BSP) CIC concluded that Political Parties in question were Public Authorities under section 2(h) of the RTI Act. The Presidents, General/Secretaries of Political Parties Were directed to designate CPIOs and the Appellate Authorities at their headquarters in 06 weeks time.

CIC was of the view that bringing the Political Parties in the ambit of RTI Act is likely to usher an era of transparency in their functioning. Besides it would result in strengthening of democracy and democratic institutions in the country.

Chapter - 6

RECOVERY OF TAXES FROM THE POLITICAL PARTIES[33]

Facts in Nutshell

The Appellant vide his RTI application sought information regarding the amount of Rs. 709.85 crore mentioned in a news item to be lying pending as tax for recovery from the political parties for the period between December, 2013 to June, 2015 and issues related thereto.

Reply by CPIO (Central Public Information Officer) and First Appellate Authority

The CPIO vide its letter dated 30.12.2015 denied disclosure of information under Section 8(1)(d), 8(1)(e) and 8(1)(h) of the RTI Act, 2005 read with Section 138(1)(a) of the IT Act, 1961. Dissatisfied by the response of the CPIO, the Appellant approached the FAA.

Dissatisfied by the response of FAA, the Appellant approached the Commission (Central Information Commission, CIC). Furthermore he also approached the Hon'ble High Court of Punjab and Haryana for issuance of appropriate direction in the matter. The Hon'ble High Court of Punjab and Haryana vide order dated 02.04.2019 in CWP No. 8869/2019 issued the following direction:

"In the light of the submissions made by counsel for the petitioner and without commenting upon the merits of the case, the present petition is disposed of with directions to the Central Information Commission-respondent No. 2 to consider and decide the application dated 06.06.2017 in accordance with law by fixing a date therein after hearing the petitioner or his counsel at an early date. The date

---

33 Ram Kumar vs. CPIO and Asst. Commissioner of Income Tax (E), Circle-1(1) and Ors. (01.05.2019 - CIC) : MANU/CI/0184/2019
Hon'ble Judges/Coram:
Bimal Julka, Information Commissioner

for hearing of the application be fixed not beyond a period of four weeks from today."

Contention by Respondent (Commissioner of Income Tax) before CIC

The Respondent reiterated the submissions of the CPIO/FAA and stated that due to the sensitivities of the matter, the information could not be disclosed. On being queried by the Commission about the amount of tax recovery due from the six political parties viz Congress, BJP, CPI (M), All India Trinamool Congress, Samajwadi party, NCP and BSP as contained in the news report published in HT Chandigarh dated 11.12.2013, the Respondent feigned ignorance and stated that no further details could be shared. It was noted by the Commission that the FAA did not follow the procedure laid down under Section 11 of the RTI Act, 2005 and merely sought shelter under Section 8(1)(d) & (j) of the RTI Act, 2005 without giving a reasoned response.

Report of the Law Commission (1999) is Reproduced below

" On the parity of the above reasoning, it must be said that if democracy and accountability constitute the core of our constitutional system, the same concepts must also apply to and bind the Political Parties which are integral to parliamentary democracy. It is the Political Parties that form the Government, man the Parliament and run the governance of the country. It is therefore, necessary to introduce internal democracy, financial transparency and accountability in the working of the Political Parties. A political party which does not respect democratic principles in its internal working cannot be expected to respect those principles in the governance of the country. It cannot be dictatorship internally and democratic in its functioning outside."

Transparency and Accountability

Much before the legislative enactment of the RTI Act, 2005, our Judiciary, in a progressive interpretation of the Constitutional provisions, had paved the way towards delineating the Right to Information. In 1975, in State of UP vs. Raj Narain (MANU/SC/0032/1975 : 1975 AIR 865, 1975 SCR (3) 333), Justice

Mathew had ruled:

"In a government of responsibility like ours, where all the agents of the public must be responsible for their conduct, there can be but few secrets. The people of this country have a right to know every public act, everything that is done in a public way by their public functionaries."

Subsequently in judgments such as S.P. Gupta v. Union of India[1981] Supp. SCC 87, the Hon'ble Supreme Court of India had held that "the concept of an open government is the direct emanation from the right to know which seems to be implicit in the right of free speech and expression guaranteed under Article 19(1)(a)."

Transparency and sanctity in the election process and disclosure of particulars of candidates representing citizens in Parliament is critical to enable members of a democratic society to be sufficiently informed so that they may cast their votes intelligently in favour of persons who are to govern them. Even the Hon'ble Supreme Court of India vide its important and significant decision passed by way of resolution dated 03.10.2017 declared that decisions of collegiums with reasons should be uploaded on website for ensuring transparency of collegium system.

"THAT the decisions henceforth taken by the Collegium indicating the reasons shall be put on the website of the Supreme Court, when the recommendation(s) is/are sent to the Government of India, with regard to the cases relating to initial elevation to the High Court Bench, confirmation as permanent Judge(s) of the High Court, elevation to the post of Chief Justice of High Court, transfer of High Court Chief Justices/Judges and elevation to the Supreme Court, because on each occasion the mater...

The Resolution is passed to ensure transparency and yet maintain confidentiality in the Collegium system."

Political parties continuously perform public functions and play a critical role in governance and socio-economic development in the country. The RTI Act, 2005 was enacted to ensure smoother and greater access to information, maximum disclosure and minimum exemptions and effective mechanism for access of information.

The importance of right to information and subordination of right to privacy to the right to information due to larger public interest had been recognized by P. Venkatarama Reddi J. in his judgment in People's Union for Civil Liberties (PUCL) and Anr. V. Union of India and Anr. WRIT PETITION (CIVIL) No. 490 OF 2002 with WRIT PETITION (CIVIL) No. 509 OF 2002 AND WRIT PETITION (CIVIL) No. 515 of 2002 wherein it had been held as under:

"By calling upon the contesting candidate to disclose the assets and liabilities of his/her spouse, the fundamental right to information of a voter/ citizen is thereby promoted. When there is a competition between the right to privacy of an individual and the right to information of the citizens, the former right has to be subordinated to the latter right as it serves larger public interest. The right to know about the candidate who intends to become a public figure and a representative of the people would not be effective and real if only truncated information of the assets and liabilities is given."

Furthermore, Justice M.B. Shah in its decision in the aforementioned case of People's Union for Civil Liberties (PUCL) and Anr. V. Union of India and Anr. WRIT PETITION had held as under:

"In our view, the aforesaid decision nowhere supports the said 30 contention. This Court only considered—to what extent a citizen would have right to privacy under Article 21. The court itself has carved out the exceptions and restrictions on absolute right of privacy. Further, by declaration of a fact, which is a matter of public record that a candidate was involved in various criminal cases, there is no question of infringement of any right of privacy. Similarly, with regard to the declaration of assets also, a person having assets or income is normally required to disclose the same under the Income Tax Act or such similar fiscal legislation. Not only this, but once a person becomes a candidate to acquire public office, such declaration would not affect his right of privacy. This is the necessity of the day because of statutory provisions of controlling wide spread corrupt practices as repeatedly pointed out by all concerned including various reports of Law Commission and other Committees as stated above."

Furthermore, the Commission in the decision in CIC/AT/A/2007/01029, CIC/AT/A/2007/01263, CIC/AT/A/2007/01264, CIC/AT/A/2007/01265, CIC/AT/A/2007/01266, CIC/AT/A/2007/01267, CIC/AT/A/2007/01268, CIC/AT/A/2007/01269, CIC/AT/A/2007/01270 dated 29.04.2008 had held as under:

"38. The laws of the land do not make it mandatory for political parties to disclose the sources of their funding, and even less so the manner of expending Page 17 of 24 those funds. In the absence of such laws, the only way a citizen can gain access to the details of funding of political parties is through their Income Tax Returns filed annually with Income Tax authorities. This is about the closest the political parties get to accounting for the sources and the extent of their funding and their expenditure. There is unmistakable public interest in knowing these funding details which would enable the citizen to make an informed choice about the political parties to vote for. The RTI Act emphasizes that "democracy requires an informed citizenry", and that transparency of information is vital to flawless functioning of constitutional democracy. It is nobody's case that, while all organs of the State must exhibit maximum transparency, no such obligation attaches to political parties. Given that political parties influence the exercise of political power; transparency in their organization, functions and, more particularly, their means of funding is a democratic imperative, and, therefore, is in public interest. Insofar as the Income Tax Returns of political parties contain funding details these are liable for disclosure."

Fiduciary Relationship and RBI

Similarly, in the case of Reserve Bank of India & Ors. vs. Jayantilal N. Mistry & Ors., MANU/SC/1463/2015 : (2016) 3 SCC 525 the Supreme Court while dealing with the defence of RBI that it was in the fiduciary relationship with the Bank noted as follows:-

The Advanced Law Lexicon, 3rd Edition, 2005, defines fiduciary relationship as a relationship in which one person is under a duty to act for the benefit of the other on the matters within the scope of the fiduciary relationship. Fiduciary relationship usually arise in one of the four situations (1) when one person places trust in the faithful integrity of another, who as a result gains superiority or influence over the first, (2) when one person assumes control and responsibility over another, (3) when one person has a duty to act or give advice to another on matters falling within the scope of the relationship, or (4) when there is specific relationship that has traditionally be recognized as involving fiduciary duties, as with a lawyer and a client, or a stockbroker and a customer.

The term fiduciary relationship has been well discussed by this Court in the case of Central Board of Secondary Education and Anr. v. Aditya Bandopadhyay and Ors. (supra). In the said decision, their Lordships referred various authorities to ascertain the meaning of the term fiduciary relationship and observed thus : 20.1) Black's Law Dictionary (7th Edition, Page 640) defines 'fiduciary relationship' thus : A relationship in which one person is under a duty to act for the benefit of the other on matters within the scope of the relationship. Fiduciary relationships-such as trustee beneficiary, guardian-ward, agent-principal, and attorney client-require the highest duty of care. Fiduciary relationships usually arise in one of four situations : (1) when one person places trust in the faithful integrity of another, who as a result gains superiority or influence over the first, (2) when one person assumes control and responsibility over another, (3) when one person has a duty to act for or give advice to another on matters falling within the scope of the relationship, or (4) when there is a specific relationship that has traditionally been recognized as involving fiduciary duties, as with a lawyer and a client or a stockbroker and a customer."

Disclosure of Income Tax

The Commission (CIC) observed that the matter of disclosure of Income Tax Return of an individual/person is no longer res Integra and has been adjudicated by several High Courts and the Hon'ble Supreme Court of India in a series of decisions, most notably by the Apex Court in Girish Ramchandra Deshpande vs. Central Information Commission & Ors. SLP(C) No. 27734 of 2012 dated 03/10/2012 wherein it was held as under:

" The details disclosed by a person in his income tax returns are "personal information" which stand exempted from disclosure under clause (j) of Section 8(1) of the RTI Act, unless involves a larger public interest

and the Central Public Information Officer or the State Public Information Officer or the Appellate Authority is satisfied that the larger public interest justifies the disclosure of such information."

The Hon'ble High Court of Delhi in the decision of Naresh Kumar Trehan v. Rakesh Kumar Gupta in W.P.(C) 85/2010 & CM Nos. 156/2010 & 5560/2011 dated 24.11.2014 while observing that the act of filing returns with the department cannot be construed as public activity held that information contained in the income tax returns would be personal information under Section 8(1)(j) of the Act. The relevant extract of the decision is mentioned below:

"Indisputably, Section 8(1)(j) of the Act would be applicable to the information pertaining to Dr. Naresh Trehan (petitioner in W.P.(C) 88/2010) and the information contained in the income tax returns would be personal information under Section 8(1)(j) of the Act. However, the CIC directed disclosure of information of Dr. Trehan also by concluding that income tax returns and information provided for assessment was in relation to a "public activity." In my view, this is wholly erroneous and unmerited. The act of filing returns with the department cannot be construed as public activity. The expression "public activity" would mean activities of a public nature and not necessarily act done in compliance of a statute. The expression "public activity" would denote activity done for the public and/or in some manner available for participation by public or some section of public. There is no public activity involved in filing a return or an individual pursuing his assessment with the income tax authorities. In this view, the information relating to individual assessee could not be disclosed. Unless, the CIC held that the same was justified "in the larger public interest"

However, the aforesaid observations were made in reference to individual assesses and not bodies/organizations/institutions incorporated entities such as listed or private limited companies and other legal entities such as societies. The Hon'ble High Court of Delhi in the matter of Naresh Trehan had clarified on this issue in the following paragraphs:

" It has been contended by the petitioners that the expression "personal information" must also extend to information relating to corporate entities.

Inasmuch as they may also fall within the definition of expression "person" under the General Clauses Act, 1897 as well as under the Income Tax Act, 1961. However, I am unable to accept this contention for the reason that the expression "personal information" as used in clause (j) of Section 8(1) of the Act has to be read in the context of information relating to an individual. A plain reading of the aforesaid clause would indicate that the expression "personal information" is linked with "invasion of privacy of the individual". The use of the word "the" before the word "individual" immediately links the same with the expression "personal information"

Black's law dictionary, sixth edition, inter alia, defines the word "personal" as under:-"The word "personal" means appertaining to the person; belonging to an individual; limited to the person; having the nature or partaking of the qualities of human beings, or of movable property."

In my view, the aforesaid reasoning would also be applicable to the expression "personal" used in Section 8(1)(j) of the Act. The expression 'individual' must be construed in an expansive sense and would include a body of individuals. The said exemption would be available even to unincorporated entities as also private, closely held undertaking which are in substance alter egos of their shareholders. However, the expression individual cannot be used as a synonym for the expression 'person'. Under the General Clauses Act, 1897 a person is defined to "include any company or association or body of individuals, whether incorporated or not". Thus, whereas a person would include an individual as well as incorporated entities and artificial persons, the expression 'individual' cannot be interpreted to include such entities. The context in which, the expression "personal information" is used would also exclude it application to large widely held corporations. While, confidential information of a corporation is exempt from disclosure under Section 8(1)(d) of the Act, there is no scope to exclude other information relating to such corporations under Section 8(1)(j) of the Act as the concept of a personal information cannot in ordinary language be understood to mean information pertaining to a public corporation."

Information which is Held and Available with the Public Authority in Its Regulatory Capacity Ought to be Disclosed to The Information Seekers:

A perusal of the above definition also indicates that the ordinary usage of the word "personal" is in the context of an individual human being and not a corporate entity. The U.S. Supreme Court has also interpreted the expression "personal" to be used in the context of an individual human being and not a corporate entity. In the case of Federal Communications Commission v. AT & T Inc : MANU/USSC/1892/2011 : 2011 US IEXIS 1899 the US Supreme Court considered the meaning of the expression "personal privacy" in the context of the Freedom of Information Act, which required Federal Agencies to make certain records and documents publically available on request. Such disclosure was exempt if the records "could reasonably be expected to constitute an unwarranted invasion of personal privacy". The U.S. Supreme Court held that the expression "Personal" used in the aforesaid context could not be extended to corporations because the word "personal" ordinarily refers to individuals. The Court held that the expression "personal" must be given its ordinary meaning. The relevant extract of the said judgment is as under : "Person" is a defined term in the statute; "personal" is not. When a statute does not define a term, we typically "give the phrase its ordinary meaning, "[Johnson v. United States, MANU/USSC/1500/2010 : 559 U.S., 559 U.S. 133, 130 S. Ct. 1265, 1761. Ed. 2d 1, 8 (2010)]. "Personal" ordinarily refers to individuals. We do not usually speak of personal characteristics, personal effects, personal correspondence, personal influence, or personal tragedy as referring to corporations or other artificial entities. This is not to say that corporations do not have correspondence, influence, or tragedies of their own, only that we do not use the word "personal" to describe them. Certainly, if the chief executive officer of a corporation approached the chief financial officer and said, "I have something personal to tell you," we would not assume the CEO was about to discuss company business. Responding to a request for information, an individual might say, "that's personal." A company spokesman, when asked for information about the company, would not. In fact, we often use the word "personal" to mean precisely the opposite of business related: We speak of personal expenses and business expenses, personal life and work life, personal opinion and a company's view."

Therefore it is clear from the above observations that the expression "personal information" as used in clause (j) of Section 8(1) of the Act has to be read in the context of information relating to an individual and that the ordinary usage of the word "personal" is in the context of an individual human being and not bodies/organizations/institutions incorporated entities such as listed or private limited companies and other legal entities such as societies. Moreover, the information which is held and available with the Public Authority in its regulatory capacity ought to be disclosed to the information seekers.

Exemption from Providing Information

Hon'ble Supreme Court of India in Reserve Bank of India v. Jayantilal N. Mistry and Ors., dated 16.12.2015, wherein interpreting section 2(f) and 8(1)(e) of the RTI Act, 2005, the following was held:

" The exemption contained in Section 8(1)(e) applies to exceptional cases and only with regard to certain pieces of information, for which disclosure is unwarranted or undesirable. If information is available with a regulatory agency not in fiduciary relationship, there is no reason to withhold the disclosure of the same. However, where information is required by mandate of law to be provided to an authority, it cannot be said that such information is being provided in a fiduciary relationship. As in the instant case, the Financial institutions have an obligation to provide all the information to the RBI and such an information shared under an obligation/ duty cannot be considered to come under the purview of being shared in fiduciary relationship. One of the main characteristic of a Fiduciary relationship is "Trust and Confidence". Something that RBI and the Banks lack between them.

And in this case the RBI and the Banks have sidestepped the General public's demand to give the requisite information on the pretext of "Fiduciary Relationship" and "Economic Interest". This attitude of the RBI will only attract more suspicion and disbelief in them. RBI as a regulatory authority should work to make the Banks accountable to their actions.

From reading of the above section it can be inferred that the Legislature's intent was to make available to the general public such information which had been obtained by the public authorities from the private body. Had it been the case where only information related to public authorities was to be provided, the Legislature would not have included the word "private body". As in this case, the RBI is liable to provide information regarding inspection report and other documents to the general public."

Meaning of Public Interest

The Hon'ble Supreme Court in the matter of Bihar Public Service Commission v. Saiyed Hussain Abbas Rizwi: MANU/SC/1103/2012 : (2012) 13 SCC 61 while explaining the term "Public Interest" held:

"The expression "public interest" has to be understood in its true connotation so as to give complete meaning to the relevant provisions of the Act. The expression "public interest" must be viewed in its strict sense with all its exceptions so as to justify denial of a statutory exemption in terms of the Act. In its common parlance, the expression "public interest", like "public purpose", is not capable of any precise definition. It does not have a rigid meaning, is elastic and takes its colour from the statute in which it occurs, the concept varying with time and state of society and its needs (State of Bihar v. Kameshwar Singh([MANU/SC/0020/1952 : AIR 1952 SC 252]). It also means the general welfare of the public that warrants recognition and protection; something in which the public as a whole has a stake [Black's Law Dictionary (8th Edn.)]."

The Hon'ble Supreme Court in the matter of Ashok Kumar Pandey vs. The State Of West Bengal (decided on 18 November, 2003Writ Petition (crl.) 199 of 2003) had made reference to the following texts for defining the meaning of "public interest', which is stated as under:

"Strouds Judicial Dictionary, Volume 4 (IV Edition), 'Public Interest' is defined thus:

"Public Interest is a matter of public or general interest does not mean that which is interesting as gratifying curiosity or a love of information or amusement but that in which a class of the community have a pecuniary interest, or some interest by which their legal rights or liabilities are affected."

In Black's Law Dictionary (Sixth Edition), "public interest" is defined as follows:

Public Interest something in which the public, or some interest by which their legal rights or liabilities are affected. It does not mean anything the particular localities, which may be affected by the matters in question. Interest shared by national government..."

In Mardia Chemical Limited v. Union of India MANU/SC/0323/2004 : (2004) 4 SCC 311, the Hon'ble Supreme Court of India while considering the validity of SARFAESI Act and recovery of non-performing assets by banks and financial institutions in India, recognised the significance of Public Interest and had held as under:

".............Public interest has always been considered to be above the private interest. Interest of an individual may, to some extent, be affected but it cannot have the potential of taking over the public interest having an impact in the socio-economic drive of the country..........."

Decision by CIC

The Commission (CIC) instructed the CPIO and Asst. Commissioner of Income Tax (E) to provide point wise generic information regarding the recovery of taxes from the Political Parties failing which penal action under Section 20(1) of the RTI Act, 2005 could be initiated.

Chapter - 7

DISCLOSURE OF THE INCOME TAX RETURNS AND THE ASSESSMENT ORDERS PERTAINING TO POLITICAL PARTIES[34]

Facts in Nutshell

This second-appeal by the appellant, Ms.Anumeha has been filed under Section 19(3) of the RTI Act against the orders of nine Appellate Authorities of the Department of Income Tax, in regard to disclosure of the Income Tax Returns and the Assessment Orders pertaining to political parties. The appellant filed an application under Section 6(1) of the Right to Information Act, 2005 before the CPIO, Central Board of Direct Taxes, Department of Revenue, Ministry of Finance, North Block, New Delhi-110001 vide letter dated 28.02.2007, seeking information on the following points:- (i) Whether the political parties mentioned in the RTI-application have submitted their Income Tax Returns for the years 2002-03, 2003-04, 2004-05, 2005-06, 2006-07. (ii) PAN Nos. allotted to these parties. (iii) Copies of the Income Tax Returns filed by the political parties for the afore-mentioned years along-with the corresponding assessment orders.

Reply by CPIO, Income Tax Department

The CPIO, Ms. Renu Johri, Director (ITA-II) transferred the application to the appropriate CPIOs in the office of Chief Commissioners of Income Tax at New Delhi, Delhi, Chennai, Mumbai, Chandigarh, Hyderabad, Guwahati, Jammu & Kashmir and Bhubaneswar vide her letter dated 07.03.2007. The CPIO in the office of Commissioner of Income Tax, Jammu & Kashmir, Jammu,

---

[34] Ms. Anumeha vs. Chief Commissioner of Income Tax-XI, New Delhi and ors.
CIC/AT/A/2007/01029, CIC
Hon'ble Judges/Coram:
A.N. Tiwari, Information Commissioner

provided information in respect of Income Tax Returns of Jammu & Kashmir People's Democratic Party and the CPIO in the office of Commissioner of Income Tax, Guwahati provided information in respect of Income Tax Returns of Asom Gana Parishad. All other CPIOs declined to divulge the information citing various reasons, some of which are summarized as below:-

(i) Information is exempt under Section 8(1)(d) of the Right to Information Act, 2005 since it contains details and particulars of commercial activities of the political parties. The CPIO, Mumbai stated that information has been submitted by the assessees in commercial confidence. (ii) The returns are submitted by the assessees in fiduciary capacity and they are confidential in nature and, as such, disclosure thereof is exempted under Section 8(1)(e). (iii) The disclosure of information has no relationship with public activity and no public interest is involved and, as such, it cannot be disclosed under Section 8(1)(j). (iv) Permanent Account Number (PAN) is a statutory number which functions as an unique identification of each taxpayer. Making PAN number public can result in misuse of this information by other persons and could compromise the privacy of the financial transactions linked with PAN. (v) Information relates to third parties who have objected to the disclosure of this information. (vi) Information is subject to confidentiality under Section 138 of the Income Tax Act, 1961. (vii) Sections 8(1)(g), 8(1)(h) and 8(1)(j) of the Right to Information Act, 2005 make it amply clear that there is no obligation to give any information which had been tendered in confidence for law enforcement or information which would impede the process of investigation or prosecution of offenders or information the disclosure of which would cause unwarranted invasion of the privacy of the individual.

The appellant thus received varying replies from the CPIOs in response to her main RTI-application submitted before the CBDT, Department of Revenue, Ministry of Finance. The appellant filed separate appeals before the appropriate Appellate Authorities. An appeal was separately filed before the Commissioner of Income Tax (ITA), Department of Revenue, Ministry of Finance.

Reply by First Appellate Authority, Chief Commissioner of Income Tax

The First Appellate Authority, Chief Commissioner of Income Tax, Bhubaneswar remanded back the matter to the CPIO, Commissioner of Income

Tax, but other First Appellate Authorities, i.e. Chief Commissioners of Income Tax, Chennai, Hyderabad, Mumbai, Delhi and Chandigarh dismissed the appeals.

Second Appeal before CIC by Appellant

The appellant in her appeal petition before Commission (CIC) has submitted that: (i) The avowed objective of a political party in a democracy is to represent people in Parliament and Legislature that are lawmaking bodies through the process of elections and that their very existence is indicative of their goal of representing the interests of the people who elect them to power. (ii) Each and every act of theirs should be open to public scrutiny. Transparency in their working and financial operation is essential in larger public interest and all sections of government, including the Income Tax Department are duty bound to hold the public interest above the interests of political parties. (iii) The disclosure of financial information relating to political parties including I.T. Returns and Assessment Orders to general public would promote such transparency and reduce the role of black money and other undesirable, even illegal activities in the operation of political parties. (iv) Various political parties in respect of whom information has been sought from Central Board of Direct Taxes and the Income Tax Department have all enjoyed fruits of political power at the national level or in one or more of the States. (vi) The information sought by the applicant in respect of political parties should be made available to the applicant and also to general public, in wider public interest.

The appellant vide her written-submission dated 21.01.2008 has stated as follows:- (i) That she herself and her organization are completely non-political and non-partisan. The Association for Democratic Reforms (ADR) which she represents works for improving the governance, democratic, political and electoral processes in the country. Earlier also, they have filed Public Interest Litigations (PIL) in the Delhi High Court, which resulted in the landmark and historic judgment of Supreme Court (March 13, 2003) making it mandatory for candidates contesting elections to State Assemblies and Parliament to disclose their criminal antecedents, if any; assets and liabilities; and educational qualifications, by way of a sworn affidavit to be filed as an essential part of the nomination form.

(ii) Since political parties are working in public domain and using public funds as mentioned above, it is obvious that disclosure of financial information about political parties is, and will be, in the public interest.

The appellant also made additional written-submissions stating that RTI Act was a special statute qua matters relating to seeking of information. To ascertain as to whether an act is general or special, one must focus on the principal subject matter of the Act and its particular perspective. For certain purposes, an Act may be general and for certain other purposes it may be special. It is a settled position of law that when there is a special enactment in respect of a particular subject (for e.g. Right to Information) it would oust the jurisdiction of all other enactments having similar provisions albeit the fact that those enactments are special in respect of the subject matter it deals with (e.g. Income Tax).

In support of this, the appellant cited the case of LIC vs. D.J. Bahadur, 1981 (1) SCC 315 in which, the issue before the Hon'ble Supreme Court was whether the Life Insurance Corporation Act, 1956 was a special statute and the Industrial Disputes Act, 1947 a general statute. Applying the above test, the Hon'ble Supreme Court held – "The Industrial Disputes Act is a special statute devoted wholly to investigation and settlement of industrial disputes which provides definitionally for the nature of industrial disputes coming within its ambit. It creates an infrastructure for investigation into, solution of and adjudication upon industrial disputes. It also provides the necessary machinery for enforcement of awards and settlements. From alpha to omega the ID Act has one special mission – the resolution of industrial disputes through specialized agencies according to specialized procedures and with special reference to the weaker categories of employees coming within the definition of workmen. Therefore, with reference to industrial disputes between employers and workmen, the ID Act is a special statute, and the LIC Act does not speak at all with specific reference to workmen. On the other hand, its powers relate to the general aspects of nationalization, of management when private businesses are nationalized and a plurality of problems which incidentally, involve transfer of service of existing employees of insures. The workmen quaworkmen and industrial disputes between workmen and the employer as such are beyond the orbit of and have no specific or special place in the scheme of the LIC Act."

The appellant submitted that in the instant case, the Income Tax Act, 1961 is an Act regulating the levy and recovery of income tax. The Right to Information Act, 2005 (RTI Act) on the other hand, is a specific and special piece of legislation directed towards providing for access to information under the control of public authorities and as such with regard to citizen's access to information, the RTI Act is the special statute while the Income Tax Act is the special statute on matters of levy, assessment and collection of income tax.

Reply by Respondent before CIC Negating Appellant Plea

The second appeal was received in the Commission on 31.07.2007. The CPIO, New Delhi, submitted his written-submissions on 17.10.2007 stating, inter-alia, as follows:- (i) Information sought in this case relates to the third parties, most of who have objected to the disclosure of the same. Therefore, information with regard to PAN Number, Income Tax Returns and the Assessment Orders and copies thereof may not be made available to the applicant. (ii) Information regarding PAN Number, details and copies of the Income Tax Returns and the Assessment Order of tax payers is personal information of the concerned tax payers which is subject to confidentiality under Section 138 of the Income Tax Act. Although the provisions of the RTI Act override the provisions of Section 138 of the Income Tax Act, Section8(1)(j) of the RTI Act itself clearly envisages that personal information, the disclosure of which has no relationship to any public interest or disclosure of which would cause unwarranted invasion of privacy cannot be disclosed. (iii) Since the disclosure of information has been objected to by most of the political parties, a uniform decision was taken not to disclose information.

Election Commission View on Furnishing of Income Tax Returns

The Election Commission in their response stated that under the law the political parties are not required to furnish to the Commission information about their Income Tax Returns. However, under Section 29C of the Representation of the People Act, 1951, the political parties are required to prepare a report in respect of the contributions received by them from any person or company in excess of Rs.20,000/- in a financial year and the report is to be submitted to the

Commission under the Conduct of Elections Rules, 1961. However, filing of this report is optional. The Commission also stated that they have submitted a proposal suggesting an amendment so as to make it mandatory for the political parties to publish their audited accounts annually for information and scrutiny of the general public.

According to the appellant, there is absolutely no exception made to Section 22, which makes it abundantly clear that access to information held by public authorities is wholly governed by the RTI Act, 2005. While enacting the RTI Act the legislature was cognizant of the fact that several statues had disclosure provisions and yet no exception was provided in the RTI Act unlike the RBD Act above. Therefore, the only interpretation which furthers the intention of the legislature would be the one which gives overriding effect to the RTI Act. Even otherwise, the RTI Act, 2005 being a later enactment would prevail over the Income Tax Act, 1961, particularly in matters of access to information by citizens.

Response of Political Parties before CIC

The Communist Party of India, vide their letter dated 04.04.2007 addressed to the Commissioner of Income Tax, New Delhi, stated that they have had no objection if information concerning them was disclosed. The Communist Party of Marxists also submitted 'no objection' to the disclosure of information. The Communist Party of India, vide their letter dated 28.08.2007, reiterated the position before the Commission.

The Bahujan Samaj Party objected to the disclosure of information on the following grounds:- (i) The disclosure of information is exempted under Section 8(1)(d) of the Right to Information Act, 2005. It also stated that there could not be any public interest, much less larger public interest, warranting disclosure of desired information. (ii) The Income Tax Department cannot divulge such confidential information to strangers and thereby become party to political maneuverings of the rival political parties which is not the object and purpose of Right to Information Act.

The Nationalist Congress Party (NCP) first submitted their preliminary objections as well as para-wise reply to the appeal petition on 14.12.2007.

Subsequently, they filed written submissions:- (i) The Nationalist Congress Party (NCP) is not a public authority in terms of provisions of Section 2(h) of the RTI Act and thus the basis itself of the appellant's case is incorrect and that the RTI application is liable to be dismissed on this ground alone as baseless. (ii) The disclosure of Balance Sheets, Profit & Loss statement and audit reports of political parties, from which income tax returns are derived entirely, contain both personal information of the assessees as well as commercial confidence nature of information, which can harm the competitive position of a political party. (iii) The appellant has equated the political parties with companies while the fact is that political parties are not Companies incorporated under the Companies Act, 1956 and are thus under no obligation to file their Balance Sheets etc. with the Registrar of Companies under Section 220 of the Companies. Act. (iv) The Income Tax Returns are submitted by the assessee to the Government in a fiduciary capacity. (v) The Income Tax Returns are not public documents and it is only the respondent who can generally inspect and have certified copies of the documents.

(vi) The disclosure of information pertaining to tax assessment order, which contains personal information such as PAN, sources of income and other business related details would cause unwarranted invasion of privacy of the assessee. (vii) Most of the third parties have objected to providing the required information and there is no larger public interest which justifies disclosure of this information. (viii) The information has been sought with a political motive and for causing harm and detriment to the political parties. (ix) It is denied that the disclosure of information relating to political parties including assessment returns and assessment orders to general public would promote transparency and reduce the role of black money and other undesirable and illegal activities in the operation of political parties as alleged. (x) The income tax return is not a public document. The contents of the documents filed cannot be disclosed to third parties except to the extent permitted under Section 138 of the Act. (xi) The copies of the Income Tax Returns filed by NCP; PAN number of NCP and information regarding the fact whether NCP has submitted its Income Tax Returns for the assessment years 2002-03 to 2006-07 is confidential in nature and private in character and thus cannot be disclosed.

The NCP also referred to the insertion of Section 13A to the Income Tax Act by the insertion of Section 13A by the Taxation Laws (Amendment) Act, 1978 w.e.f. 1.4.1979 and in support of their arguments they cited the "Statement of Objects and Reasons" which reads as under:-

"Political parties are essential in any democratic set-up. The taxation of their income, however, reduces their disposable funds thereby adversely affecting their capacity to finance their activities from legitimate sources of income. It is, therefore, proposed to provide for exemption from income tax in respect of specified categories of income derived by political parties, namely income from investments both in movable and immovable properties and income by way of voluntary contributions, the proposed exemption will be available only in the case of political parties which are registered or deemed to be registered with the Election Commission of India under the Election Symbols (Reservation and Allotment) Order, 1968. The exemption will not be allowed unless the political party maintains proper books of accounts; records the name and address of every person who has made a voluntary contribution of more than ten thousand Rupees at a time; and the accounts of the political party are audited by a chartered accountant or other qualified accountant."

The Samajwadi Party objected to the disclosure of information on the following grounds:- (i) Information has been asked for with a political motive. (ii) Under the provisions of Section 138(2) of the Income Tax Act, the confidentiality of information provided by the assessees is to be maintained. (iii) In Writ Petition (Civil) No. 633 of 2005, an order was passed by the Hon'ble Supreme Court directing the President of Samajwadi Party and other family members to file their Income Tax and Wealth Tax Returns and the Returns have already been filed in sealed cover before the Supreme Court. Since the matter is still pending before the Hon'ble Apex Court, the disclosure of information will be prejudicial to the sanctity of the proceedings pending before the Supreme Court.

The Bharatiya Janata Party, has objected to the disclosure of information on the ground that the Income Tax Returns were confidential information, parting with which, will amount to infringement of certain privacy rights of the members of the political parties. The BJP has contended that the disclosure of information was exempted under Section 8(1)(j).

Dravida Munnetra Kazhagam (DMK) filed their detailed written submissions vide letter dated 10th December, 2007 stating, inter-alia, as under:- (i) While making a request for information, an applicant may not be required to give any reasons or any other personal details except those that may be necessary for contacting him but Section 6(2) does not give a blanket exemption to the appellant to reveal the bonafide of her / his conduct once an appeal is preferred under the RTI Act. (ii) A request for copies of assessment orders is motivated inasmuch as an appellant has no public knowledge of an assessment made. Incomes of political parties are exempt under Section 13A of the Income Tax Act and in the absence of any violation of Section 13A, the information sought for is frivolous and academic. (iii) The appellant should have first exhausted her remedies under Section 138 of the Income Tax Act and that the provisions of RTI Act do not apply when an alternative remedy is available under the Income Tax provisions. The Returns of Income filed by the assessees under the provisions of Income Tax Act are confidential information which include details of commercial activities. These are submitted in fiduciary capacity. There is no public interest involved in the matter. Disclosure of information is, therefore, exempted under Section 8(1)(j) of the Right to Information Act.

All India Congress Committee (AICC) made following submissions:- (i) The Applicant/Appellant is a busy body having malafide intent and that they are seeking the information for ulterior motives. (ii) The Applicant/Appellant has failed to come up with any substantive/cogent reasons for its requests for the information and as to what use and purpose the said information would be put to. (iii) The documents relating to Income Tax Returns and Assessment Orders are both personal information of the political parties and also contain commercial confidential nature of data, the disclosure of which is barred under Section 8(1)(d) and (j) of the Right to Information Act. (iv) It is now a well settled proposition that Income Tax Returns filed by the assessees before Income Tax Authority are personal as well as fiduciary entrustment and thereby attract the exemptions under Sections 8(1)(e) and 8(1)(j) of the Right to Information Act, 2005. (v) The Income Tax Returns contain commercial information for enabling the Income Tax

Department to determine the tax liability flowing from it such returns also attract provisions of Section 8(1)(d) of the RTI Act. (vi) The PAN Number is a statutory number and making it public would compromise the privacy of any financial transaction linked with the PAN.

Question before Central Information Commission

Whether income tax returns of an assessee along with its assessment order and PAN of various political parties can be considered to be exempted under Sections 8(1) (d), (e), (g), (h) and (j) of the RTI Act and as to whether such information can be disclosed in larger public interest?

Political Parties and Transparency

Political parties are an unique institution of the modern Constitutional State. These are essentially civil society institutions and are, therefore, nongovernmental. Their uniqueness lies in the fact that in spite of being nongovernmental, political parties come to wield or directly or indirectly influence, exercise of governmental power. It is this link between State power and political parties that has assumed critical significance in the context of the Right of Information – an Act which has brought into focus the imperatives of transparency in the functioning of State institutions. It would be facetious to argue that transparency is good for all State organs, but not so good for the political parties, which control the most important of those organs. For example, it will be a fallacy to hold that transparency is good for the bureaucracy, but not good enough for the political parties which control those bureaucracies through political executives.

In modern day context, transparency and accountability are spoken of together ¯ as twins. Higher the levels of transparency greater the accountability. This link between transparency and accountability is sharply highlighted in the Preamble to the RTI Act. In T.N. Seshan, CEC of India Vs. Union of India & ors. the Apex Court referred to the Preamble to the Constitution of India and observed that the preamble of our Constitution proclaimed that we were a Democratic Republic and "democracy" being the basic feature of our constitutional set-up, there could be no two opinions that free and fair elections to our legislative bodies alone would guarantee the growth of a healthy democracy in the country. In People's Union for Civil Liberties (PUCL) and Ors Vs. Union of India and Anr. (AIR2003SC2363), the apex court stated that it is true that the elections are fought by the political parties, yet election would be a farce if the voters are unaware of antecedents of candidates contesting elections. Their decisions to vote either in favour of 'A' or 'B' candidate would be without any basis. Such election would be neither free nor fair. In Union of India v. Association for Democratic Reforms & another (AIR 2002 SC 2112) also, the Apex Court has observed as follows:- "To maintain the purity of elections and in particular to bring transparency in the process of election, the Commission can ask the candidates about the expenditure incurred by the political parties and this transparency in the process of election would include transparency of a candidate who seeks election or re-election. In a democracy, the electoral process has a strategic role. The little man of this country would have basic elementary right to know full particulars of a candidate who is to represent him in Parliament where laws to bind his liberty and property may be enacted."

Purpose of RTI Act, 2005 and Political Transparency

The RTI Act aims at expanding accountability through transparency at all levels of governance. It is difficult to be persuaded by the argument that though political parties control the political executive who are their appointees these parties should be allowed to be insulated from the demands of transparency. In other words, political parties be allowed to escape the obligations / norms transparency imposes, and inferentially, escape accountability, even though these parties almost always influence and, frequently control, State power through the organs of the State. That shall be an unacceptable proposition especially in a democracy as accountability is the underpinning of the actions of all stake-holders who have anything to do with State power.

The question that additionally needs to be asked is whether the avowed purpose of the RTI Act, as set out in its Preamble 'to combat corruption' is being achieved by allowing the finances of the political parties to remain beyond public scrutiny or even public view. There is now widespread concern about a hyphenated relationship developing between party finance and political corruption.

The lack of openness and transparency in party finance is matched by the lack of adequate State regulation of such finance.

The National Commission to Review the Working of the Constitution in its report submitted in March 2002 has recommended that the political parties as well as individual candidates be made subject to a proper statutory audit of the amounts they spend. These accounts should be monitored through a system of checking and cross-checking through the income-tax returns filed by the candidates, parties and their well- wishers. At the end of the election each candidate should submit an audited statement of expenses under specific heads. The National Commission has further suggested that the Election Commission should devise specific formats for filing such statements so that fudging of accounts becomes difficult. Also, the audit should not only be mandatory but it should be enforced by the Election Commission.

The Supreme Court in People's Union for Civil Liberties Vs. Union of India (AIR2003SC2363) considered the report of the Law Commission, National Commission to Review the Working of the Constitution, conclusion drawn in the report of Shri Indrajit Gupta and Ethics Manual applicable in an advance democratic country and observed that it is apparent that for saving democracy from the evil influence of criminalization of politics, for saving the election from muscle and money power, for having true democracy and for controlling corruption in politics, the candidate contesting the election should be asked to disclose his antecedents including assets and liabilities. Thereafter, it is for the voters to decide in whose favour he should cast his vote.

In Common Cause (A Registered Society) Vs. Union of India (AIR 1996 SC 3081), Supreme Court dealt with election expenses incurred by political parties and submission of return and the scope of Article 324 of the Constitution, where it was contended that cumulative effect of the three statutory provisions, namely, Section 293A of the Companies Act, 1956, Section 13A of the Income Tax Act, 1961 and Section 77 of the Representation of the People Act, 1951, was to bring transparency in the election funding. The people of India must know the source of expenditure incurred by the political parties and by the candidates in the process of election. It was contended before the Supreme Court that elections in the country were fought with the help of money power which was gathered from black sources and once elected to power, it becomes easy to collect tons of black money, which is used for retaining power and for re-election and that this vicious circle had polluted the wellspring of democracy in the country. The Court held that purity of election was fundamental to democracy and the Election Commission could ask the candidates about the expenditure incurred by the candidates and by a political party. The Apex Court summed up the position thus:- *"...The political parties in their quest for power spend more than one thousand crore of rupees on the General Election (Parliament alone), yet nobody accounts for the bulk of the money so spent and there is no accountability anywhere. Nobody discloses the source of the money. There are no proper accounts and no audit. From where does the money come nobody knows. In a democracy where rule of law prevails this type of naked display of black money, by violating the mandatory provisions of law, cannot be permitted."*

In same case (Common Cause (A Registered Society) Vs. Union of India (AIR 1996 SC 3081), the Apex Court has further observed that to combat this naked display of unaccounted/black money by the candidates, declaration of assets was likely to check violation of the provisions of the P.R. Act and other relevant Acts including Income Tax Act. The Apex Court did not agree that the declaration of assets would result in infringement of the right of privacy. The following observations of the Court in this context are quite relevant:-

"Similarly, with regard to the declaration of assets also, a person having assets or income is normally required to disclose the same under the Income Tax Act or such similar fiscal legislation. Not only this, but once a person becomes a candidate to acquire public office, such declaration would not affect his right or privacy. This is the necessity of the day because of statutory provisions of controlling wide spread corrupt practices as repeatedly pointed out by all concerned including various reports of Law Commission and other Committees as stated above.

In Dr. P. Nalla Thampy Terah v. Union of India and Ors. [1985 Suppl. SCC 189], the Apex Court considered the validity of Section 77(1) of the

Representations of People's Act and referred to the report of the Santhanam Committee on Prevention of Corruption, which says: "The public belief in the prevalence of corruption at high political levels has been strengthened by the manner in which funds are collected by political parties, especially at the time of elections. Such suspicions attach not only to the ruling party but to all parties, as often the opposition can also support private vested interests as well as members of the Government party. It is, therefore, essential that the conduct of political parties should be regulated in this matter by strict principles in relation to collection of funds and electioneering. It has to be frankly recognized that political parties cannot be run and elections cannot be fought without large funds. But these funds should come openly from the supporters or sympathizers of the parties concerned."

Decision by CIC

These judicial pronouncements unmistakably commend progressively higher levels of transparency in the functioning of political parties in general, and their funding in particular. Quite importantly, these pronouncements by the nation's Supreme Court were made much before the RTI Act came into being and, in a sense, even before transparency was enshrined, through the RTI Act, as an avowed objective of governance, Supreme Court delineated the evolutionary process that would culminate in the year 2005 in adoption of the historic enactment of RTI Act by India's Parliament. The convergence of approach of the nation's Supreme Court and its Supreme Legislature 'the Parliament' in preparing the country to embrace the values of transparency in all aspects of governance is striking. It was their response to an idea, whose time had come. And, it is in this context that the case for transparency in political funding and its concomitant, the case for disclosure of Income Tax Returns of political parties is to be evaluated.

The laws of the land do not make it mandatory for political parties to disclose the sources of their funding, and even less so the manner of expending those funds. In the absence of such laws, the only way a citizen can gain access to the details of funding of political parties is through their Income Tax Returns filed annually with Income Tax authorities. This is about the closest the political parties get to accounting for the sources and the extent of their funding and their expenditure. There is unmistakable public interest in knowing these funding details which would enable the citizen to make an informed choice about the political parties to vote for. The RTI Act emphasizes that "democracy requires an informed citizenry", and that transparency of information is vital to flawless functioning of constitutional democracy. It is nobody's case that, while all organs of the State must exhibit maximum transparency, no such obligation attaches to political parties. Given that political parties influence the exercise of political power; transparency in their organization, functions and, more particularly, their means of funding is a democratic imperative, and, therefore, is in public interest. Insofar as the Income Tax Returns of political parties contain funding details these are liable for disclosure.

In fact provision for disclosure of such information exists in the Income Tax Act itself. Section 138(1)(b) of the Income Tax Act empowers the Commissioner of Income Tax to disclose, "in public interest", any information which comes into the hands of the public authority. That Section reads as follows:- "(b) Where a person makes an application to the [Chief Commissioner or Commissioner] in the prescribed form for any information relating to any assessee [received or obtained by any income-tax authority in the performance of his functions under this Act], the [Chief Commissioner or Commissioner] may, if he is satisfied that it is in the public interest so to do, furnish or cause to be furnished the information asked for and his decision in this behalf shall be final and shall not be called in question in any court of law."

What this Section states is that any information in the hands of the Income Tax authorities would be ordinarily held as confidential, but can be made public, if in the judgement of the Commissioner of Income Tax, it serves public purpose. Therefore, the contention that all Income Tax Returns 'an information provided by assessees to Income Tax authorities' are permanently barred from disclosure, is not correct. This information can be disclosed in public interest, either in a given case, or a class of cases, under Income Tax laws.

There is no inconsistency between the Income Tax Act and the RTI Act. In the Income Tax Act, an information can be disclosed in public interest whereas under the RTI Act, every information held by the Public Authority is disclosable unless it is "exempted" as specified under Sections 8 or 9 of the Act. The Right to Information Act, 2005 was enacted to secure access to information under the control of Public Authorities in order to promote transparency and accountability in the working of every Public Authority. The Act recognizes that a functional democracy requires an informed citizenry and transparency of information is vital to its functioning and also to contain corruption and to hold the Government and their instrumentalities accountable to the governed. The Act intends to harmonize the conflict of interest between efficient operations of the Government, preservation of confidentiality of sensitive information on one hand and disclosure of information on other. The Preamble of the Act makes it very clear that while harmonizing these conflicting interests, the Act seeks to preserve the paramountcy of the democratic ideal.

Accordingly, Section 3 of the RTI Act provides that all citizens shall have the right to access information held by public authorities. This Section makes this right subject only to the various provisions of the Act. The right is, therefore, not absolute, but is subject only to the provisions of the Right to Information Act. Section 22 of the Act contains the non-obstante clause which provides an overriding power to the provisions of the Act. Section 22 reads as under: "Sec.22— The provisions of this Act shall have effect notwithstanding anything inconsistent therewith contained in the Official Secrets Act, 1923, and any other law for the time being in force or in any instrument having effect by virtue of any law other than this Act."

From the provisions of Section 3 and Section 22, read in the context of the Preamble of the Act, it can be inferred that a citizen is entitled to access information available with and held by a Public Authority unless:- (a) such information is exempted under Section 8 or Section 9; (b) The information relates to an organization exempted under Section 24 subject to exceptions provided for in the proviso to subsection (1) in case of an organization established by the Central Government and subsection (4) in the case of an organization established by State Governments; (c) Information which relates to or has been supplied by a third party and has been treated as confidential by that third-party. In case such an information is intended to be disclosed, the procedure set out in Section 11 need to be followed.

The scheme of the Act makes it abundantly clear that disclosure of information to a citizen is the norm and non-disclosure by a Public Authority an exception and it necessitates justification for any decision not to disclose an information.

CIC held that an information which is otherwise exempt, can still be disclosed if the public interest so warrants. That public interest is unmistakably present is evidenced not only in the context of the pronouncements of the Apex Court but also the recommendations of the National Commission for the Review of the Working of the Constitution and of the Law Commission.

Political financing and its potentiality for distorting the functioning of the government, has been the subject of wide public debate in contemporary democracies. It is recognized that political parties do need large financial resources to discharge their myriad functions. But this recognition is tinged with the apprehension that non-transparent political funding could, by exposing political parties, and through it the organs of State which come under the control or its influence, to the corrupting influence of undisclosed money, can inflict irreversible harm on the institutions of government. There is public purpose in preventing such harm to the body-politic.

Democratic States, the world over, are engaged in finding solutions to the problem of transparency in political funding. Several methodologies are being tried such as State subsidy for parties, regulation of funding, voluntary disclosure by donors – at least large donors – and so on. The German Basic Law contains very elaborate provisions regarding political funding. Section 21 of the Basic Law enjoins that political parties shall publicly account for the sources and the use of their funds and for their assets. The German Federal Constitutional Court has in its decisions strengthened the trend towards transparency in the functioning of political parties. It follows that transparency in funding of political parties in a democracy is the norm and, must be promoted in public interest. In the present case that promotion is being effected through the disclosure of the Income Tax Returns of the political parties.

The Commission directed that the public authorities holding such information shall provide the following information to the appellant:- Income Tax Returns of the political parties filed with the public authorities and the Assessment Orders for the period mentioned by the appellant in her RTI-application dated 28.02.2007.

The Commission also directed that the PAN of those political parties whose Income Tax Returns are divulged to the applicant shall not be disclosed. It was decided not to disclose PAN in view of the fact that there is a possibility that this disclosure could be subjected to fraudulent use. It was therefore, considered practical that while Income Tax Returns and the Assessment Orders pertaining to political parties be disclosed, there should be no disclosure of the PANs of such parties.

Chapter - 8

INFORMATION REGARDING CASTE CERTIFICATES ISSUED TO CHAMARS AS JATAVS[35]

Facts in Nutshell

Appellant — **Sultan Singh** through his RTI application sought action taken report on his various applications enclosed with RTI. As no reply received from PIO & FAA, appellant approached the Central Information Commission.

Proceedings before the Commission

Appellant was questioning why the name of the 'caste[36]' has been changed from Chamar to Jatav, while issuing the caste certificates to Scheduled Castes. His complaint was that persons belonging to Chamar are not getting certificates with that caste, instead of that, they are certified as Jatav. Appellant wanted the reasons for the same.

Reply by PIO/Respondent— PIO, Sub Divisional Magistrate (Punjabi Bagh)

Respondent authority stated that by the order dated 27.07.2011 castes of Sumar/Chamar, Chuhra and Kanjar had been incorporated in the group of 'Jatav'. Prior to this circular, Sumar/Chamar, Chuhra and Kanjar were given certificate in their respective caste. After this circular they are getting certificates in name of Jatav caste. The CPIO stated that in 2012 a notification issued which clearly stated that Chamar group was replaced with Jatav.

---

[35] Appellants: Sultan Singh Vs. Respondent: PIO, Sub Divisional Magistrate (Punjabi Bagh) Hon'ble Judges/Coram: M. Sridhar Acharyulu, Information Commissioner, Central Information Commission

Subject: Right to Information

CIC/SA/A/2015/000827, Decided On: 17.08.2015

[36] Caste is a form of social stratification characterized by endogamy, hereditary transmission of a lifestyle which often includes an occupation, ritual status in a hierarchy, and customary social interaction and exclusion based on cultural notions of purity and pollution.

The appellant questioned if they are deleted from Sumar/Chamar, Chuhra and Kanjar caste, what is their caste status and what should be name of their caste if they are not certified with those approved names. The SDM (Punjabi Bagh) does not have any information about this. The officer stated that Chamar being a derogatory word, it was deleted from the list of caste and now people belonging to Sumar/Chamar, Chuhra and Kanjar caste are being issued certificates in the name of 'Jatav'. Appellant also presented several instances where Chamars are given Jatav Certificate.

Constitutional Privileges Cannot be Denied to Scheduled Castes, Scheduled Tribes and Backward Classes by Their Caste Certificate:

Certifying a person as belonging to his particular caste is a very important aspect, which cannot be taken lightly. Especially when Constitution guaranteed certain reservations and privileges to backward classes by defining scheduled castes and scheduled tribes, the persons belonging to these castes cannot be denied with their caste certifications. There are several constitutional privileges provided for the backward classes, which are given on the bases of caste certificate. They are as follows:

"Article 15(4) of Constitution Of India says: (4) Nothing in this article or in clause (2) of Article 29 shall prevent the State from making any special provision for the advancement of any socially and educationally backward classes of citizens or for the Scheduled Castes and the Scheduled Tribes.

Article 16(4) says: (4) Nothing in this article shall prevent the State from making any provision for the reservation of appointments or posts in favor of any backward class of citizens which, in the opinion of the State, is not adequately represented in the services under the State.

The objective of the Constitution (85th Amendment) Act, 1995 was states as:

The Scheduled Castes and the Schedule Tribes have been enjoying the facility of reservation in promotion since 1955. The Supreme Court in its judgment dated 16th November 1992, in the case of *Indra Sawhney and others v Union of*

India and others[37], however, observed that *reservations or appointments or posts under Article 16(4) of the Constitution is confined to initial appointments and cannot extend to reservation in the matter of promotion.* The ruling of the Supreme Court will adversely affect the interests of the Scheduled Castes and Scheduled Tribes. Since the representation of the Scheduled Castes and Scheduled Tribes in services in the States have not reached the required level, it is necessary to continue the existing dispensation of providing reservation in promotion in the case of the Scheduled Castes and Scheduled Tribes. In view of the commitment of the Government to protect the interest of the Scheduled Castes and Scheduled Tribes, the Government have decided to continue the existing policy of reservation in promotion for the Scheduled Castes and the Scheduled Tribes. To carry out this, it is necessary to amend article 16 of the Constitution by inserting a new clause (4A) in the said article to provide reservation in promotion for the Scheduled Castes and the Scheduled Tribes.

By this amendment, following clause is added after Article 16(4).

"(4A) Nothing in this article shall prevent the State from making any provision for reservation in matters of promotion to any class or classes of posts in the services under the State in favour of the Scheduled Castes and the Scheduled Tribes which, in the opinion of the State, are not adequately represented in the services under the State."

Article 341. Scheduled Castes

(1) The President may with respect to any State or Union territory, and where it is a State after consultation with the Governor thereof, by public notification, specify the castes, races or tribes or parts of or groups within castes, races or tribes which shall for the purposes of this Constitution be deemed to be Scheduled Castes in relation to that State or Union territory, as the case may be,

(2) Parliament may by law include in or exclude from the list of Scheduled Castes specified in a notification issued under clause (1) any caste, race or tribe or part of or group within any caste, race or tribe, but save as aforesaid a

---

[37] AIR 1993 SC 477

notification issued under the said clause shall not be varied by any subsequent notification.

Article 330. Reservation of Seats for Scheduled Castes and Scheduled Tribes in the House of the People,

"(1) Seats shall be reserved in the House of the People for (a) the Scheduled Castes; (b) the Scheduled Tribes except the Scheduled Tribes in the autonomous districts of Assam; and (c) the Scheduled Tribes in the autonomous districts of Assam

(2) The number of seats reserved in any State or Union territory for the Scheduled Castes or the Scheduled Tribes under clause (1) shall bear, as nearly as may be, the same proportion to the total number of seats allotted to that State or Union territory in the House of the People as the population of the Scheduled Castes in the State or Union territory or of the Scheduled Tribes in the State or Union territory or part of the State or Union territory, as the case may be, in respect of which seats are so reserved, bears to the total population of the State or Union territory."

Article 332 provides similar reservations in legislative Assemblies of states. Article 366 defined 'Scheduled Castes' under (24) Scheduled Castes means such cases, races or tribes or parts of or groups within such castes, races or tribes as are deemed under Article 341 to be Scheduled Castes for the purposes of this Constitution;

Constitution (Scheduled Castes) (Union Territories) Order, 1951

As per the Constitution (Scheduled Castes) (Union Territories) Order, 1951, C.O. 32 in Schedule 1, pertaining to Delhi, at point 10 listed the castes: Chamar, Chanwar Chamar, Jatava or Jatav chamar, Mochi, Ramdasia, Ravidasi, Raidasi, Rehgarh or Raigar, at point 11 Chohra (Sweeper), at 12, Chuhra are included in the list of Schedule Castes. This order is made by the President in exercise of powers conferred by clause (1) of Article 341 of the Constitution as amended by the Constitution (First Amendment) Act, 1951.

This order specifically stated that subject to the provisions of this order, the castes, races or tribes or parts of, or groups within, castes or tribes specified in [Parts I to III] of the Schedule to this Order shall, in relation to the [Union Territories] to which those parts respectively relate be deemed to be Scheduled Castes so far as regards members thereof resident in the localities specified in relation to them respectively in those Parts of that Schedule.

Thus under Article 341(1) President by notifications for States and Union territories declares the Schedule Castes, and only by law by Parliament can include in or exclude from any caste. Once President notified it the Order remain in force as the list of the Scheduled Castes. In Delhi, the order of the President (1951) gives the list of Scheduled Castes, which are deemed to be the Scheduled Castes according to Article 366(24) definition.

The Cabinet of the Government of National Capital Territory of Delhi on 27.7.2011 Decided As Follows:

The Council of Ministers deliberated on the issue and decided that all such references to the caste names mentioned in this order which have derogatory connotation should be removed forthwith while issuing certificates to the applicants and Government of NCT of Delhi should also move the Ministry of Home Affairs GOI to carry out suitable amendments in this order so as to remove all words in the caste names which have derogatory connotation attached to the reference to caste in this order. The Cabinet approved the following amendment be carried out in caste names in 'The Constitution (Scheduled Castes) (Union Territories) Order, 1951":

"i. At serial number 8, the word 'Bhangi' may be substituted with "Balmiki",

ii. At serial number 10, the word "chamar/chanwar" may be deleted.

iii. At serial number 12, the word "chuhra' may be deleted,

iv. At serial number 20, the work "kanjar" may be deleted."

The Cabinet also decided that pending amendment of the Constitution (Scheduled Castes) (Union Territories) Order, 1951 the deputy Commissioners of the districts be directed to take necessary steps while issuing case certificates to the applicants.

Chamars

Author Chandel, M.P.S. [(1990). A Social Force in Politics: Study of Scheduled Castes of U.P. Mittal Publications p. 51. ISBN 9788170991939] has explained as follows:

"Jatav, also known as Jatava/Jatiya/Jatba/Jatoi is a social group that in India are considered to be a part of the Chamar caste, Dalits, who are now classified as a Scheduled Caste under modern India's system of positive discrimination, as discussed in."

Singer, Milton; Cohn, Bernard S., eds. (2007). Structure and Change in Indian Society pp. 216-217 stated:

"In the early part of the twentieth century, the Jatavs attempted the process of sanskritisation, claiming themselves to be historically of the kshatriya varna. They gained political expertise by forming associations and by developing a literate cadre of leaders, and they tried to change their position in the caste system through the emulation of upper-caste behavior. As a part of this process, they also claimed not to be Chamars and petitioned the government of the British Raj to be officially classified differently: disassociating themselves from the Chamar community would, they felt, enhance their acceptance as kshatriya. These claims were not accepted by other castes and, although the government was amenable, no official reclassification as a separate community occurred due to the onset of World War II."

It has also been suggested that the Chamars and Jats inter-married and formed the Jatavs as mentioned in Lynch, Owen M. (1969). The Politics of Untouchability. New York: Columbia University Press. p. 30. OCLC 31520. It is sometimes said that they are descendants from the marriage of Jats with Chamars.

The Chamar is one of the Dalit communities, who are classified as a Scheduled Caste. They are found mainly in the northern states of India and in Pakistan and Nepal. Ramnarayan Rawat posits that the association of the Chamar community with a traditional occupation of tanning was constructed, and that the Chamars were instead historically agriculturists[38]. According to the 2001 census of India, Chamar Population in Delhi is 893384 and their percentage is 6.45%. Chamars who have adopted the weaving profession and abandoned tanning and leathercraft, identify themselves as Julaha Chamar; R.K. Pruthi suggests this is in the hope that they might in future be considered as Julaha by other communities in the future. They believe that leatherwork is "degrading" when compared to weaving[39].

The 1st Chamar Regiment was an infantry regiment formed by the British during World War II[40]. The Chamar Regiment which was involved in the Pacific War Japanese[41] front and was awarded the Battle Honor of Kohima for theirs distinguished role in the book, Battle of Kohima. The Regiment was disbanded in 1946. Recently in 2011, several politicians have demanded that the Chamar Regiment be revived. Notable people among this caste are founder of Bahujan Samaj Party, Kanshi Ram, Former Deputy Prime Minister of India, Jagjivan Ram, former Chief Minister of UP, Mayawati, former Speaker Meira Kumar, and Mohinder Singh Kaypee, MP from Jalandhar.

Whether Chamar and Jatav Castes are One and the Same

Whether Chamar and Jatav castes are one and the same was subject matter of consideration in a case *Kishorilal Hans v. Raja Ram Singh & Ors*[42] decided by Supreme Court in 30 November 1971, by Justice AN Grover. In this case the appellant was declared elected in February 1967 from the Bhander Assembly constituency in District Datia of the State of Madhya Pradesh a seat which was reserved for a scheduled caste candidate. Under the Constitution Scheduled Castes) Order 1950 and Scheduled Tribes Lists (Modification) Order 1956 the President of India had declared in respect of District Datia the various castes which were to be recognised as Scheduled castes. In items thereof the castes

38 Yadav, Bhupendra (21 February 2012). "Aspirations of Chamars in North India". Chennai, India: The Hindu. Retrieved 2013-01-14

39 Pruthi, R.K. Indian caste system. Discovery p. 189

40 "Orders of Battle - 27/2 Punjab Regiment [British Commonwealth]" orders of battle.com

41 The Pacific War, sometimes called the Asia-Pacific War, was the theatre of World War II that was fought in the Pacific and East Asia. It was fought over a vast area that included the Pacific Ocean and islands, the South West Pacific, South-East Asia, and in China (including the 1945 Soviet–Japanese conflict).

42 1972 AIR 598, 1972 SCR (2) 632

mentioned were: 'Chamar, Ahirwar, Chamar Mangam, Mochi and Raidas.' The respondent, an unsuccessful candidate at the said election filed an election petition inter alia on the ground that the appellant, was a Jatav by caste and therefore not a member of any of the scheduled castes mentioned in the Presidential Order. The appellant contended that the Jatav caste was a sub-caste of the caste chamar mentioned in the order. The High Court decided against the appellant who appealed to Supreme Court. From the evidence there was little room for doubt that although at one time Jatavs might have been chamars but they became a distinct caste or came to be recognised as a separate caste several years ago. The fact that they were shown separately as a caste in the Madhya Bharat and several others states in the Scheduled Caste or Scheduled Tribes Order (Amendment) Act 1956 shows that the existence of Jatav caste was recognised.

Decision by CIC

CIC held that Chamar case cannot be equated with Jatav, and persons belonging to caste of Chamar cannot be certified as Jatavs. The Constitutional provisions clearly indicate that there cannot be any changes in the list of castes, sub-castes and other entries in the list of Scheduled Castes as ordered by the President under the Constitutional authority.

Article 338(9) of the Constitution says the Union and every State Government shall consult the Commission (National Commission for Scheduled Castes[43]) on all major policy matters affecting Scheduled Castes. This means that the Delhi Administration cannot alter the Order of the President referred above or delete from or include in the list any caste that was already notified without consulting the National Commission for Scheduled Castes and following the process prescribed by the Constitution.

The Cabinet of the Government of National Capital Territory of Delhi on 27.7.2011 has noted in its decision that certain nomenclatures like Bhangi, Chamar, Chuhra and Kanjar have acquired derogatory connotations in the public

[43] National Commission for Scheduled Castes is an Indian constitutional body established with a view to provide safeguards against the exploitation of Scheduled Castes to promote and protect their social, educational, economic and cultural interests, special provisions were made in the Constitution.

mind and it was necessary to change the same to more appropriate nomenclature which do not carry stigma. In doing so, the Government has, in fact removed these names from the lists of Scheduled Castes, without following the procedure prescribed by the Constitution. Because they have not provided alternative names in place of names which they felt derogative, there was a serious injustice to Chamars etc. as they were not getting certificates, which they were entitled to under the Constitution of India.

Though Cabinet understood the serious lapse in the earlier decision and reversed it, it appears that the latest information did not percolate to all offices, because of which they continued to issue certificates denoting the caste of Chamars as Jatavs, which is questioned in this second appeal. At present, there is no proposal to amend the Presidential Order on Scheduled Castes. Hence there is a Constitutional obligation on the Revenue department to certify 'chamars' as belonging to caste of 'chamars' only. The Political Executive has ignored the fact that they cannot amend the list and names of castes among the Scheduled Castes, but after realizing the mistake, they have not taken sufficient measures to instruct the revenue department to give corrected certificates.

The Commission directed the Deputy Commissioner of Revenue Department Head Quarters to explain the appellant and CIC, what measures they have taken to correct the caste certificates issued to Chamars as "Jatavs etc., since 2011 till today, when do they start certifying the applicants with their original caste names, and how do they compensate if any loss is suffered by the applicants because of such issuance of wrong certificates. The Commission also directed the respondent authority to issue necessary instructions specifically directing the revenue officers to issue certificates in accordance with list concerning Delhi under the Constitution (Scheduled Castes) (Union Territories) Order 1951 and place that order in their official website.

Chapter - 9

INFORMATION REGARDING MINISTER BEING A PUBLIC AUTHORITY UNDER RTI ACT, 2005[44]

Facts in Nutshell

Appellant— Hemant Dhage by his RTI application dated 20.11.2014 addressed to the additional private secretary of Hon'ble Minister for Law and Justice, sought to know ***"Whether any time is scheduled for common people to meet the Cabinet Minister and Minister of State in the Minister's office in the Mantraalay (Secretariat)?*** If yes, please inform the timing of meeting the minister, both in English and Hindi". He claimed that he belonged to below the poverty line and hence the information could be given free of cost.

The appellant wanted information from Minister's office. It is about process of meeting the Minister. Appellant approached office of Minister through RTI to know either general time of meeting or the procedure to have appointment as he could find any means for that.

Reply by PIO, Ministry of Law and Justice

The PIO of Ministry of Law and Justice replied on 16.01.2015 citing information sent by office of the Hon'ble Minister, that no specific time was given for general public to meet the Minister. However, as and when requests are received appointments are given subject to the convenience of Hon'ble Minister.

Reply in First Appeal

There was no order in first appeal.

---

44 Appellants: Hemant Dhage Vs. Respondent: Department of Legal Affairs, GOI
Hon'ble Judges/Coram: M. Sridhar Acharyulu, Information Commissioner, Central Information Commission
Subject: Right to Information
Decided On: 12.03.2016, CIC/SA/A/2015/000435

Therefore, appellant approached the Central Information Commission.

Question before the Central Information Commission

(a) Is Minister or his office a 'public authority' under RTI Act, 2005?

(b) Whether a citizen has right to information sought, and does the minister has corresponding obligation to give?

Is 'Minister' a 'Public Authority'?

The term Public Authority is defined by Section 2(h) of Right to Information Act, 2005 as follows:

"public authority" means any authority or body or institution of self-government established or constituted—

(a) by or under the Constitution;

(b) by any other law made by Parliament;

(c) by any other law made by State Legislature;

(d) by notification issued or order made by the appropriate Government, and includes any—(i) body owned, controlled or substantially financed; (ii) non Government organization substantially financed, directly or indirectly by funds provided by the appropriate Government.

Both commonsense and Constitution suggests Minister is an authority constituted 'by and under the Constitution'. There are many specific provisions which prove this statement. Minister is authority constituted by Constitution, because:

(a) Article 74[45] says there shall be a Council of Ministers to aid and advise President

[45] Article 74 in The Constitution Of India 1949

74. Council of Ministers to aid and advise President

(1) There shall be a Council of Ministers with the Prime Minister at the head to aid and advise the President who shall, in the exercise of his functions, act in accordance with such advice: Provided that the President may require the council of Ministers to reconsider such advice, either generally or otherwise, and the President shall act in accordance with the advice tendered after such reconsideration

(2) The question whether any, and if so what, advice was tendered by Ministers to the President shall not be inquired into in any court

(b) Article 75[46] says that Ministers shall be appointed by the President on the advice of Prime Minister. [Refer Section 2(h)(a) of RTI Act]

(c) Article 75(2) says that the Minister shall hold the office during the pleasure of the President. This signifies the pervasive control of government over their functioning, which is prerequisite to declare an authority as 'public authority' as ordained by Hon'ble Supreme Court in Thalappalam Ser. Coop.Bank Ltd. vs State Of Kerala & Ors[47].

(d) Minister's salaries are determined by law made by Parliament from time to time by law-the Salary, Allowances and Pension of Members of Parliament Act, 1954. This is another characteristic that makes Minister a public authority. [Refer S. 2(h)(b) of RTI Act, 2005]

(e) Similarly, regarding the Council of Ministers in States, the Articles 163[48] and 164[49] provided for the appointment and salaries of the Ministers.

---

[46] Article 75 in The Constitution Of India 1949

75. Other provisions as to Ministers

(1) The Prime Minister shall be appointed by the President and the other Ministers shall be appointed by the President on the advice of the Prime Minister

(2) The Minister shall hold office during the pleasure of the President

(3) The Council of Ministers shall be collectively responsible to the House of the People

(4) Before a Minister enters upon his office, the President shall administer to him the oaths of office and of secrecy according to the forms set out for the purpose in the Third Schedule

(5) A Minister who for any period of six consecutive months is not a member of either House of Parliament shall at the expiration of that period cease to be a Minister

(6) The salaries and allowances of Ministers shall be such as Parliament may from time to time by law determine and, until Parliament so determines, shall be as specified in the Second Schedule

[47] 2013 (16) SCC 82

[48] Article 163 in The Constitution Of India 1949

163. Council of Ministers to aid and advise Governor

(1) There shall be a council of Ministers with the chief Minister at the head to aid and advise the Governor in the exercise of his functions, except in so far as he is by or under this constitution required to exercise his functions or any of them in his discretion

(2) If any question arises whether any matter is or is not a matter as respects which the Governor is by or under this Constitution required to act in his discretion, the decision of the Governor in his discretion shall be final, and the validity of anything done by the Governor shall not be called in question on the ground that he ought or ought not to have acted in his discretion

(3) The question whether any, and if so what, advice was tendered by Ministers to the Governor shall not be inquired into in any court

[49] Article 164 in The Constitution Of India 1949

164. Other provisions as to Ministers

Each member of Council of Ministers both at State level and Union is provided with the office, sufficient staff and other resources and infrastructure. Some senior scale civil servants also serve them. Entire expenditure of provision and maintenance of the office along with salaries to the staff members is borne by the Government and paid from the tax-payers money. Thus state Minister is 'public authority' as per Section 2(h)(a) of RTI Act, 2005.

(f) Without being an MP or MLA, one cannot hold office of the Minister in the Council of Ministers. The Representation of People Act, 1950 which is enacted to provide the allocation of seats in, and the delimitation of constituencies for the purpose of election to, the House of the People and the Legislatures of States, the qualifications of voters at such elections, the preparation of electoral rolls, the manner of filling seats in the Council of States to be filled by representatives of Union territories. Thus this law made by Parliament explained how the office of MP or MLA has been instituted to become Minister, which also a public authority. Representation of People Act, 1951 which was made to provide for the conduct of elections of the Houses of Parliament and to the House or Houses of the Legislature of each State, the qualifications and disqualifications for membership of those Houses, the corrupt practices and other offences at or in connection with such elections. Thus the Minister is constituted as public authority by 'law made by Parliament' as per Section 2(h)(b) of RTI Act.

---

(1) The chief Minister shall be appointed by the Governor and the other Ministers shall be appointed by the Governor on the advice of the Chief Minister, and the Ministers shall hold office during the pleasure of the Governor: Provided that in the State of Bihar, Madhya Pradesh and Orissa, there shall be a Minister in charge of tribal welfare who may in addition be in charge of the welfare of the Scheduled Castes and backward classes or any other work

(2) The Council of Ministers shall be collectively responsible to the Legislative Assembly of the State

(3) Before a Minister enters upon his office, the Governor shall administer so him the oaths of office and of secrecy according to the forms set out for the purpose in the Third Schedule

(4) A Minister who for any period of six consecutive months is not a member of the Legislature of the State shall at the expiration of that period cease to be a Minister

(5) The salaries and allowances of Ministers shall be such as the Legislature of the State may from time to time by law determine and, until the Legislature of the State so determines, shall be as specified in the Second Schedule

(g) The Member of Parliament or Legislature is declared as a public servant in *P.V. Narasimha Rao v. State*[50], by the Supreme Court of India in 1998. The Ministers have public duties to perform and they too have certain privileges prescribed under the Constitution under Article 105[51]. The Constitution in several other articles prescribed similar duties for MLAs in State legislatures. Tenth schedule explains the disqualification process for legislators, which means they have a duty not to defect to a party different from the party from which he was elected as a representative of people who voted for them. This reaffirms the position that MPs and MLAs are constituted by the Constitution of India [Refer Sec. 2(h)(a) of RTI Act, 2005]

Article 75(3) says the Council of Ministers shall be collectively responsible for the House of the People. For the decisions taken in the Cabinet Meeting, whether good or bad, moved by one individual or two, it will become decision of the entire cabinet, once approved, and makes all together responsible. However it does not exclude individual minister's responsibility as overall in charge of a portfolio and independent decision maker in that area. The Minister's privileged issues if any are rightly excluded by the exceptions in RTI Act, such

---

[50] 2002 CriLJ 2401, 97 (2002) DLT 45

[51] Article 105 in The Constitution Of India 1949

105. Powers, privileges, etc of the Houses of Parliament and of the members and committees thereof

(1) Subject to the provisions of this constitution and the rules and standing orders regulating the procedure of Parliament, there shall be freedom of speech in Parliament

(2) No member of Parliament shall be liable to any proceedings in any court in respect of anything said or any vote given by him in Parliament or any committee thereof, and no person shall be so liable in respect of the publication by or under the authority of either House of Parliament of any report, paper, votes or proceedings

(3) In other respects, the powers, privileges and immunities of each House of Parliament, and of the members and the committees of each House, shall be such as may from time to time be defined by Parliament by law, and, until so defined shall be those of that House and of its members and committees immediately before the coming into force of Section 15 of the Constitution (Forty fourth Amendment) Act 1978

(4) The provisions of clauses (1), (2) and (3) shall apply in relation to persons who by virtue of this constitution have the right to speak in, and otherwise to take part in the proceedings of, a House of Parliament or any committee thereof as they apply in relation to members of Parliament

as Section 8(1)(a)[52], (c)[53], (f)[54], (i)[55]. The proviso at the end of the section 8(1) which says "the information which cannot be denied to the Parliament or a State Legislature shall not be denied to any person" makes it clear wherever Minister is answerable to Legislators, he can also answerable to the ordinary citizen.

The expression "authority" would also include all persons or bodies that have been conferred a power to perform the functions entrusted to them under the constitution and merely because the Ministers are individuals, the same would not render the office of the Cabinet Minister any less authoritative than other constitutional functionaries. The expression "authority" as used in Section2(h) cannot be read as a term to exclude bodies or entities which are, essentially, performing functions in their individual capacity. The expression "authority" as used in Section 2(h) of the Act would encompass any office that is conferred with any statutory or constitutional power.

---

[52] Section 8 1(a) in The Right To Information Act, 2005

8. Exemption from disclosure of information.—

(1) Notwithstanding anything contained in this Act, there shall be no obligation to give any citizen,—

(a) information, disclosure of which would prejudicially affect the sovereignty and integrity of India, the security, strategic, scientific or economic interests of the State, relation with foreign State or lead to incitement of an offence

[53] Section 8 1(c) in The Right To Information Act, 2005

8. Exemption from disclosure of information.—

(1) Notwithstanding anything contained in this Act, there shall be no obligation to give any citizen,—

(c) information, the disclosure of which would cause a breach of privilege of Parliament or the State Legislature

[54] Section 8 1(f) in The Right To Information Act, 2005

8. Exemption from disclosure of information.—

(1) Notwithstanding anything contained in this Act, there shall be no obligation to give any citizen,—

(f) information received in confidence from foreign government

[55] Section 8 1(i) in The Right To Information Act, 2005

8. Exemption from disclosure of information.—

(1) Notwithstanding anything contained in this Act, there shall be no obligation to give any citizen,—

(i) cabinet papers including records of deliberations of the Council of Ministers, Secretaries and other officers: Provided that the decisions of Council of Ministers, the reasons thereof, and the material on the basis of which the decisions were taken shall be made public after the decision has been taken, and the matter is complete, or over: Provided further that those matters which come under the exemptions specified in this section shall not be disclosed

The office of the Cabinet Minister is an office established under the Constitution of India; the incumbent appointed to that office discharges functions as provided under the Constitution. Indisputably, the appointee to that office is, by virtue the constitution, vested with the authority to discharge those functions.

The probable claim that Cabinet Minister does not have the necessary infrastructure to support the applicability of the RTI Act in as much as, the Minister is a singular person office and, therefore, would have to act as a CPIO as well as the Appellate Authority and hence cannot be held as 'Public Authority" is not tenable. If lack of infrastructure is prescribed as the criteria for imposing transparency obligations, then none would be obliged to inform. That was never the intention of the RTI Act. It is quite relevant to quote the Judgment of Delhi High Court in ***W.P.(C) 1041/2013 in the case of S.C. Agrawal Vs. Office of the Attorney General of India***, dated 10.03.2015 where court observed, "it has been contended that there would be a practical difficulty as the office of the Attorney General is only a skeletal office which only consists of the appointee and the appointee's is personal staff. In court view, this cannot be considered as a reason for excluding the applicability of the Act on a public authority." Accordingly, the Court directed the office of the AGI to reconsider the RTI application.

Whether A Citizen Has Right To And Minister Has Corresponding Obligation to Provide Information?

It is borne by epics that Emperor Maryada Purushottam Shri Ram[56] used to have a bell in front of his palace, and whoever rings it he could come out of his residence to meet the citizen and hear him, reflecting grievance redressal mechanism in Ram Rajya. The history is replete with stories and Indian forts have built-in durbar halls where Emperors of Mughals, Rajputs and others used to meet the people to hear their submissions at a stipulated hour. Those are all dictatorial regimes. In democratic governance also people heard and saw that some of Prime Ministers, Chief Ministers and Ministers held janata darbars (public

[56] *Rama* or *Ramachandra* is the seventh avatar of the Hindu God Vishnu. He is the central figure of the Hindu epic Ramayana, which is the principal narration of the events connected to his incarnation on earth, his ideals and his greatness.

meetings) to receive people's representations/complaints etc in open. To meet or not, when and how to, etc are to be processed and informed by the concerned Minister, as that is totally prerogative of the Minister. Thus it may not be mandatory to have a fixed or prescribed timing for meeting the general public. Meeting by appointment is also difficult to be regulated or fixed with time schedules. Being an elected public representative, the Minister has a democratic duty to meet the common people and thus, citizens have a corresponding right to meet him. However this right should be subjected to limitations to ensure that it does not result in any form of chaos leading to a situation where he cannot perform his legal responsibilities as minister or public representative or bring Minister into physical security risk.

Subject to availability and convenience of the Minister at office in capital city or in Constituency, the minister owes a moral and democratic responsibility to meet his voters or people in the constituency. It will be in fitness of democratic requirements that every Minister makes it a regular practice once or twice or thrice in a week or month at any frequency of his choice, that he/she will be made available for meeting the people in a scheduled hour for a better people-oriented decision making or governance or hearing the grievances of public. Or, the Minister can publish dates of his meeting in coming month or fortnight, in a schedule as per his choice. It is the democratic right of voters to meet him and also it's his duty to meet voters which will go a long way in achieving the objectives of good governance through transparency as envisaged by the RTI Act.

Extending logically, this duty includes a genuine responsibility of the office of the Minister for Law & Justice/Minister of State (not the Ministry) to inform the people when they could meet him. This is a facility that they are expected to provide to the people who elected the Ministers. The information about such facility should be disclosed voluntarily by the office of Minister under section 4(1)(b) within 120 days from the date of commencement of RTI law. If there is no such facility of meeting, the Minister's office should declare that "there is no such facility" in a particular week/fortnight/month/year, as required under Section 4(1)(b).

Decision by CIC

The Commission considers it is the duty of both the Centre and States to provide required support to each minister, to ensure transparency in their functions.

Maharashtra State Chief Information Commissioner has declared on 25th September 2015 that each Minister of Maharashtra state as public authority and directed the Chief Secretary to appoint PIOs and First Appellate Authorities accordingly.

The Ministers debate the issues in the cabinet meetings and their collective opinion in the form of advice to the President or Governor is crucial in governance. President or Governor is a nominal head while executive head of each department is the Minister. They sanction for several state development activities and introduce people welfare schemes involving huge amounts. They are answerable to the Houses of Parliament and Legislature, being the representatives of the people. The Ministers are responsible individually to lead their departments/ministries and are also answerable to Legislature. They are expected to provide much needed leadership to the department taking assistance from the senior civil servants. The Constitution has entrusted the Ministers with higher powers and responsibilities over and above the IAS and IPS officers appointed through a rigorous examination process, only to facilitate the opinion of the people, their needs and duty and to keep in mind their welfare. They are all public duties, and Minister is a public body. Minister should not forget that he/she is elected by the people for the people on his request based on his promises and performances.

Thus there is no reason why Ministers should be kept beyond the purview of Right to Information, as their answerability is well established by the Constitution and Representation of People Act, 1951. Very title of the Act, 1951 suggests that they are expected to represent the people who elected them and also because they administer them in their capacity as Ministers of a particular portfolio of the Government. No honest and sincere minister would refuse to inform the people who elected him/her.

Though the definition in Section 2(h) provides several conditions and circumstances to declare an authority as 'public authority', the first clause in that definition itself substantially covers each and every Minister of both Center and State Governments. The 'Minister' is an institution within the scheme of the democratic Constitution. Being a Minister itself is public authority and as minister is associated with and assisted by an office, he cannot escape from the responsibilities under Right to Information Act. That office should facilitate access to people to the information held by it.

CIC observes that it is pitiful that a citizen has to file a RTI request to know the timings and process of meeting their chosen minister, which should have been ordinarily provided on their own. It is difficult for the PIO of the Ministry of Law, or Department of Legal Affairs to know and inform the people as to how and when the Cabinet Minister and Minister of State for Law will meet or what are the schedules or plans or processes for such meetings. It is not reasonable to ask the PIO of Ministry/Department of Legal Affairs to give that information. The Minister or his office alone is the appropriate authority to decide and inform about the facility of meeting the minister with details like days and timings, and also about the process of seeking appointment.

CIC observed that the being accessible to people is an essential representative character of democracy. Voter has a right to meet his representative, who has a corresponding duty. In mature democracy the people will reject and defeat a minister/legislator, who does not inform the means to meet his people.

No party lags behind in promising the people/voters that they will be within the reach or they will serve better etc. It is their moral duty to keep up their promises he made and programs forming part of manifesto of the political party. In a nation whose motto is '*Satyamev Jayathe*[57]', the Ministers under the leadership of the Prime Minister and respective Chief Ministers, have a moral responsibility to realize their promises truthfully.

It is pertinent to read the language of 'the oath of office and affirmations' made by each Minister when they were sworn in by the President or Governors:

57 "Satyameva Jayate" is a *mantra* from the ancient Indian scripture *Mundaka Upanishad.* Upon independence of India, it was adopted as the national motto of India. It is inscribed in script at the base of the national emblem.

... I will bear true faith and allegiance to the Constitution of India as by law established.... that I will faithfully and conscientiously discharge duties as a Minister for the Union/State and that I will do right to all manner of people in accordance with the Constitution and the law, without fear or favour, affection or ill-will. (The Constitution, Third Schedule, I).

The significant duty of the Minister is to be within the reach of people, answerable to them and keeping them posted with information as promised.

In addition, the Minister is asked to take oath of secrecy, as follows:

I will not directly or indirectly communicate or reveal to any person or persons any matter which shall be brought under my consideration or shall become known to me as a Minister except as may be required for the due discharge of my duties as such Minister. (Constitution of India, Third Schedule, II).

The National Commission to Review the Working of the Constitution (NCRWC) headed by Justice M.N. Venkatachalaiah[58], former Chief Justice of India, in 2002, referring to the Right to Information stated:

Government procedures and regulations shrouded in a veil of secrecy do not allow the clients to know how their cases are being handled. They shy away from questioning officers handling their cases...... In this regard, government must assume a major responsibility and mobilize skills to ensure flow of information to citizens. The traditional insistence on secrecy should be discarded. In fact, we should have an oath of transparency in place of an oath of secrecy.

It needs no mention that in a welfare state, Minister is a key functionary being in charge of a portfolio, or group of departments in a ministry. Instead of leaving it to the individual discretion, the law should mandate the transparency including the information about facilitating the 'meeting' with people. In this information age, the Right to Information Act, 2005 has relegated the Official

[58] M. N. Venkatachaliah was the 25th Chief Justice of India.[1][2][3][4] He served as Chief Justice from 1993 to 1994. He currently serves as the Chancellor of Sri Sathya Sai Institute of Higher Learning (Deemed University), a Modern Gurukula, a place where the teacher-student interaction occurs in the backdrop of the process of Integral Education that includes the five dimensions of: Intellectual, Cultural, Physical, Service and Devotional.

Secrets Act, 1923[59] into irrelevance in many aspects except protecting security related secrets. It will be more appropriate to pledge for transparency rather than confining to oath of secrecy. The Right to Information Act, 2005 has been deliberated and cleared by the Union Cabinet and passed by both the Houses of Parliament. Similarly several State Cabinet Ministers discussed and presented to their respective Legislative Assemblies who passed transparency laws. When Ministers wanted every other authority answerable, why should they also not be answerable under RTI Act?

Even if he takes oath of transparency, it will not oblige him to disclose various kinds of information, such as that prejudicially affect the sovereignty[60] and integrity of India etc as delineated in 8(1)(a), information, the disclosure of which would cause a breach of privilege of Parliament or State Legislature (c); information received in confidence from foreign government (f), and cabinet papers including records of deliberations of the Council of Ministers, Secretaries and other officers (with a proviso) (i). Section 8(2) allows the public authority to provide access to papers not withstanding anything contained in Official Secrets Act, 1923 in cases of public interest. In addition, Section 22[61] of RTI Act gives information law an overriding effect over the Official Secrets Act or any other law if that contradicts with RTI. Hence the Minister has to take an oath of transparency in place of obsolete 'oath of secrecy' or at least in addition to it.

CIC held that it wais not proper for the Public Authority (Ministry of Law and Justice) to direct the appellant to check with the Minister himself and take the appointment. Such a task is a mere impossibility for a common man, in the absence of a published schedule of meeting time or process of securing

---

59 The Official secret Act 1923 is India's anti espionage (Spy" and "Secret agent") act held over from British colonisation. It states clearly that any action which involves helping an enemy state against India. It also states that one cannot approach, inspect, or even pass over a prohibited government site or area.

60 Meaning of sovereignty:

1. Supremacy of authority or rule as exercised by a sovereign or sovereign state.
2. Royal rank, authority, or power.

61 Section 22 in The Right To Information Act, 2005

22. Act to have overriding effect.—The provisions of this Act shall have effect notwithstanding anything inconsistent therewith contained in the Official Secrets Act, 1923 (19 of 1923), and any other law for the time being in force or in any instrument having effect by virtue of any law other than this Act.

appointment through transparent means. Giving such an advice to applicant is no information at all, or at least, it is incomplete information. CIC held that the Ministers in the Union Government and all State Governments are 'public authorities' under Section 2(h) of RTI Act, 2005. Thus the Commission holds that the Ministers have a statutory obligation to inform the people as mandated by the Right to Information Act, 2005.

The Commission strongly recommended the Centre and States to provide necessary support to each minister, including designating some officers, or appointing as Public Information Officers and First Appellate Authorities. They also shall be given an official-website for suo moto[62] disclosure of the information with periodical updating as prescribed under Section 4 including the facility of meeting people since the Ministers deserve necessary assistance to receive, acknowledge and provide response to the representations given by the people and as Constitutional functionaries, the Ministers have a duty to inform the people about their efforts to fulfill the promises they have made, through Section 4(1)(b) of RTI Act and also to furnish the information as sought by their voters under other provisions of RTI Act. Exercising the power given under Section 19(8)(a)(ii)[63] the Commission requires the public authority, especially, the Cabinet Secretary of Union and all Chief Secretaries of States, to take such steps as may be necessary to secure compliance of the Right to Information Act and appointing a Public Information Officer.

---

[62] Meaning of suo moto:

A court takes *suo moto* action, meaning it starts a legal process on its own.

[63] Section 19 in The Right To Information Act, 2005

19. Appeal.—

(1) Any person who, does not receive a decision within the time specified in sub-section (1) or clause

(a) of sub-section (3) of section 7, or is aggrieved by a decision of the Central Public Information Officer or the State Public Information Officer, as the case may be, may within thirty days from the expiry of such period or from the receipt of such a decision prefer an appeal to such officer who is senior in rank to the Central Public Information Officer or the State Public Information Officer, as the case may be, in each public authority: Provided that such officer may admit the appeal after the expiry of the period of thirty days if he or she is satisfied that the appellant was prevented by sufficient cause from filing the appeal in time.

(2) Where an appeal is preferred against an order made by a Central Public Information Officer or a State Public Information Officer, as the case may be, under section 11 to disclose third party information, the appeal by the concerned third party shall be made within thirty days from the date of the order.

The Commission declares that the office of the Minister for Law as public authority under Section 2(h) of Right to Information Act, and under Section 19(8)(a)(ii) require the Government of India to appoint a Central Public Information Officer to answer the information requests of the citizen and publish the information as per Section 4(1)(b) including facility of meeting people.

---

(3) A second appeal against the decision under sub-section (1) shall lie within ninety days from the date on which the decision should have been made or was actually received, with the Central Information Commission or the State Information Commission: Provided that the Central Information Commission or the State Information Commission, as the case may be, may admit the appeal after the expiry of the period of ninety days if it is satisfied that the appellant was prevented by sufficient cause from filing the appeal in time.

(4) If the decision of the Central Public Information Officer or State Public Information Officer, as the case may be, against which an appeal is preferred relates to information of a third party, the Central Information Commission or State Information Commission, as the case may be shall give a reasonable opportunity of being heard to that third party.

(5) In any appeal proceedings, the onus to prove that a denial of a request was justified shall be on the Central Public Information Officer or State Public Information Officer, as the case may be, who denied the request.

(6) An appeal under sub-section (1) or sub-section (2) shall be disposed of within thirty days of the receipt of the appeal or within such extended period not exceeding a total of forty-five days from the date of filing thereof, as the case may be, for reasons to be recorded in writing.

(7) The decision of the Central Information Commission or State Information Commission, as the case may be, shall be binding.

(8) In its decision, the Central Information Commission or State Information Commission, as the case may be, has the power to,—

(a) require the public authority to take any such steps as may be necessary to secure compliance with the provisions of this Act, including—

(i) by providing access to information, if so requested, in a particular form;

(ii) by appointing a Central Public Information Officer or State Public Information Officer, as the case may be;

(iii) by publishing certain information or categories of information;

(iv) by making necessary changes to its practices in relation to the maintenance, management and destruction of records;

(v) by enhancing the provision of training on the right to information for its officials;

(vi) by providing it with an annual report in compliance with clause (b) of sub-section (1) of section 4;

(b) require the public authority to compensate the complainant for any loss or other detriment suffered;

(c) impose any of the penalties provided under this Act;

(d) reject the application.

(9) The Central Information Commission or State Information Commission, as the case may be, shall give notice of its decision, including any right of appeal, to the complainant and the public authority.

(10) The Central Information Commission or State Information Commission, as the case may be, shall decide the appeal in accordance with such procedure as may be prescribed.

Chapter - 10

INFORMATION REGARDING ACCESS TO NAMES OF ALL THOSE Z+ SECURITY COVER PROTECTEES WHO ARE NOT HOLDING ANY CONSTITUTIONAL OR STATUTORY OFFICE[64]

Facts in Nutshell

Queries of the appellant contained in the RTI application:

"It has been reported in the media that Mr. Amit Shah or Bhartiya Janta Party will be provided Z + Plus security cover by the government. Kindly provide the following information regarding it:

1. Are private citizens, who are not holding any public office entitled to such security cover.
2. Kindly provide a certified copy of the rules and regulations governing the entitlement and determination of type of security cover to be given to a person.
3. What is the estimated monthly or annual cost of providing the Z-Plus security cover to Mr. Amit Shah
4. Who will be responsible for paying the bill of this cover. The Government of India or Mr. Amit Shah or the Bhartiya Janta Party.
5. Kindly provide complete list of persons currently under security cover, the type of security cover being provided, the individual amount being spent, and who is paying for it."

---

64 Deepak Juneja vs. Central Public Information Officer, Ministry of Home Affairs (20.08.2018 - CIC) : MANU/CI/0524/2018

Hon'ble Judges/Coram:

Yashovardhan Azad, Information Commissioner

Reply by PIO and FAA

The PIO replied vide letter dated 01.08.2018 thereby denying information sought citing exemption clause (g) & (j) of the Section 8(1) of the RTI Act, 2005. The appellant preferred the first appeal whereupon the FAA (First Appellate Authority) upheld the decision of PIO and elaborated upon the exemptions availed by PIO. The same reads as:

"You have sought copy of rules and regulations governing the entitlement and determination of types of security cover to be given to a person. CPIO vide reply dated 01.08.2014 has stated that security to an individual (including private citizen) is provided on the basis of threat assessment carried out by the Central Security Agencies. Further details in this regard were not disclosed citing sections 24(I), 8(1)(g) and 8(1)(j) of the RTI Act, 2005.

I find that the CPIO was justified in denying the details including rules and regulations on the subject. In this connection, it is point out that the guidelines regarding provision of security to an individual have been framed in consultation with the security agencies. Since security agencies have been exempted from the provision of RTI Act 2005 in terms of Section 24(1) read with Schedule -II of the RTI Act, details with regard to modalities of assessment of threat and categorization of security to be provided to an individual cannot be disclosed.

You have requested details of months/annual cost of security to Mr. Amit Shah. The information was not provided by the CPIO on the grounds that the expenditure on security is incurred by concerned police force(s) providing security to an individual and such details are not maintained in this office.

The responsibility for provision of security to an individual rests with the concerned State Government under whose jurisdiction such an individual is ordinarily resident or happens to be. In case a protectee, who is ordinarily resident of Delhi, visits any place outside Delhi, it will be the responsibility of the concerned State Government to provide him the requisite security cover. The expenditure on provision of such security is incurred by the concerned police force(including Delhi Police) out of their normal budget under different heads of account and details of the same are not reported to this office. In view of this, details of expenditure incurred on provision of security to protectee are not been maintained in this office and hence could not be provided to you.

You have requested for complete list of persons currently under the security cover provided, the amount being spent and who is paying for it. CPIO vide his letter dated 01.08.2014 had observed that details of security provided, being exempt under Sections 8(1)(g) and 8(1)(j) cannot be disclosed.

It may be stated that the details of the types of security provided to an individual would reveal nature of security arrangements made for a person, as categorization of a protectee itself indicates the level of security provided. Such security categorization is made on the basis of inputs provided by the security agencies who are exempt in terms of Section 24(1) of the RTI Act 2005. In view of this the details with regard to persons being provided with the security cover and types of security provided, being exempt under Sections 24(1), 8(1)g) and 8(1)(j) if the RTI Act 2005 cannot be disclosed."

Appellant Submission before CIC

The plea of appellant aimed at gaining access to names of all those Z+ security cover protectees who are not holding any Constitutional or Statutory office. The appellant submitted that the plea taken by the PIO is contrary to the law as well as the facts since merely publicizing the names of security protectees, the rules for granting such protection, the cost of providing Z+ security cover and the source for defraying the cost incurred for security cover would not ipso facto comprise the security. He contended that the information sought is not exempt under clauses (g) and (j) of Section 8(1) of the RTI Act as invoked by the respondent PIO. While addressing arguments against applicability of clause (g); the appellant contended that the protectees are already under a threat perception for which they are adequately provided with security. He submitted that the security cover at state expense is a largesse and the same cannot be kept classified from the citizenry. Adverting to the proviso appended to clause (j), he submitted that the details of protectees under the Z+ security cover cannot be kept from the Parliament and hence the same cannot be denied to a citizen. The appellant pointed out that Mr. Amit Shah who happens to be the National

President of Bhartiya Janta Party has been granted Z+ security cover by MHA since July 2014 despite him not being holding any constitutional or statutory office. The appellant sought the reasons for grant of such security cover and the expenses incurred due to the same. He relied on various media reports wherein it has been reported that Mr. Mukesh Ambani Chairman of the Reliance Industries Ltd. has been granted with 'Z' security cover on cost reimbursement basis (approximately 15 to 18 lacs per month) to the Govt. of India. He argued that grant of security cover to eminent persons under threat is the duty of state in cases where the beneficiary holds a high office. As per the appellant, the act of bearing expenses for providing security cover to key State functionaries & Constitutional dignitaries by Govt. of India is justified since they cannot perform their vital functions while reeling under threat. However, the appellant submitted that defraying cost of elite Z+ security cover to private persons must not be meted out from the state exchequer. He submitted that since the cost of security cover granted to Mr. Amit Shah is borne out from the exchequer, the Parliament and similarly, the public has a right to know about the arrangement. He further relied on certain media reports claiming that Z security cover has also been extended to Shri Swami Ramdev, who does not hold any constitutional office. He filed on record the order dated 22.03.2017 passed by a 3 judge bench of the Hon'ble Supreme Court in Sanjay Laloo versus State of Meghalaya & Ors. and invited attention towards the relevant excerpts wherein the address of a former Judge despite being a Y category protectee was revealed in the judicial order. The contention of the appellant was thus aimed at exhibiting that revelation of identity and address of a protectee was not deemed classified by the Apex Court.

Respondent Submission before CIC

The PIO reiterated and relied upon the observations of the FAA. It was contention of the PIO that that the queries of the appellant have no bearing with public interest and the same would be prejudicial to the security cover of the Z+ protectees. He submitted that the protection granted to various political and non-political dignitaries is as per standard operating manuals which are classified. He submitted that the extension of security cover is on the basis of threat perception and the whole process of security assessment is thus classified and any revelation of the specific security assessment of a person or the rules by which such assessment is guided would render the whole security cover to be futile. Another contention of the respondent was that revelation of expenses incurred in providing security cover would lead to revelation of the intricacies as well as the magnitude and rigour of security cover. Another contention of respondent was that the rules governing the entitlement of grant of security cover and process of threat assessment etc are framed in consultation with Central Security Agencies. Citing the bar of Section 24(1) of the RTI Act, the respondents claimed, that the rules so framed in consultation with various agencies which are exempted under the mandate of RTI Act. He submitted that revelation of the rules framed in consultation with various exempted organizations would be nullifying the effect of Section 24 besides unveil the whole process of security assessment to public at large.

RTI Act, 2005

The RTI Act is a central legislation aimed at promotion of transparency in governance. The preamble to RTI Act, 2005 reads as:

An Act to provide for setting out the practical regime of right to information for citizens to secure access to information under the control of public authorities, in order to promote transparency and accountability in the working of every public authority, the constitution of a Central Information Commission and State Information Commissions and for matters connected therewith or incidental thereto.

Whereas the Constitution of India has established democratic Republic;

And whereas democracy requires an informed citizenry and transparency of information which are vital to its functioning and also to contain corruption and to hold Governments and their instrumentalities accountable to the governed;

And whereas revelation of information in actual practice is likely to conflict with other public interests including efficient operations of the Governments, optimum use of limited fiscal resources and the preservation of confidentiality of sensitive information;

And whereas it is necessary to harmonise these conflicting interests while preserving the paramountcy of the democratic ideal;

Now, therefore, it is expedient to provide for furnishing certain information to citizens who desire to have it.

The RTI Act aims at setting out the practical regime of RTI. The expression 'practical' qualifies the RTI. The preamble further acknowledges that "revelation of information in actual practice is likely to conflict with other public interests including efficient operations of the Governments". To counter the equally important rival facets of governance, Section 8 has been enacted which incorporates various situations wherein the Right of a citizen to secure Information from a public authority can be curtailed.

Clauses (g) & (j) of Section 8(1) of the RTI Act provide:

8. Exemption from disclosure of information.- (1) Notwithstanding anything contained in this Act, there shall be no obligation to give any citizen,-

......

(g) Information, the disclosure of which would endanger the life or physical safety of any person or identify the source of information or assistance given in confidence for law enforcement or security purposes; ....

(j) information which relates to personal information the disclosure of which has not relationship to any public activity or interest, or which would cause unwarranted invasion of the privacy of the individual unless the Central Public Information Officer or the State Public Information Officer or the appellate authority, as the case may be, is satisfied that the larger public interest justifies the disclosure of such information: Provided that the information, which cannot be denied to the Parliament or a State Legislature shall not be denied to any person.

Decision by CIC

Clause (g) of Section 8 of RTI Act is based on the 'potential harm' theory. While assessing the disclosability of a piece of information, the PIO is enjoined to apply his mind as what effects the revelation may produce. There has to be something more to mere guesswork by the PIO as the expression "which would endanger" cannot be read as "which may endanger". However, in the present case, information regarding the beneficiaries of Z+ security cover has been sought. Judicial notice can be taken of the fact that the protectees are already facing highest level of threat and that is why they have been accorded with the highest level of security cover. Revelation of names of protectees if not adding on to the danger their life or physical safety would be counterproductive to the efficacy of security cover. The query, when seen from this perspective attracts the exemption under clause (g).

The exemption clause of section 8 clause (h) prevents disclosure of personal information. The names of private Z+ protectees are personal since they do not owe the security cover to their public office but private position in life. It was not the case that each and every private person would get Z+ cover at the mere asking. The public eminence of the private person; threat perception and the potential harm which may ensure to the national interest if the private person is left exposed to the potential threat are the key determinative factors while granting the security cover. Despite being an eminent person under threat; the protectee is entitled to his Right of privacy. A nine judge bench of the Supreme Court in Justice K.S. Puttaswamy and Ors. v. Union of India (UOI) and Ors. (24.08.2017 - SC) : MANU/SC/1044/2017 held 'Right to privacy' as a right guarded by the Constitution of India. The identity, specific threat perception analysis etc. are personal information of a protectee who does not hold a public office. For instance, if the Govt. extends a Z+ cover to a spiritual leader or an ace sportsman or any eminent personality in acknowledgement of his/her contribution to the national interest, would that person be left bereft of his/her right to privacy? The right to know, in such case must make a way for the right to privacy of the individual and the efficiency of governance since the same furthers the concept of 'practical regime' of RTI as conceptualized in the preamble of the RTI Act.

On 09.12.2015, The MoS for Ministry of Home Affairs Tabled Reply to the Following Queries.

RAJYA SABHA

UNSTARRED QUESTION No. 1192

SECURITY TO PERSONS OF POLITICAL AND JUDICIAL FIELD

+1192. SHRI NARAYAN LAL PANCHARIYA:

Will the Minister of HOME AFFAIRS be pleased to state:

(a) the criteria for providing security to persons of political and judicial field;

(b) the category of persons of both fields for whom there is a provision for providing security guard;

(c) whether there is a provision to provide security to Members of Parliament, if so, the number of Member of Parliament to whom security guards have been provided so far in the country along with details thereof; and

(d) the names of persons and families in the country to whom security has been provided, the category-wise details thereof?

ANSWER: MINISTER OF STATE IN THE MINISTRY OF HOME AFFAIRS (SHRI HARIBHAI PARATHIBHAI CHAUDHARY)

(a) Security arrangements for President of India, Vice President of India and Prime Minister of India are made in accordance with the guidelines contained in their respective Blue Books issued by Ministry of Home Affairs and the SPG Act. Security arrangements for other political personalities are made as per the guidelines laid down in the "Yellow Book" titled "Security arrangement for the protection of individuals". The security arrangements for such individuals are made after careful assessment of their threat perception emanating from terrorists/militant/fundamentalist outfits and organized criminal gangs. The degree of threat varies from individual to individual, depending on factors, such as nature of activities, status, and likely gains for the terrorists, etc. Accordingly, categorized security cover (Z+, Z, Y & X) is provided to them on the basis of gravity of the threat.

The security so provided is periodically reviewed by Committee specially constituted for this purpose. Certain categories of individuals, such as Union Ministers, State CMs and Judges of Supreme Court and High Courts, are provided positional/statutory security cover to facilitate bold and impartial decision making.

(b) The protectees falling under Z+, Z, Y(threat) and Y category are entitled for getting the deployment of Static Armed Guard at their residence. Besides, Static Armed Guard are also provided to the protectee of any category based on the threat assessment.

(c) Security cover to individuals, including MPs is provided only on the basis of individual threat perception. State Governments have their own criteria to provide security to MPs. The list of MPs provided security under various categories is not maintained centrally.

(d) The details of individuals, who are being provided security cover, by Central Government cannot be disclosed in the public interest.

Thus, in terms of the above quoted parliamentary proceeding, there was an actual instance of denial of names of beneficiaries of all categories of the Central protectees to the Parliament. Hence, the argument of application of proviso to clause (j) in the present case does further the cause of appellant.

As a sequel to the aforesaid, CIC found that RTI application has been dealt with adequately. The appeal was disposed of.

Chapter - 11

INFORMATION REGARDING MISPLACED AND STOLEN ANTIQUES[65]

Facts in Nutshell

The appellant sought information regarding efforts made by the Government of India along with the related documents and correspondence for bringing into India (i) Koh-i-Noor diamond, (ii)Sultanganj Buddha, (iii) Nassak Diamond (iv) The Sword and ring of Tipu Sultan, (v) The golden throne of Maharaja Ranjit Singh (vi) Royal Jade wine cup of Shahjahan, (vii) Amaravathi railings and Buddhapade (viii) Saraswathi Marble idol- Vagdevi (ix) Mechanical Tiger of Tipu etc., & jewels.

Reply by CPIO

The CPIO, Archaeological Survey of India (ASI) replied stating that under the Antiquities and Art Treasure Act, 1972, the ASI can take up the issue of retrieval of only those antiquities, which have been illegally exported out of the country in violation of the above Act which became operational in 1976. So far 25 antiquities have been retrieved from various other countries during the years 2014 to 2017.

As no information was given and all his first appeals were also transferred to ASI without any purpose, the appellant filed second appeal before Central Information Commission (CIC).

Contention by Appellant before CIC

Appellant contented that our finest jewels like Koh-i-Noor, precious

---

[65] B.K.S.R. Ayyangar vs. PIO, Archaeological Survey of India (20.08.2018 - CIC)
CIC/ALSOI/A/2018/111930
Hon'ble Judges/Coram:
M. Sridhar Acharyulu, Central Information Commissioner

treasures, artifacts were looted by the invaders especially the British, and he wanted to know wonderful efforts of our government to bring them back to India, but did not receive any thing. He filed RTI request with the PMO, Ministry of External Affairs and Ministry of Culture, as he knew that it is difficult to expect such information from the ASI officers.

Contention by CPIO before CIC

CPIO (antiquity) stated that she had received the RTI application from Nodal officer of ASI, the ASI could take up the issue of the retrieval of antiquities from the foreign country only in case of illegally exported article as per Antiquities and Art Treasures Act 1972 which came in to force in April 1976. The objects/ Antiquities referred by the applicant were taken away prior to Independence, therefore ASI has no authority to process the case of retrieval of "Koh-I-Noor diamond" and other objects under reference. The reply was given by CPIO of Antiquity Section within stipulated time under the provision of RTI Act. 2005.

The CPIO submitted that two writ petitions number 185 of 2016 and 367 of 2016 were filed for retrieval of Koh-i-Noor Diamond before Supreme Court by All India Human Rights & Social Justice Front v. the High Commissioner of UK (Britain) & ors. and Heritage Bengal. Supreme Court held on 21.04.2017 Government was mindful of the sentiments that have been expressed by the Indian public and the Parliament from time to time, about the return of the Koh-i-Noor and other items of India. The Ministry of External Affairs, Government of India continues to explore ways and means for obtaining a satisfactory resolution to the issue with the U.K. Government.

Historic Koh-I-Noor

Some people believe that history of Koh-I-Noor diamond goes back more than 5000 years and its original name was Syamantaka Mani during the age of Lord Krishna, later it changed hands in 1304 from Rajas of Malwa to Emperor of Delhi, Allaudin Khilji, came to Samarkhand in 1339, where it stayed for 300 years, before it was mentioned in Baburnama in 1526, said to be gifted by Babur to Sultan Ibrahim Lodi, which came back to Mughal Sultans, passed on to Persian

General Nadir Shah in 1739, who believed to have given the name Koh-I-Noor ("mountain of light"), from whom it reached his General Ahmad Shah Durrani, who brought it back to India in 1813 to gift to Ranjit Singh in exchange of throne of Afghanistan. After conquest of East India Company forces in 1849, it went to their treasury in Lahore, finally shipped to Britain to adore the crown of Queen Victoria in 1850. Hence the people have high sentimental attachment with this Diamond.

Nassak Diamondis: believed to be a unique blue diamond that graced the crown of Lord Shiva at Triambakeswar in Nasik during 15th century and disappeared during third Anglo-Maratha war in 1817. Also called 'eye' of Shiva, Nassak is a large diamond weighed 43.38 carats (8676 gram) when it was found in the Golconda mines of Kollur. The British East India Company captured the diamond and sold it to British jewelers Rundell and Bridge in 1818. Rundell and Bridge recut the diamond in 1818, after which it made its way into the handle of the 1st Marquess of Westminster's dress sword. It was imported into United States in 1927 and was considered one of the first 24 great diamonds of the world by 1930, and it was sold in auction in New York in 1970. Trustees of temple recently requested President and Prime Minister Modi to bring it back from private museum in Lebanon[66].

Sultanganj Buddha: When Railway Engineer EB Harris was excavating for building a Railway Station at Sultanganj, contractor Mr. Samuel Thronton has discovered Buddha statute in 1862. He shifted it to Birmingham Museum in 1867. It is a splendid example of Gupta-Pala transitional sculpture, the largest substantially complete copper Buddha figure known from the time. The archaeologists dated it back to between 500 and 700 AD. The Buddha's Sangathi (monastic robe) clings so closely to the body that it is almost invisible, but for a series of string-like folds, giving the figure a wet-looking appearance.[67]

Tipu's Mechanical Tiger: Tipu Sultan is most popular ruler of Mysore who died defending independence from British soldiers. Tipu's Tiger is a mechanical tiger created for him. It is an 18th century automaton or mechanical toy.

[66] http://www.thehindu.com/society/history-and-culture/bring-back-indias-nassak-diamond-from-lebanon/article23346247.ece

[67] http://www.bbc.co.uk/birmingham/content/articles/2006/05/10/sultanganj_bud dha_feature.shtml

Mechanisms inside the tiger and man's bodies make one hand of the man move, emit a wailing sound from his mouth and grunts from the tiger. In addition a flap on the side of the tiger folds down to reveal the keyboard of a small pipe organ with 18 notes. The carved and painted wood casing represents a tiger savaging a near life-size European man. It is on display in the Victoria and Albert Museum, London[68].

Tipu's Sword: The last sword used by Tipu in his last battle, at Srirangapatnam, and the ring worn by him were taken by the British forces as war trophies. Until April 2004, the sword was kept on display at the British Museum London as gifts to the museum from Major General Augustus W.H. Meyrick and Nancy Dowager. When the legendary sword was auctioned in 2004, Rajyasabha MP and economic offender Vijay Mallya purchased it. This is considered to be one of the world's rare artifact. The curved steel blade made of fine steel has inscribed with verses from the Holy Quran. It has wooden sheath covered with maroon velvet.

Tipu's Ram Ring is 'an Indian antique gold ring' with 'Rama' in raised Devenagri script surrounded by chased floral buds to the octagonal base and ornate shoulders and hoop, the inside of which is engraved Major General Lord Fitz Roy Somerset KCB, late 18th century. It has been weighed to be of 41.2 gms. A catalogue dated 1908 of the Royal United Service Museum, Whitehall described as '3064. Ring was taken from Tipu's finger by Colonel Honorable A. Wellesley (Duke of Wellington) in battle field of Seringapatam, 1799, and given by him to his niece, Lady FitzRoy Somerset.'

Marble Vagdevi: The most beautiful marble statue of Vagdevi- Goddess Saraswati was taken from Bhoj Sala of Madhra Pradesh. Raja Bhoj was king in 1034 reputed for have nine gems of literary personalities in his royal court. It is said Lord Curzon looted it and shifted it to England.

Singhasan of Maharaja Ranjit Singh made of wood and resin core with sheets of repousse, chased and engraved gold by goldsmith Hafez Muhammad Multani. It was made between 1820 and 1830, reflecting splendour of Ranjit Singh. When British annexed Punjab after second Anglo-Sikh war in 1849, the

---

[68] https://www.ripleys.com/weird-news/tipus-tiger-ancient-mechanical-wonder/

throne was taken over as one of the state property, displayed with other looted treasures at the Great Exhibition in 1851. It is kept in the V&A Museum with inventory number 2518(IS).[69]

Wine Cup of Shah Jahan is of white nephrite Jade, inscribed with his title, "Second Lord of the Conjunction" as per Persian titulature convention. It specially alludes to Timur, the central Asian ruler from whom the Mughals descended. It belongs to year 1657 CE. Colonel Charles Seton Guthrie of 19th Century acquired most probably after the Indian Rebellion of 1857. It changed several hands and finally acquired by the Victoria and Albert Museum in 1962.[70]

Decision by CIC

More than three thousand five hundred sites and monuments which are notified and under the ASI protection, other ancient monuments which are not under any official protection form part of India's and indeed the World's heritage. The Constitution of India enjoins upon all Indian nationals to protect and preserve this heritage. Laws prohibit removal and smuggling of these antiquities, whether protected or not. Such thefts from officially notified sites, the offence is greater. There is a steady stream of thefts and smuggling of antiques after destruction and mutilation. If in the past foreign invaders destroyed, now in these days, criminals are mutilating artifacts and removing them for smuggling. They cut off the head of a sculpture to steal, smuggle and sell it. Tragedy is that there is no centralized documentation exists in India about thefts or smuggling of art objects. Actionable information is not made available by the ASI. The monument from where artifacts are stolen, description of stolen antique, measurements and photographs and details of the FIR should be made public through all possible media. The complaints and FIRs should also contain photographic evidence of stolen objects, which should have duly publicized so that smuggling becomes difficult. There should be such public documentation of thefts which will help in preventing stolen things from crossing borders. Because of the alerts issued www.plunderedpast.in two stolen sculptures could be recovered. The

69 https://en.wikipedia.org/wiki/Maharaja_Ranjit_Singh%27s_throne#/media/File: Ranjit_Singh%27s_golden_throne.jpg?100

70 http://collections.vam.ac.uk/item/O73769/wine-cup-of-shah-jahan-wine-cup-unknown/

Commission recommended that ASI should take similar efforts to publish alerts, photos and FIRs about thefts, besides developing centralized public documentation of thefts with full details and photographs.

These precious artifacts reflect India's glorious culture and valiant history cannot be in the hands of looters, offenders or lying in foreign government and private museums. Deep sentiments are associated with these heritage objects as some of them are religiously considered sacred such as Marble Vagdevi of Bhoj Raj, Buddha's statue from Sultanganj, Nassak Diamond called 'eye' of Shiva, and objects with high historic value like Koh-I-Noor, Tipu's sword, ring and mechanical tiger etc. They legitimately belonged to India and people of past, present and future generations are interested in re-possessing them.

The information requested under RTI demand an initiative from the PMO to secure the details from the concerned, possibly including Ministry of External Affairs or of Culture to take needful measures. If they have initiated any such measures, they should have given the details. Appellant and people will be disappointed if nothing was done, at least that should have been stated. If some measures were taken but not fruitful, or if they are still in the process, that information could be satisfactory.

The PMO and Ministry of Culture should take note of the concerns expressed by this enthusiastic independent archeologist. This shows that India need to show matching interest in recovering these artifacts of immeasurable value. Ministry of Culture and ASI has a duty to respond to queries of such organizations. Similarly if any of such efforts are gaining results that could be possibly within the reach of PMO. If they have done something to regain those symbols of our glorious past either through diplomatic means or ARCA (Association for Research into Crime against Art),the PMO would be better equipped to inform the appellant rather than others. The Government cannot ignore these sentiments which are reflected by representations, Public Interest Litigations and RTI requests.

Chapter - 12

NGOs ANNUAL REPORTS AND INCOME-EXPENDITURE STATEMENTS ARE NOT THIRD PARTY INFORMATION[71]

Facts in Nutshell

The appellant filed RTI application seeking information about J&K NGO's availing GIA under BAJSS/Centralized System of Rajiv Gandhi National Creche Scheme from Central Social Welfare Board and following documents relating to the said information: (1) Copy of Registration Certificate of NGO (2) Copy of PAN Card of the NGO (3) Copy of 12AA Registration with Income Tax Department (4) Copy of 80-G Registration with Income Tax Department (5) Copy of Office Bearers/Managing Committee Members (6) Consolidated Income & Expenditure Account of the Organization for the Financial Year 2013-14, 2014-15 & 2015-16 (7) Copy of ITR with Computation Statement for the Assessment Year 2014-15, 2015-16 & 2016-17.

The appellant alleged that several NGOs in Jammu and Kashmir are not filing IT returns and seeks to know competition assessment including grants, funds that are received by such organisations in light of the new amendment in Income Tax Act as per which an organisation cannot receive more than Rs. 2,000 in cash.

Reply by CPIO

The Deputy Director of Central Social Welfare Board stated that the information sought by the appellant is third party information, hence, cannot be provided.

---

[71] Ashok Kumar vs. PIO, Central Social Welfare Board (17.05.2017 - CIC)
CIC/CSWBO/A/2017/109115
Hon'ble Judges/Coram:
M. Sridhar Acharyulu, Central Information Commissioner

The CPIO could not show how the information sought is personal information of NGO, how it could be classified as 'third party' information, or whether he examined the existence of public interest before rejecting the RTI request. Ms. Pavitra Gupta, Deputy Director (CPIO) contended that it was 'personal' information of the NGO and hence could not be given. Officers could not answer how an organization could have 'personal' information.

NGO's and Transparency

The Intelligence Bureau (IB) submitted a classified document identifying several foreign-funded non-governmental organizations (NGOs) that are negatively impacting economic development of the country[72]. It was alleged that these NGOs provide field reports to foreign donors who in turn build a record against India and these reports are used for the strategic foreign policy interests of the Western government. It shows how NGOs are unfettered in their approach. In Sept. 2016, a bench of Supreme Court led by T.S. Thakur observed that there is no central legislation to ensure accountability and transparency in the working of NGOs[73]. Moreover, there is no legal brainwork done at the center level to control these NGOs. In Jan 2017, the Supreme Court in Writ Petition (Crl.) Nos. 172 of 2011 between Manohar Lal Sharma, Advocate v. State of Maharashtra and Ors. ordered a compulsory audit of nearly 30 lakh NGOs by March 31, 2017[74]. In this matter, the bench headed by Chief Justice J.S. Khehar and Hon'ble Justice N.V. Ramana and Hon'ble Justice D.Y. Chandrachud said mere blacklisting of NGOs who do not file annual statements will not suffice but also action must be initiated like criminal proceedings for misappropriation and civil action for recovery of given funds. The bench also asked Centre to lay down guidelines for accreditation of NGOs and devise a proper accounting system.[75]

The Court suggested that the government ought to frame a statutory law to regulate the flow of public money to the NGOs. The court said the guidelines

---

72 (http://indianexpress.com/article/india/india-others/foreign-aided-ngos-are-actively-stalling-development-ib-tells-pmo-in-a-report/)

73 (http://www.thehindu.com/new s/national/Unaccounted-flow-of-funds-to-NGOs-a-%E2%80%98major-problem%E2%80%99-SC/article14638269.ece)

74 (http://www.thehindu.com/todays-paper/SC-orders-audit-of-30-lakh NGOs/article17020950.ece)

75 (http://ngo.india.gov.in/auth/default.php)

might not prove sufficient for systematizing the entire process of accreditation, fund utilization and audit of NGOs.

Decision by Central Information Commission (CIC)

In a division bench matter between Anil Bairwal v. Commissioner of Income Tax-1, vide file Nos. CIC/DS/A/2011/004218 along with 7 other second appeals, decided on 10.08.2016 by the Hon'ble Central Information Commissioners Shri Basant Seth and Shri M. Sridhar Acharyulu held as under:

"29. Section 138(1)(b) of the Income Tax Act is also similarly couched with requirement of examining the public interest factor, which is very significant. In fact provision for disclosure of such information exists in the Income Tax Act itself. Section 138(1)(b) of the Income Tax Act empowers the Commissioner of Income Tax to disclose, "in public interest", any information which comes into the hands of the public authority. That Section reads as follows:-

"(b) Where a person makes an application to the [Chief Commissioner or Commissioner] in the prescribed form for any information relating to any assessee [received or obtained by any income-tax authority in the performance of his functions under this Act], the [Chief Commissioner or Commissioner] may, if he is satisfied that it is in the public interest so to do, furnish or cause to be furnished the information asked for and his decision in this behalf shall be final and shall not be called in question in any court of law."

That this Section states is that that any information in the hands of the Income Tax authorities would be ordinarily held as confidential, but can be made public, if in the judgement of the Commissioner of Income Tax, it serves public purpose. Therefore, the contention that all Income Tax Returns - an information provided by assessees to Income Tax authorities - are permanently barred from disclosure, is not correct. This information can be disclosed in public interest, either in a given case, or a class of cases, under Income Tax laws.

30. The CPIOs being authorities are under R.T.I. Act, should proceed according to procedure prescribed under that law and consult each and every third party about whose ITR related information is being sought.

31. The Bench (CIC) directed the respondents to examine each point of RTI request, issue notices to all third parties as required under Section 11 in all eight cases, secure responses, duly consider the larger public interest after giving sufficient opportunity to the appellants, and decide on with speaking orders on each point, within three months from the date of receipt of this order."

The Commission (CIC) found that the Central government have formulated new guidelines for bringing transparency and accountability in the working of NGOs. NGOs are now required to register with the NITI Aayog's portal NGO Darpan in order to get grants. Darpan also requires a number of new disclosures like the Aadhaar number and PAN numbers of chief executives of not-for-profit organizations.

If an NGO registers itself with Income Tax department, it has to tell people that it has a PAN registration; similarly, if it registers under 12AA or 80G of the Income Tax Act, it has to inform the same and even should give the registration details. In fact, these 3 factors i.e., (1) PAN registration, (2) registration under Section 12AA and (3) registration under Section 80G of Income Tax Act would give an NGO a credit and credibility to collect donations with information given to donors to secure some rebate in taxation. Hence, these documents cannot be claimed as third party information. Consolidated income and expenditure account of an NGO/political party has to be in public domain are given on demand in the interest of transparency and accountability, there is no point in considering this statement as confidential. The Central Social Welfare Board being regulatory of social welfare activities has every authority to check whether the concerned NGO has registered a PAN card for it, whether they are filing IT returns regularly, what is the IT assessment and how much of tax was paid by it, besides, the amount of donations and also donors etc. The appellant is interested in knowing these aspects of Jammu & Kashmir NGOs which indicates the enormous public interest in disclosure.

The R.T.I. Act emphasizes that "democracy requires an informed citizenry", and that transparency of information is vital to flawless functioning of constitutional democracy. It is nobody's case that, while all organs of the State must exhibit maximum transparency, no such obligation attaches to political parties. Given that political parties influence the exercise of political power; transparency in their organization, functions and, more particularly, their means of funding is a democratic imperative, and, therefore, is in public interest. Insofar as the Income Tax Returns of political parties contain funding details these are liable for disclosure.[76]

Hence, on the same lines the NGO is expected to be transparent. NGOs annual reports, income-expenditure statements and ITRs cannot be considered somebody's 'personal' or 'third' party information. An NGO similarly cannot hide its income tax returns. Hence, Commission directed the respondent authority to provide the certified copies of the information sought along with the PAN number, if not the copy of PAN card. In light of the above developments, the Commission directed the respondent authority to provide complete details regarding Jammu & Kashmir NGOs including the certified copies of registration certificate duly attested by Registrar of Societies and the copy of PAN number. Commission suggested that in fact, the NGOs in their capacity as public authorities should voluntarily disclose all the information sought under Section 4(1)(b) along with their activities report. The respondent authority is under an obligation to disclose this information as mandated under Section 4(1)(b) of the R.T.I. Act.

---

[76] Anil Bairwal v. Commissioner of Income Tax-1, vide file Nos. CIC/DS/A/2011/004218

Chapter - 13

RIGHT TO INFORMATION AND FRAMING POLICIES FOR THE GUIDES BY MINISTRY OF TOURISM[77]

Facts in Nutshell

Appellant sought information on following 9 points:

(i) Gazette notification dated 31.01.2017 with subject Policy for Archaeological Survey of India guides to perform within Centrally protected Monuments, after this notification the Ministry got authority to issued new guide license and to renew existing guide license, whether the Ministry is still renewing existing guide license

(ii) Does he have to get his guide license by Ministry of Tourism, Government of India or any of its department or ASI

(iii) If Ministry of Tourism or any of its department still renewing above guide license even after the Gazette Notification of ASI then provide the reason in detail

(iv) if Ministry is renewing, what is the last date for submission of it and where it needs to be submitted

(v) can a person from Jaipur submit above license for renewal at India Tourism office in Jaipur

(vi) if no, provide reason in detail

(vii) reason as to why after 1996 ASI delegated its power to make guides for its monuments to Ministry of Tourism

[77] Ajay Duti
Vs.
CPIO, M/o Tourism
Hon'ble Judges/Coram:
M. Sridhar Acharyulu, Central Information Commissioner
Second Appeal Nos. CIC/ALSOI/A/2018/112427, CIC/ALSOI/A/2018/614623 and CIC/MTOUR/A/2018/614620

(viii) reason as to why ASI has to take power to make guides for its monuments back from Ministry of Tourism vide gazette notification dated 31-01-2017

(ix) if there is any opinion/rule regarding guides taking clients to shopping as per travel agents itinerary/condition.

In Short:

Through RTI the Following Issues Were Raised

i. Why regional guides are being replaced by zonal one.

ii. Why thousands of guides are being asked to come to Delhi to get stamps on the application of renewal of license. Only to collect 500 bribe.

iii. Why don't you do it Jaipur

iv. Expressing his frustration. On the 2 departments functioning of.. resulting in the destruction of tourism industry in India, he openly demanded to officialise/legalise the bribe, fix the rates. At least that would be a solution continuing some system in the 2 dept.

v. Why the department of ASI handed over its power to appoint/license the guides to the tourism dept. in 2003 and why it was taken back in 2017

vi. Who will be responsible for the damage caused to the guides because of this unthoughtful shifting of power between the 2 depts. And what is the solution.

Decision by CPIO and FAA

The CPIO replied on 08.12.17 with an answer to points 1 to 5 that the guide policy of 31.01.2017 is sub-judice, however, Ministry of Tourism has issued instructions to all Regional Director for renewal of existing Regional level guide license till March 2018. He stated that information sought under points 8 and 9 are not covered in the RTI act. Vide order dated 22.12.2017, the FAA order directed the CPIO to provide the copy of the stay order of the High Court regarding the renewal of licenses, instructions of renewal of licenses and zonal jurisdiction of the RDs issued by Ministry of Tourism. The part of the RTI which pertains to ASI has been transferred. The appellant still not satisfied filed second appeal before Central Information Commission (CIC).

Contention by Appellant before CIC

The appellant pointed out that the regional level guides have lost the authority to enter monuments. He suggested that the monument guides could have been regional level guides instead of eliminating or separating them. He said that a particular guide cannot enter because he is not a monument guide and without these aspects for a tourist guide are very narrow.

The appellant framed his arguments on three grounds: (i) Ministry of Tourism has no policy for Regional level guides (ii) there are no training programmes for guides (iii) IATO is acting as an agent in hiring tour guides. He stated that MoT renews RLG license and central ASI & state ASI (Rajasthan) counter sign it, as used to happened till ASI gazette notification dated 31-01-2017 (new comprehensive policy of ASI). In India there are 3 category of Monuments:

i. Central ASI guide with ASI license or countersign only can enter.

ii. State ASI guides with state ASI license or counter sign only can enter

iii. Private License issued by both ASI or MOT not allowed.

He stated that before this new policy was introduced by ASI in January 2017, RLG license was countersigned by central & state ASI, however now MOT would reinstate his RLG license without counter sign by central ASI & state ASI, this RLG is meaningless he would not be allowed to enter any monuments in India. He stated that MoT must ask IATO to stop using unauthorized people as tour escort or replacement of RLG. The terms like Tour escort, Trip Leader, Tour manager, Tour Director, RLG means same and all of them do the same job. The appellant suggested that MOT/ASI should reinstate original condition of refresher course for RLG i.e no interview or test.

The appellant alleged that the Ministry of Tourism has given IATO (Indian association of tour operator) Tour operator unconditional discretion to bring in foreign tourist through their tours and is the main body for obtaining inputs, suggestions, data, new requirements including that of RLG (regional level guides).

Decision by CIC

The Commission gave the following directions

i. Directs department of tourism and ASI to explain reasons for a shifting of power/responsibility for appointing or framing policies for the guides between them.

ii. To consider the RTI applications of this applicant as a complaint and directs to provide an action taken report in 30 days

iii. To show-cause why maximum penalty be not imposed on Ms. Sunita Tewatia, CPIO, ASI, Mr. Ranjan Lahiri, CPIO, Ministry of Tourism and Mr. Kalyan Sengupta, CPIO for a delay and denial of info sought besides harassing the appellant by kicking the matter into each other's courts.

The Commission also recommended Secretary, Ministry of Tourism, Government of India to review the feud between the 2 departments harming the guides and the tourism industry and inform the appellant about the steps taken to resolve the problem reflected in his appeal. The Secretary, Ministry of Tourism, Government of India was also recommended to seriously consider the problem pointed out by the appellant that the policies of the Ministry are compelling the guides and others to file 3 court cases each year because of which the activities are slowing down.

The Ministry of Tourism is involved in licensing of only Regional Level Guides (RLG) who are given licenses on the basis of five zones as already defined by the Ministry of Tourism. Hence the contention of any change in policy is not true. At present there are about 3269 Regional Level Guides. As Northern Region has many states having zonal licenses gives greater coverage and mobility. By providing guide licenses, Ministry of Tourism is only facilitating guides by recognizing the training knowledge. Ministry of tourism is not involved in job placement of trained guides. Ministry of Tourism only provides the guide license and does not provide any employment. Guiding is voluntary job taken up by the individual. Since no work is allocated by Ministry of Tourism or its field offices, the question of dismissal from 4 tours does not arise. It is pertinent to mention that as per direction of Hon'ble High Court of Delhi, Secretary, Tourism and

Culture took meeting with ASI and all stake holders to resolve the issue and the status report was submitted to the Hon'ble High Court of Delhi.

The Commission finds that the policy of January 2017 indicates that the Ministry of Tourism intends to create quality tourists. However, the Ministry of Tourism could not put before the Commission any concrete plans with definite timelines with respect to appointment of new regional level guides or renewal of licenses. In absence of definitive timeline, the appellant apprehends continuation of existing policy will be detrimental to young generations aspiring to become tourist guides. There is a need that the Ministry of Tourism to put in place a specific and certain program for conducting refresher courses, inviting applications and granting new licenses renewing licenses of existing tourist guides, without red tape or lethargy. The Commission directed that the process of licensing should be completely transparent to eliminate corruption or abuse of power to discriminate against some guides, as apprehended by appellant.

Commission recommended Ministry of Tourism and Archaeological Survey of India to have fixed timeline for accepting applications for participation in fresher course, which is now a mandatory requirement for grant and renewal of guide licenses

Chapter - 14

RIGHT TO INFORMATION ABOUT COMPLAINTS RECEIVED BY THE NATIONAL COMMISSION FOR PROTECTION OF CHILD RIGHTS[78]

Facts in Nutshell

Appellant sought information about the number of complaints received by the National Commission for Protection of Child Rights, copy of inquiry proceedings in such complaints, date-wise decisions of cases where the accused persons were found guilty and what reliefs were granted. He was emphasising for information about what action was taken, why action was not taken on certain complaints, the time taken for considering those complaints, how many of complaints were found to be true, whether accused were punished, whether any relief was provided to victims along with the details of dates and kind of relief provided. He also wanted to know how many of complaints on child rights violations were proved to be truthful since beginning of the Commission.

Appellant's request for action taken information on four-year old complaints before National Commission for Protection of Child Right (NCPCR), which is in public interest and relates to its core function.

If one properly tries to understand the requirement of information of the complainant, it strikes that he sought to know how the NCPCR acted on complaints under Section 13(j). Even under Section 15, the NCPCR has to take certain steps after inquiry.

---

[78] Appellants: Ajit Kumar Singh

Vs.

Respondent: PIO, National Commission for Protection of Child Rights

Hon'ble Judges/Coram:

M. Sridhar Acharyulu, Central Information Commissioner

Ajit Kumar Singh vs. PIO, National Commission for Protection of Child Rights (31.10.2018 - CIC) : MANU/CI/0718/2018, CIC/NCPCR/C/2017/143655

Section 15. Steps after inquiry.—The Commission may take any of the following steps upon the completion of an inquiry held under this Act, namely:—(i) where the inquiry discloses, the Commission of violation of child rights of a serious nature or contravention of provisions of any law for the time being in force, it may recommend to the concerned Government or authority the initiation of proceedings for prosecution or such other action as the Commission may deem fit against the concerned person or persons; 8 (ii) approach the Supreme Court or the High Court concerned for such directions, orders or writs as that Court may deem necessary; (iii) recommend to the concerned Government or authority for the grant of such interim relief to the victim or the members of his family as the Commission may consider necessary.

Section 16. Annual and special reports of Commission.—(1) The Commission shall submit an annual report to the Central Government and to the State Government concerned....

This is the core area of its activity. The applicant wanted to know what steps Commission has taken either on complaints under Section 13(j) or after inquiry under Section 15 or what they reported under Section 16 in their annual reports. Instead of culling out this information from their annual reports, they have used Section 7(9) of RTI Act, saying collection diverts the substantial sources of the public authority, which is absolutely not convincing.

Decision by PIO

The PIO replied stating that all this information was not disclosable as per exemption under section 8(1)(j) of RTI Act.

NCPCR

The Commissions for Protection of Child Rights Act, 2005 was "an Act to provide for the constitution of a National Commission and State Commissions for Protection of Child Rights and Children's Courts for providing speedy trial of offences against children or of violation of child rights and for matters connected therewith or incidental thereto".

Section 13 prescribed its functions of Commission.—(1) The Commission shall perform all or any of the following functions, namely:—

(a) examine and review the safeguards provided by or under any law for the time being in force for the protection of child rights and recommend measures for their effective implementation;

(b) present to the Central Government, annually and at such other intervals, as the Commission may deem fit, reports upon the working of those safeguards;

(c) inquire into violation of child rights and recommend initiation of proceedings in such cases;

....

(j) inquire into complaints and take suo motu notice of matters relating to,—

(i) deprivation and violation of child rights;

(ii) non-implementation of laws providing for protection and development of children;

(iii) non-compliance of policy decisions, guidelines or instructions aimed at mitigating hardships to and ensuring welfare of the children and to provide relief to such children, or take up the issues arising out of such matters with appropriate authorities; and.

Contention by PIO before CIC

The CPIO, adviser and consultant vehemently argued with the Commission refusing the disclosure without forwarding any justification. They have bluntly rejected entire information abusing section 8(1)(j) of RTI Act. It is most unfortunate that the Consultant and Advisor have guided the CPIO and Public Authority to breach the RTI Act. Then the Commission directed:

The Commission directed the respondent authority to provide information regarding cases pending for over two years pertaining to Bihar Circle and details of disposal of cases where accused were found guilty, after removing names and personal details of children; within 15 days from date of receipt of this order.

Decision by CIC (Central Information Commission)

The Commission on 21.09.2017 held: It is absolutely not convincing that the National Commission for Protection of Child Rights is refusing the information about action taken on complaints pending since years before it. The NCPCR uses a privacy exception to refuse entire information en bloc. No effort is done to provide information which could have been disclosed on their own under Section 4(1)(b). Except the name of the child, nothing could be denied. The NCPCR has hired services of a consultant and adviser, who instead of guiding the CPIO properly to disclose the information, misguided him to deny the entire information. These two experienced seniors did not even provide reasons to justify the denial. They failed to perform their duty to separate information that could be given from that cannot be given and provide, as prescribed under Section 10(1) of RTI Act. They do not know that Section 10 provide for severability. When appellant was not seeking names and personal information and wanted information about the number of cases left out without any action, or action taken and pending before the Commission for years, public authority cannot invoke Section 8(1)(j) at all.

As per commission this is a complaint, which cannot be rejected on the ground that first appeal was not filed. Secondly in deciding the penalty proceedings under Section 20 RTI Act, 2005 in a complaint, the Commission has to see whether the public authority was having valid reasons to deny, whether inclined to give information. But, unfortunately all of them were in uniform in their response to show cause notices also that reflected their anti-RTI attitude.

In the present scenario of continuous violation of child rights, the NCPCR that is legitimately expected to initiate measures to safeguard childhood, especially of the girl children in the wake of pouring-in news about violation of their body.

Watching spurt in the media reports on sexual offences on minor children, which is a serious matter of national concern the NCPCR is expected to look into them either on complaint or suo-motu. The Protection of Children from Sexual Offences Act 2012 (POCSO Act) made provisions for avoiding the re-victimisation of the child at the hands of the judicial system. Section 44(1) of this Act entrusted NCPCR with the responsibility of monitoring implementation of this Act, in addition to functions assigned to them under Commissions for Protection of Child Rights Act, 2005. Section 44(2) says that NCPCR have the same powers as are vested in it under Act of 2005. Section 44(3) says NCPCR shall also include its activities under this section in the annual Report referred to in Section 16 of the Commissions for Protection of Child Rights Act, 2005.

The Officers representing the NCPCR explained that the information systems were improved and voluntary disclosures were also systematised. Easy mechanisms to receive and act on complaints are also being made available. They said a user-friendly POCSO e-box was created on website http://ncpcr.gov.in/index2.php. wherein the children or any person could file a complaint straight away and status of action could be obtained, besides the helpline numbers i.e. 1098/9868235077, wherein the calls will be received and acted upon. http://ncpcr.gov.in/index2.php. The Commission suggests that the NCPCR could have added a post box number where anyone could post a letter of complaint, a traditional method of sending a written copy, which is essential as most of the people are not web connected or e-savvy. The information about their responses and action taken with positive results from even silent calls to helpline numbers, which was about 1.3 crore last year, should have been put on the website of the NCPCR. The Media is a very effective organ to take these messages to people, the NCPCR may request them to run a scrolling or video message free of cost, use Doordarshan and Akashvaani for the same. When media runs a report of child sexual abuse news, they should invariable carry the helpline number, POSCO e-box, or post box number or address & email of the NCPCR of NCW to facilitate the viewers to report if they knew any such incidents within their vicinity. The media may also be requested to report the successful stories ending in punishment to culprits and relocation of victims etc.

The Commission directed the respondent authority to update their website time to time and provide the information on their website with details of action taken on wrong doers in homes, help rendered to children in distress, admissions given in schools, audit of Homes to check installation CCTVs, checking of the videos and action taken etc. along with disposal of cases of child right sincluding the nature of complaint, their status, time taken in disposal and if pending for more than 30 days, reasons for the same etc.

Commission observed that the NCPCR should understand that mere providing the numbers will not amount to information. They have duty to provide the detailed information under the RTI Act, except where the law protects the names of the children, in all other cases entire details including their names as beneficiaries need be provided proactively on their website as per the Section 4(1)(b) of the RTI Act.

Chapter - 15

NO RIGHT TO INFORMATION REGARDING SHRI RAHUL GANDHI'S RELIGION AND PASSPORT DETAILS[79]

Facts in Nutshell

The appellant filed an application under the Right to Information Act, 2005 (RTI Act) before the Central Public Information Officer (CPIO), M/o. External Affairs, New Delhi seeking following information regarding the passport details and religion of Mr. Rahul Gandhi, Member of Parliament, Lok Sabha:-

"1. How many passports have been issued by any Government in the world to Mr. Rahul Gandhi or alias, if any, bearing photograph of Mr. Rahul Gandhi, Member of Parliament, Lok Sabha, India?

2. If more than one passport has been issued bearing his photograph, address and details of all passports be provided.

3. What was his religion at the time of birth?

4. What is his religion by virtue of his faith at present?"

2. The CPIO responded on 06-06-2018. The appellant filed the first appeal dated 19-06-2018 which was disposed of by the first appellate authority on 02-072018. Thereafter, he filed a second appeal u/Section 19(3) of the RTI Act, 2005 before the Commission (Central Information Commission) requesting to take appropriate legal action against the CPIO under Section 20 of the RTI Act, 2005 and also to direct him to provide the sought for information.

[79] Dr. Sanjeev Goel ... Appellant VERSUS CPIO, M/o. External Affairs, New Delhi. Respondent
Second Appeal No. CIC/MOEAF/A/2018/146793
Neeraj Kumar Gupta, Information Commissioner, Central Information Commission
Date:- 17-04-2020

Argument by Appellant before CIC

The appellant submitted that Mr. Rahul Gandhi is a 'public servant' as per the provisions of Section 2(c) of the Prevention of Corruption Act, 1988 and the information which cannot be denied to the parliament or a State Legislature shall not be denied to any person. He further submitted as follows:- "Mr. Rahul Gandhi is already on bail in a criminal case, so he should declare details of all passports issued to him by any country in the world in his name or alias bearing photograph of Mr. Rahul Gandhi, Member of Parliament, Lok Sabha, India. There are all possibilities to jump his bail by using other passports, if, he possesses more than one passport i.e. passport issued by authorities of various countries. The third party information which is exempted from disclosure u/Section 8(1)(j) of RTI Act, 2005 is not applicable in this case, as Mr. Rahul Gandhi is a public representative/figure/public servant and meets any head of the state out of India in the same capacity and not as an individual person. Being a public servant, he is in public life and should disclose all his identity, if such revelation does not harm him in any manner, whatsoever. Section 9(1) of the Citizenship Act, 1955 provides that any citizen of India who by naturalization or registration acquires the citizenship of another country shall cease to be a citizen of India. Persons who acquire another citizenship lose their Indian citizenship from the date on which they acquire that citizenship or another country's passport."

The appellant also emphasized that he has a right to know the religion of Mr. Rahul Gandhi who is a public figure. Therefore, considering the public interest in the matter, the information pertaining to his passport details and religion should be disclosed to him, as no exemption is applicable in this case.

Argument by Respondent before CIC

The learned counsel, appearing on behalf of the respondent submitted that the information pertaining to the passport details and religion of Mr. Rahul Gandhi is personal in nature which attracts the exemption available u/Section 8(1)(j) of the RTI Act, 2005. Further, he submitted that disclosure of the information sought would cause unwarranted invasion of the third party's privacy and will have no larger public interest involved.

Provisions of RTI Act, 2005

Provisions of Section 8(1)(j) of the RTI Act, 2005 which is being accordingly extracted hereunder:- "8. Exemption from disclosure of information.— (1) Notwithstanding anything contained in this Act, there shall be no obligation to give any citizen, ... (j) information which relates to personal information the disclosure of which has not relationship to any public activity or interest, or which would cause unwarranted invasion of the privacy of the individual unless the Central Public Information Officer or the State Public Information Officer or the appellate authority, as the case may be, is satisfied that the larger public interest justifies the disclosure of such information: Provided that the information which cannot be denied to the Parliament or a State Legislature shall not be denied to any person."

Meaning of Public Interest

In Union of India v. Association for Democratic Reforms and Another, (2002) 5 SCC 294, recognising the voters' right to know the antecedents of the candidates and the right to information which stems from Article 19(1)(a) of the Constitution, it was held that directions could be issued by the Court to subserve public interest in creating an informed citizenry, observing:

"46. The right to get information in democracy is recognised all throughout and it is natural right flowing from the concept of democracy. At this stage, we would refer to Article 19(1) and (2) of the International Covenant of Civil and Political Rights which is as under:

(1) Everyone shall have the right to hold opinions without interference.

(2) Everyone shall have the right to freedom of expression; this right shall include freedom to seek, receive and impart information and ideas of all kinds, regardless of frontiers, either orally, in writing or in print, in the form of art, or through any other media of his choice.

Clearly, the larger public interest in having an informed electorate, fair elections and creating a dialectical democracy had outweighed and compelled Court to issue the directions notwithstanding disclosure of information relating to the personal assets, educational qualifications and antecedents including previous involvement in a criminal case of the contesting candidate. Public interest, sometimes criticised as inherently amorphous and incapable of a precise definition, is a time tested and historical conflict of rights test which is often applied in the right to information legislation to balance right to access and protection of the conflicting right to deny access."

The RTI Act is no exception. Section 8(1)(j) of the RTI Act prescribes the requirement of satisfaction of 'larger public interest' for access to information when the information relates to personal information having no relationship with any public activity or interest, or would cause unwarranted invasion of privacy of the individual. Proviso to Section 11(1) states that except in case of trade or commercial secrets protected by law, disclosure may be allowed if the public interest in disclosure outweighs in importance any possible harm or injury to the interest of the third party. The words 'possible harm or injury' to the interest of the third party is preceded by the word 'importance' for the purpose of comparison. 'Possible' in the context of the proviso does not mean something remote, farfetched or hypothetical, but a calculable, foreseeable and substantial possibility of harm and injury to the third party.

Comparison or balancing exercise of competing public interests has to be undertaken in both sections, albeit under Section 8(1)(j) the comparison is between public interest behind the exemption, that is personal information or invasion of privacy of the individual and public interest behind access to information, whereas the test prescribed by the proviso to Section 11(1) is somewhat broader and wider as it requires comparison between disclosure of information relating to a third person or information supplied and treated as confidential by the third party and possible harm or injury to the third party on disclosure, which would include all kinds of 'possible' harm and injury to the third party on disclosure.

In Bihar Public Service Commission v. Saiyed Hussain Abbas Rizwi and Another, (2012) 13 SCC 61, court held that the phrase 'public interest' in Section 8(1)(j) has to be understood in its true connotation to give complete meaning to the relevant provisions of the RTI Act. However, the RTI Act does not specifically identify factors to be taken into account in determining where the public interest lies. Therefore, it is important to understand the meaning of the expression 'public interest' in the context of the RTI Act. Court held 'public interest' to mean the general welfare of the public warranting the disclosure and the protection applicable, in which the public as a whole has a stake. Thus, the public interest has to be construed while keeping in mind the balance factor between right to privacy and right to information with the purpose sought to be achieved and the purpose that would be served in the larger public interest, particularly when both these rights emerge from the constitutional values under the Constitution of India.

Public interest in access to information refers to something that is in the interest of the public welfare to know. Public welfare is widely different from what is of interest to the public. "Something which is of interest to the public" and "something which is in the public interest" are two separate and different parameters. For example, the public may be interested in private matters with which the public may have no concern and pressing need to know. However, such interest of the public in private matters would repudiate and directly traverse the protection of privacy. The object and purpose behind the specific exemption vide clause (j) to Section 8(1) is to protect and shield oneself from unwarranted access to personal information and to protect facets like reputation, honour, etc. associated with the right to privacy. Similarly, there is a public interest in the maintenance of confidentiality in the case of private individuals and even government.

The public interest test in the context of the RTI Act would mean reflecting upon the object and purpose behind the right to information, the right to privacy and consequences of invasion, and breach of confidentiality and possible harm and injury that would be caused to the third party, with reference to a particular information and the person.

In an article 'Freedom of Information and the Public Interest: the Commonwealth experience' published in the Oxford University Commonwealth Law Journal, Published online on 28th August, 2017, the factors identified as favouring disclosure, those against disclosure and lastly those irrelevant for consideration of public interest have been elucidated as under: "it is generally accepted that the public interest is not synonymous with what is of interest to the public, in the sense of satisfying public curiosity about some matter.

For example, the UK Information Tribunal has drawn a distinction between 'matters which were in the interests of the public to know and matters which were merely interesting to the public (i.e. which the public would like to know about, and which sell newspapers, but... are not relevant). Factors identified as favouring disclosure include the public interest in: contributing to a debate on a matter of public importance; accountability of officials; openness in the expenditure of public funds, the performance by a public authority of its regulatory functions, the handling of complaints by public authorities; exposure of wrongdoing, inefficiency or unfairness; individuals being able to refute allegations made against them; enhancement of scrutiny of decision-making; and protecting against danger to public health or safety.

Factors that have been found to weigh against disclosure include: the likelihood of damage to security or international relations; the likelihood of damage to the integrity or viability of decision-making processes: the public interest in public bodies being able to perform their functions effectively; the public interest in preserving the privacy of individuals and the public interest in the preservation of confidences. Factors irrelevant to the consideration of the public interest have also been identified. These include: that the information might be misunderstood; that the requested information in overly technical in nature; and that disclosure would result in embarrassment to the government or to officials."

Public interest has no relationship and is not connected with the number of individuals adversely affected by the disclosure which may be small and insignificant in comparison to the substantial number of individuals wanting disclosure. It will vary according to the information sought and all circumstances of the case that bear upon the public interest in maintaining the exemptions and those in disclosing the information must be accounted for to judge the right balance. Public interest is not immutable and even time-gap may make a significant difference. The type and likelihood of harm to the public interest behind the exemption and public interest in disclosure would matter. The delicate balance requires identification of public interest behind each exemption and then cumulatively weighing the public interest in accepting or maintaining the exemption(s) to deny information in a particular case against the public interest in disclosure in that particular case.

Under Section 11(1) RTI Act, 2005 reference is made to the 'possible' harm and injury to the third party which will also have to be factored in when determining disclosure of confidential information relating to the third parties.

In the RTI Act, in the absence of any positive indication as to the considerations which the PIO has to bear in mind while making a decision, the legislature had intended to vest a general discretion in the PIO to weigh the competing interests, which is to be limited only by the object, scope and purpose of the protection and the right to access information and in Section 11(1), the 'possible' harm and injury to the third party. It imports a discretionary value judgment on the part of the PIO and the appellate forums as it mandates that any conclusion arrived at must be fair and just by protecting each right which is required to be upheld in public interest. There is no requirement to take a fortiori view that one trumps the other.

RTI and Privacy

The RTI Act also defines the legitimate aim, that is a public interest in the dissemination of information which can be confidential or private (or held in a fiduciary relationship) when larger public interest or public interest in disclosure outweighs the protection or any possible harm or injury to the interest of the third party.

The public may be interested in private matters with which the public may have no concern and pressing need to know. However, such interest of the public in private matters would repudiate and directly traverse the protection of privacy. The object and purpose behind the specific exemption vide clause (j) to Section 8(1) is to protect and shield oneself from unwarranted access to personal information and to protect facets like reputation, honour, etc. associated with the right to privacy. Similarly, there is a public interest in the maintenance of confidentiality in the case of private individuals and even government.

As per Black's Law Dictionary, 8th Edition, the word 'personal' means 'of or affecting a person or of or constituting personal property'. In Collins Dictionary of the English Language, the word 'personal' has been defined as under: "1. Of or relating to the private aspects of a person's life. 2. Of or relating to a person's body, its care or its appearance. 3. Belonging to or intended for a particular person and no one else. 4. Undertaken by an individual himself. 5. Referring to, concerning, or involving a person's individual personality, intimate affairs, etc., esp. in an offensive way. 6. Having the attributes of an individual conscious being. 7. Of or arising from the personality. 8. Of or relating to, or denoting grammatical person.

9. Of or relating to movable property (Law). 10. An item of movable property (Law)."

The right to privacy though not expressly guaranteed in the Constitution of India is now recognized as a basic fundamental right vide decision of the Constitutional Bench in K. S. Puttaswamy and Another v. Union of India and Others, (2017) 10 SCC 1, holding that it is an intrinsic part of the right to life and liberty guaranteed under Article 21 of the Constitution and recognised under several international treaties, chief among them being Article 12 of the Universal Declaration of Human Rights, 1948 which states that no one shall be subjected to arbitrary interference with his privacy, family, home or correspondence, nor to attacks upon his honour and reputation. The judgment recognises that everyone has a right to the protection of laws against such interference or attack.

It is observed that privacy involves a person's right to his physical body; right to informational privacy which deals with a person's mind; and the right to privacy of choice which protects an individual's autonomy over personal choices. While physical privacy enjoys constitutional recognition in Article 19(1)(d) and (e) read with Article 21, personal informational privacy is relatable to Article 21 and right to privacy of choice is enshrined in Articles 19(1)(a) to (c), 20(3), 21 and 25 of the Constitution.

Privacy and confidentiality encompass a bundle of rights including the right to protect identity and anonymity. Anonymity is where an individual seeks freedom from identification, even when and despite being in a public space. In K. S. Puttaswamy (supra) reference is made to Spencer v. R., 2014 SCC Online Can SC 34: (2014) 2 SCR 212: 2014 SCC 43, which had set out three key elements of informational privacy: privacy as secrecy, privacy as control, and privacy as anonymity, to observe:

"214. [...] anonymity may, depending on the totality of the circumstances, be the foundation of a privacy interest that engages constitutional protection against unreasonable search and seizure.

xx xx xx

[...] The disclosure of this information will often amount to the identification of a user with intimate or sensitive activities being carried out online, usually on the understanding that these activities would be anonymous. A request by a police officer that an ISP voluntarily disclose such information amounts to a search."

Privacy and confidentiality, therefore, include information about one's identity. In the context of the RTI Act, suffice would be to say that the right to protect identity and anonymity would be identically subjected to the public interest test

Clause (j) to sub-section (1) of Section 8 of the RTI Act specifically refers to invasion of the right to privacy of an individual and excludes from disclosure information that would cause unwarranted invasion of privacy of such individual, unless the disclosure would satisfy the larger public interest test. This clause also draws a distinction in its treatment of personal information, whereby disclosure of such information is exempted if such information has no relation to public activity or interest.

In Peck v. United Kingdom, (2003) EMLR 15, the European Court of Human Rights had held that private life is a broad term not susceptible to exhaustive definition but includes the right to establish and develop relationships with other human beings such that there is a zone of interaction of a person with others, even in a public context, which may fall within the scope of private life. Recognised facets of an individual's private life include a person's health, ethnicity, personal relationships, sexual conduct; religious or philosophical convictions and personal image. These facets resemble what has been categorised as sensitive personal data within the meaning of the Data Protection Act, 2018 as applicable in the United Kingdom.

Public and Private Information

With respect to what is public and private information, the relevant portion is quoted as under:-

"50. Gleeson CJ in Australian Broadcasting Corporation v. Lenah Game Meats Pty Ltd, (2001) 185 ALR 1, had distinguished between what is public and private information in the following manner:

An activity is not private simply because it is not done in public. It does not suffice to make an act private that, because it occurs on private proper property, it has such measure of protection from the public gaze as the characteristics of the property, the property owner combine to afford. Certain kinds of information about a person, such as information relating to health, personal relationships, or finances, may be easy to identify as private, as may certain kinds of activity which a reasonable person, applying contemporary standards of morals and behaviour, would understand to be meant to be unobserved. The requirement that disclosure or observation of information or conduct would be highly offensive to a reasonable person of ordinary sensibilities is in many circumstances a useful practical test of what is private."

In Girish Ramchandra Deshpande v. Central Information Commissioner and Others, (2013) 1 SCC 212, the applicant had sought copies of all memos, show-cause notices and censure/punishment awarded to a Government employee from his employer and also details of his movable/immovable properties, details of investment, loan and borrowings from financial institutions, details of gifts accepted by the employee from his family members and relatives at the time of the marriage of his son. In this context, it was observed that copies of all memos issued to the third respondent, show-cause notices and orders of censure/punishment, etc. are qualified to be personal information as defined in clause (j) of Section 8(1) of the RTI Act. The performance of an employee/officer in an organisation is primarily a matter between the employee and the employer and normally those aspects are governed by the service rules which fall under the expression "personal information", the disclosure of which has no relationship to any public activity or public interest. The details disclosed by a person in his income tax returns are "personal information" which stand exempted from disclosure under clause (j) of Section 8(1) of the RTI Act, unless involves a larger public interest and the Central Public Information Officer or the State Public Information Officer or the appellate authority is satisfied that the larger public interest justifies the disclosure of such information.

In Canara Bank v. C. S. Shyam and Another, (2018) 11 SCC 426, the applicant had sought information on parameters with regard to transfer of clerical staff with details of individual employees, such as date of their joining, promotion earned, date of their joining the branch, the authorities who had posted the transfer letters, etc. The information sought was declared to be personal in nature, which was conditionally exempted from disclosure under Section 8(1)(j) of the RTI Act.

In Subhash Chandra Agarwal v. Registrar, Supreme Court of India and Others, (2018) 11 SCC 634, the applicant had sought information relating to details of medical facilities availed by individual judges of the Supreme Court and their family members, including information relating to private treatment in India and abroad in last three years. Supreme Court had held that the information sought by the applicant was 'personal' information and was protected under Section 8(1)(j) of the RTI Act, for disclosure would cause unwarranted invasion of privacy which prohibition would not apply where larger public interest justifies disclosure of such information.

In R. K. Jain v. Union of India and Another, (2013) 14 SCC 794, the applicant had sought inspection of documents relating to Annual Confidential Reports (ACRs) of a Member of Customs Excise and Service Tax Appellate Tribunal (CESTAT) and follow up action taken by the authorities based on the ACRs. The information sought was treated as personal information, which, except in cases involving overriding public interest, could not be disclosed. It was observed that the procedure under Section 11 of the RTI Act in such cases has to be followed. The matter was remitted to examine the aspect of larger public interest and to follow the procedure prescribed under Section 11 of the RTI Act which, it was held, was mandatory.

In Union of India v. R. Jayachandran, WP (C) 3406/2012 dated 19-02-2014 court held that After all passport number is not only personal information but also an identification proof, specifically when one travels abroad. If passport number of a third party is furnished to an applicant, it can be misused.

Personal records, including name, address, physical, mental and psychological status, marks obtained, grades and answer sheets, are all treated as personal information. Similarly, professional records, including qualification, performance, evaluation reports, ACRs, disciplinary proceedings, etc. are all personal information. Medical records, treatment, choice of medicine, list of hospitals and doctors visited, findings recorded, including that of the family members, information relating to assets, liabilities, income tax returns, details of investments, lending and borrowing, etc. are personal information. Such personal information is entitled to protection from unwarranted invasion of privacy and conditional access is available when stipulation of larger public interest is satisfied. This list is indicative and not exhaustive.

Decision by CIC

CIC held that Mr. Rahul Gandhi being a public figure his personal information such as religion and passport details cannot be disclosed. Furthermore, the appellant has also failed to substantiate that the information sought is in line with the proviso appended to Section 8(1)(j) of the RTI Act, 2005. Hence, in the absence of any larger public interest in the matter, Commission (CIC) came to a conclusion that the information sought by the appellant qualifies to be the 'personal information' of third party which is exempted under Section 8(1)(j) of the RTI Act, 2005 and therefore, it cannot be provided to the appellant.

Chapter - 16

INFORMATION REGARDING WORKING OF INDIAN BANK ASSOCIATION (IBA)[80]

Facts in Nutshell

In response to the RTI applications filed by the complainants, the Indian Bank Association (IBA) refused to provide the information stating that they are not a Public Authority as defined under section 2(h) of the RTI Act.

R.K. Jain/Complainant sought the information from Indian banks Association, Mumbai as follows:

(a) Certified copy of documents reflecting Legal status of IBA.

(b) List of present office bearers along with their date of joining.

(c) Composition of managing committee of IBA for the first year i.e. from when it is formed.

(d) Date of its formation and name of the founding members.

(e) Source of funds and contribution received by IBA in the first 5 years since the formation of IBA.

(f) Address of IBA head office and regional office along with documents reflecting whether premise is rented or granted free of charge

(g) Name of auditors and PAN of IBA,

(h) Memorandum of association of IBA.

(i) Source of funding the IBA and details of donation/contribution received since the date of its inception.

---

[80] Appellants: R.K. Jain and Ors.
Vs.
Respondent: Indian Bank Association (IBA)
Hon'ble Judges/Coram:
Manjula Prasher and M. Sridhar Acharyulu, Central Information Commissioners
R.K. Jain and Ors. vs. Indian Bank Association (IBA) (13.11.2017 - CIC)
Complaint Nos. CIC/MP/C/2015/000044 and CIC/SH/C/2016/000123

Aggrieved with the reply of the IBA, both the complainants filed complaints under section 18 of the RTI Act to the Central Information Commission (CIC) praying that an enquiry be conducted in the matter and the IBA should be declared as public authority.

Question before Central Information Commission (CIC)

Whether the IBA is a Public Authority under the provisions of section 2(h) of the RTI Act, 2005.

Whether IBA is directly or indirectly funded by Government, and whether there is any nexus between Indian Banks Association and Reserve Bank of India along with Ministry of Finance Union of India.

Submissions of the Complainants before CIC

The Managing Committee of the IBA comprises of 29 member banks of which around 18 banks are public sector banks. Thus the IBA is a body which is controlled by the appropriate Government and thereby fall under the definition of public authority as given in section 2(h) (i) of the RTI Act. Further, the IBA acts as an "advisory body" or "think tank" for banks. It tenders its advice on several important matters, such as, award of punishment to the employees of banks, implementation of provisions of statues e.g. RTI Act, Human Resources of the banks etc. It shows that it performs 'public function', thereby satisfying the requirement to be declared as public authority under the RTI Act. Complainant further submitted that the IBA is an 'Agency' or 'instrumentality' of the State (Public Sector Banks). The IBA also negotiates wage settlements on behalf of its member banks - majority of which are the public sector banks who mandate it to do so, with the Bank Unions/Associations under Industrial Disputes Act, 1947. Besides, being an agency and instrumentality of the State and under the control of the appropriate Government, the IBA is also substantially financed by the appropriate Government. All the expenses of the IBA, which is a non-profit making Association of Banks, are shared by the member banks, majority of which are public sector banks. It receives an annual subscription of nearly 4 crores from more than 100 Indian and foreign banks. Besides this, the IBA collects other funds from its members. As per the information displayed on the official website of the IBA, it has 189 members. Thus, the IBA also meets the criteria of substantial financing by appropriate Government and thereby falls under the definition of public authority as defined in section 2(h) of The RTI ACT.

Complainant stated that the IBA performed various activities indirectly as per instructions of the Reserve Bank of India (RBI) and Department of Financial Services (DFS). He produced a letter No. 4/3/2012-SCT(B)/Welfare dated 30.12.2013 from DFS addressed to the Chairman, IBA to issue necessary guidelines to the public sector banks regarding pay fixation of ex-servicemen/ Ex-ECOs/SSCOs in a uniform way to avoid disparity in pay fixation across public sector banks. He stated that the RBI entrusted the IBA with the following tasks: (i) drafting a Master Joint Lenders' Forum (JLF) agreement between all lenders in respect of Special Mention Accounts (SMA) with an aggregate exposure (AE) exceeding Rs. 100 crores; (ii) constituting an Independent Evaluation Committee (IEC) to carry out evaluation of Techno-Economic Viability study and the proposed restructured packages for AE exceeding Rs. 500 crores; and (iii) put a database on the IBA's website in respect of delinquent third party service providers such as Advocates, Chartered Accountants and Valuers reported by the lender banks.

The IBA took a decision to implement the task assigned by the RBI. So the IBA has to work in consultation with Ministry of Finance and RBI for achieving common objectives. He further stated that the IBA is a major stake holder and part of the administrative structure for monitoring Mission Document of Pradhan Mantri Jan Dhan Yojana (PMJDY). Under the PMJDY, the Government had assigned the job to the IBA to have a monitoring committee to review the progress on weekly basis. The information for monitoring was to be extracted from the DFS portal and adequate publicity needed to be carried out in structured manner based on different tiers at Central level, State level and Districts/Local level structure. The mechanism for public was to be devised by the IBA and NABARD in coordination with banks and other stake holders. A common fund had to be contributed by the banks for publicity in States. State level Bankers Committees would coordinate based on broad guidelines of the IBA/NABARD. Under the heading of roles of major stakeholders of the scheme the IBA was assigned the role of coordination in financial inclusion efforts with all banks, key monitoring role in financial literacy campaign; coordination in publicity and campaign, coordination in centralized handling of customers' grievances/issues through toll free numbers in coordination with banks; a dedicated desk to be set up for monitoring of implementation of the scheme. The Finance Ministry had directed LIC to immediately operationalize the benefit of live cover under PMJDY and the LIC had been asked to expeditiously enter into a memorandum of understanding with the IBA. He further stated that the Department of Financial Services vide letter No. 7/07/2016-P & C dated 22.01.2016 addressed a letter to the Chairman, IBA along with heads of public sector banks issuing guidelines regarding the study visit of the Select Committee of Rajya Sabha on Prevention of Corruption (Amendment) Bill, 2013 to Mumbai and Kolkata from 12 to 18th February, 2016. He added that the IBA functions on the principle of 'mutuality' where 'members' of the 'association' are one and the same.

The Managing Committee of the IBA consisted of 31 members out of which 19 members are Chairman cum Managing Directors of public sector banks or public authorities under RTI Act. Thus 61.29 % of members of managing committee are public servants or belong to public authorities. Therefore, the IBA is a body which is being managed and controlled by public servants of Govt. of India, since Chairman and Managing Directors (CMDs) are employees of Central Govt.

The IBA is a society or voluntary organization and it provides expertise to member banks in host of matters relating to service conditions of employees, periodical wage revision, formulation of policies for banks, execution of govt. directives/schemes/policies, legal issues of member banks, customer service defending banks in courts by being party to Litigation, technology for banks, recovery of loans, approval of transport companies, security printers, couriers for banks including PSB etc. Thus, the IBA has substantial contribution in functioning of public sector banks. The advice of the IBA is followed by public sector banks in toto by getting formal approval of Board of Directors and/or Central Govt. The IBA provides expertise to Government of India in the matter of banking industry and execution of govt. policies and schemes. The IBA is associated with Pradhan Mantri Jandhan Yojana (PMJDY) and other social schemes. The IBA plays a public role in the matter of banking industry of the country and its working, advice, decisions affect large number of employees of banks and customers of banks including trade, industry, common citizens, marginalized segment of society, etc. *Hence, there is need for transparency in its working in view of legislative intent and preamble of RTI Act.*

The IBA provides expertise to member banks in service related matters like periodical wage revision, formulation of policies, execution of Government directives/schemes/policies, legal issues of member Banks, customer service, defending banks in courts by being party to litigation, technology for banks, recovery of loans, approval of transport companies, security printers, couriers for banks including PSB, etc. The IBA makes substantial contribution in functioning of entire public sector banks and its advice is followed by public sector banks into getting formal approval of Board of Directors and/or Central Government.

Submissions of the IBA before CIC

The IBA is an unregistered, voluntary association of banks or of like minded people. The IBA is not a statutory body nor has it been incorporated under any law. The IBA was formed on 26th September 1946 by 22 banks coming together to discuss issues of common interest. It may be noted that all these banks were private banks at that time. Over the years, the membership grew. It was just a turn of events that some of these banks were nationalized in the year 1970. However, the working of the IBA has continued in the same manner over the years. Currently, the IBA has Public Sector Banks, Private Sector Banks, Foreign Banks, Urban Co-operative Banks, Asset Reconstruction Companies, Credit Rating Companies, Credit Guarantee Funds, Financial Services Companies, Credit Bureaus and others as Members. As on 30th September 2016, the membership of the IBA stood at 239 of which 137 were Ordinary Members and 102 Associate Members. Of the 137 Ordinary Members, only 27 i.e. less than 20% are Public Sector Banks. Of the total 239 banks, public sector members are 27 PSB and 38 RRBs which is just 27% of total membership. The key Officers of the IBA such as Chairman, Deputy Chairman and Honorary Secretary of the IBA are elected by the Members of the Managing Committee and rules of the Association do not specify that only Public Sector Bank Chairman can become Chairman/Deputy Chairman/Honorary Secretary. Further, funding of the IBA is by way of Basic Annual Subscription collected from all members of the Association in terms of their working fund and is not sectoral specific i.e. private or public. Further, the IBA's vision is "To work proactively for the growth of a healthy, professional and forward looking banking and financial services industry, in a manner consistent with Public Good". However, working for public good alone does not make an institution a Public Agency. The IBA is a premier service organization representing all banks in India. Therefore, the Government, the Reserve Bank of India or any other trade or industry body/association find it convenient to use the IBA as a single point of contact while interacting with the banking industry. The IBA provides certain pooled services to its members. The pooled service can be anything - wage negotiation, contribution to publicity under Pradhan Mantri Jan Dhan Yojana/Pradhan Mantri Mudra Loan Yojana, representing cases in Courts of industry interest, price discovery of technological investments and so on, and the service may cover all sectors of banks or some specific sector as the case may be. In PMJDY and PMMLY initiatives, Public Sector Member Banks and Private Sector Member Banks including Foreign Banks with more than 20 branches participated.

IBA is purely a voluntary Association of Banks or of like minded people, working in common interest, using collective wisdom to arrive at consensus based decisions for the benefit of its members. The expenses of the association are shared among the members in a fair manner, it is neither substantially owned nor controlled nor financed by the Government nor is it under the control of the Government. Therefore, the IBA does not fall within the definition of a public authority as defined in Section 2(h) of the RTI Act and accordingly the IBA is not a public authority.

Public Authority and RTI Act, 2005

Definition of public authority is provided in section 2(h) of the RTI Act, which is reproduced below:

"public authority" means any authority or body or institution of self government established or constituted,-

(a) by or under the Constitution;

(b) by any other law made by Parliament;

(c) by any other taw made by State Legislature;

(d) by notification issued or order made by the appropriate Government, and includes any-

(i) body owned, controlled or substantially financed;

(ii) non-Government organisation substantially financed, directly or indirectly by funds provided by the appropriate Government;

It is noted that funding of the IBA is by way of basic annual subscription from all members of the Association. The members of the IBA consist of public sector as well private banks and financial institutions.

For the purpose of Section 2(h) of the RTI Act, what is to be seen is whether the body is owned and controlled or substantially financed by the government Whether the funding is For specific programs/projects carried on by the petitioner or funds are given not for any specific program to the petitioner will not make the petitioner not financed by the Government The Government can give the funds without specifying as to how the funds are to be utilized: Specifying the manner in which the funds are to be utilized rather will show more control of the government on the petitioner. [81]

State and State Instrumentality

Hon'ble Supreme Court held in Bank of India & Ant. V.K. Mohandas & Ors. Civil Appeal No. 1942 of 2009; 27-3-2009, that public sector banks are 'State' within the meaning of Article 12 of the Constitution of India. As the Managing Committee of IBA comprises 29 member banks, of which around 18 banks are public sector banks, it can be reasonably inferred that a body consisting of 18 "state's operates as the 'state.

---

[81] Electronics and Computer Software Export Promotion Council v. CIC, (in LPA 1802/2006 & CM 11865/2006)

The Punjab & Haryana High Court in DAV College Trust and Management Society & Ors. Vs. The Director of Public Institution & Ors. (Civil Writ petition No. 2626 of 2008) laid down that a crucial touchstone for determining "whether an organization qualifies to be a public authority (PA)' is "whether it performs a public duty'.

The IBA performs an important role in the decision making process of banking industry and in that sense performs 'public function', one of the important factors or requirements making a body a public authority under the RTI Act.

The IBA thus, is an 'agency' or 'instrumentally' of the State (Public Sector Bank PSB in the present case). One of the objectives of IBA, as displayed on its website, is "to act as an agent or a representative of a member or members in respect of matters connected with any of their operations working or administration." Government of India through its Department of Financial Services has entrusted the IBA with the responsibility of issuing guidelines in the matter of employment of public sector banks. This is a public function. The Reserve Bank of India also has entrusted the IBA with several tasks, besides soliciting the advice of IBA in matters concerning the implementation of law (e.g. RTI Act). This establishes that the IBA functions as an agency of the State.

Also, the IBA negotiates wage settlements on behalf of its member banks-majority of which are the public sector banks-who mandate it to do so, with the Bank Unions/Associations under Industrial Disputes Act, 1947, Thus, the IBA also functions as an agent/representative of its member banks in order to resolve the industrial disputes arising between employer and workmen. If not resolved it may hamper the public functions which are being discharged by the banks with the workmen, resorting to strike. Thus the functioning of the IBA is also of public importance that makes it liable to be accountable to the public.

The IBA enters into Bipartite Wage Settlements with the recognized and registered Trade Unions. These settlements are registered under Rule 58 of Industrial Disputes (Central) Rules, 1957 and therefore have a statutory force. Thus the IBA has an onerous responsibility to maintain the sanctity of statutorily enforceable rules.

The role and functions of the IBA have been well crystallized in its Annual Report under the head Focus and Priorities. It also admitted its critical role in coordination of project PMJDY. It has been asked by the GOI to issue necessary guidelines in the matter of Pay fixation of Ex-servicemen reemployed in banks. Not only the banks, other ministries, departments e.g. Ministry of Defence too rely on such lists of transporters, empanelled by the IBA. Therefore, the procedure cannot be hidden from the public who are the ultimate beneficiaries.

The Hon'ble Supreme Court in its decision dated 27-3-2009 Bank of India & Anr. vs. K. Mobandass & Ors. Civil Appeal No. 1942 of 2009 has declared every public sector bank as "state" within meaning of Article 12 of the Constitution of India.

IBA provides expertise to Government of India in banking regarding execution of govt. policies and schemes. An advertisement released by Department of Financial Services, Ministry of Finance, Government of India jointly with IBA shows this. The letter No. 10/30/7/2010-IR dated 25-07-2012 of Ministry of Finance addressed to IBA shows that the IBA works closely with Central Govt. in the matter of banking.

Decision by CIC

The respondent/IBA failed to convince the Bench that there was no control of the appropriate government over its affairs. The Complainants explained that besides being an agency and instrumentality of the State under the control of appropriate Government, the IBA is also substantially financed by the appropriate Government.

Free Accommodation in 20 Cities: In terms of Annual Report of IBA for the year 2004-05, IBA has 20 Local Chapters functioning at Ahmedabad, Bangalore, Bhopal, Bhubaneshwar, Chandigarh, Chennai, Delhi, Goa (Panaji), Guwehati, Hyderabad, Jaipur, Kochi, Kolkata, Lucknow, Ludhiana, Mumbai, Patna, Pune, Vadodra and New York. All the Local Chapters were housed in the buildings of PSBs and manned by public servants whose salary & perks were paid from public funds. No rent is paid by the IBA. It is an admitted fact that the Delhi Chapter of IBA is housed in 5, Sansad Marg, New Delli-110001. No rent is paid by the IBA for the same. The maintenance and cost of infrastructure is paid by the Punjab National Bank.

Commission observed that the Supreme Court in Thalappalam case[82] has propounded a litmus test that if the substantial assistance provided by the state is withdrawn, body should not be able to function in which case that body has to be considered as substantially funded and thus, it has to be declared as the Public Authority". The respondent IBA shall cease to exist but for 43% of funds provided by the PSBs.

A File Noting received from RBI is sufficient to establish that IBA plays a significant role in deciding the accounting standards to be followed by the banks while making contribution towards Pension and Gratuity.

The Indian Banks Association was declared as a public authority under Section 2(h) of RTI Act 2005 The Commission under Section 19(8)(a)(ii) directed the IBA to appoint CPIO and to provide the information sought to both the complainants..

---

[82] (2013)16SCC82

Chapter - 17

INFORMATION REGARDING THE DELHI & DISTRICT CRICKET ASSOCIATION[83]

Facts in Nutshell

Sri Subhash Chandra Agrawal filed a complaint on 8.6.2012 stating that there was no response from respondents to his RTI petition dated 30.4.2012 seeking details about a) land provided to stadium of DDCA at Feroz Shah Kotla Ground, b) title, ownership/lease/freehold/rent, rate of rent, subsidy given, other facilities, security, etc. provided by Government or state resources, c) activities undertaken, eligibility criterion for enrolment of membership of Association, total number, various categories, d) number of voters, e) powers and facilities available to office bearers, f) number of mailed envelopes containing proxy-forms returned undelivered, g) number votes received at elections held last, h) system of distribution of complimentary tickets/passes during several matches conducted by BCCI and IPL etc, i) number of envelops with such passes for matches held till 30th April 2012, along with, j) envelopes returned undelivered, k) utilization of seats fell vacant due to return of complimentary tickets, l) relationship of DDCA with BCCI, etc and m) any other related information along with file-notings on movement of the RTI petition as well.

The complainant sought a direction to provide documents free of cost as per Section 7(6) and compensation under S 19(8)(b) besides invoking the penal provisions.

[83] Appellants: Subhash Chandra Agrawal Vs. Respondent: Delhi & District Cricket Association
Hon'ble Judges/Coram:
Basant Seth, Sharat Sabharwal and M. Sridhar Acharyulu, Information Commissioners
Subhash Chandra Agrawal vs. Delhi and District Cricket Association (13.04.2015 - CIC), File No. CIC/LS/C/2012/000714

Complainant's Case before CIC

The complainant's case is: the DDCA is a Public Authority under section 2(h) of the R.T.I. Act because it is substantially financed by the Central Government in as much as a plot of land measuring 14.281 acres at Ferozshah Kotla has been allotted to it on temporary basis for a period of 33 years w.e.f. 1.4.2002 and DDCA is required to pay license fee @ Rs. 5,500/- per acre per annum for the open space and at the rate of 5% per annum @ Rs. 88 lacs per acre for built up area, revisable after every 11 years on the basis of land rates prevailing at that time. The land is located in the heart of the capital city of Delhi and the fee structure grossly falls short of the prevailing market rates and this can be construed as indirect substantial financing of DDCA. It is an Association under the Companies Act, which has its office at Willington Pavilion, Kotla Ferozshah, New Delhi. The object of this Association is to encourage and promote the game of cricket in the Province of Delhi and districts of Karnal, Meerut, Aligarh, Bulandshahr, Gurgaon etc. The other objects of the Association are to finance or assist in the organization or promotion of Provincial Cricket Association and of Inter Provincial Tournaments as also to promote and hold/ organize, either singly or jointly with other Associations, Clubs or persons, cricket matches and competitions etc.

Complainant Contended

"a. The Delhi & District Cricket Association is a "public authority" as defined under section 2(h) of the Right to Information Act for the reason that it is substantially funded, directly or indirectly, by the appropriate Government(s).

b. The DDCA is one of the 30 Member State Cricket Associations of the BCCI and has an umbilical cord attached to its parent National Sports Federation BCCI which is responsible for the promotion and development of the game of cricket across the length and breadth of India just like the DDCA is solely responsible for the promotion and development of cricket within the entire territory of the National Capital Region of Delhi.

c. Besides, affiliated Member State Associations of the BCCI like the Respondent DDCA, also avail huge concessions from the Government in the form of providing them free of cost security while hosting cricket matches commonly known as "police bandobast". But for such substantial largesse's, grants and concessions or funding by the Centre and/or State Government it would be almost impossible for the DDCA and its parent body BCCI to function as such leave alone generate revenues to the tune of Crores of Rupees annually. Thus huge amount of financial benefits accrue to the Respondent DDCA."

On behalf of complainants, Hon'ble M.P. (Lok Sabha) Mr. Kirti Azad, former test cricketer and member of World Cup winning team in 1983, presented following points explaining the concessions granted by Government, controls exercised and made serious allegations of irregularities against the DDCA:

"a. The DDCA occupies 14.28 acres of lakhs of prime land in Delhi, for which it pays nearly Rs. 24.64 lakh of license fee annually. Since 2002, no lease executed by MoUD with DDCA, for want of compliance with various requirements listed by L&DO vide their letter L&DO/L11/17(32)02/512 dt. 10th July, 2002- DDCA therefore is clearly in unauthorized possession of this land that is conservatively estimated to be worth Rs. 5000 crores.

b. L&DO have been repeatedly requesting DDCA to fulfill certain conditions, yet DDCA have not cared to complete the requisite formalities.

c. There are no approvals from statutory bodies like DUAC, ASI, MCD, Fire Department etc.

d. Every time there is a match, temporary approvals are sought from MCD on purely political considerations- endangering the lives of 45000 spectators.

e. While no Government property can be sub-leased, DDCA has illegally constructed 10 Corporate Boxes and have sub -leased these boxes for 10 years to corporate such as ONGC and have collected Rs. 36 crore, without seeking approval of the land owners i.e. Government of India.

f. Nearly Rs. 158 crore has been spent on building an unauthorized stadium for which no accounts are available. SFIO has confirmed that no tenders have been issued for work carried out/materials purchased even for non-routine items.

g. There is rampant cheating of entertainment tax by pricing a large number of tickets at a mere Rs100 while paying spectators have to fork out Rs. 10000-Rs. 50000/per seat.

h. While no member of DDCA can be paid any fees for doing any work for DDCA, many members who are close to the powers that be are being regularly paid money. DDCA keeps on fighting with Government departments contesting property tax, ESI etc and keeps paying crores in legal fees alone.

i. Benefit of Sec 25 Companies Act enables DDCA to retain power with dubious characters who misuse the proxy system, and through the conduct of fraud elections, some office bearers manage to perpetuate themselves.

j. The DDCA selects players, and this activity is akin to a state function-no one can play for Delhi without being selected by DDCA to represent Delhi in various age groups.

Complainant further contended that the DDCA had government nominees on its Board of Directors, it got exemption from Entertainment tax, and Income Tax, besides it was holding IPL with its own team - Delhi Dare Devils, which are attributes that characterize DDCA as 'public authority' under R.T.I. Act.

Complainant relied on the judgment of Indian Olympic Association v. Veeresh Kumar Malik [(2010) ILR 4 Delhi 1] decided by Delhi High Court on 7.10.2012, wherein 'substantial funding' of Common Wealth Games Committee was explained and concluded that the financing or funding of the Games Committee, concededly a non-governmental organization, is substantial; it is therefore, a public authority, within the meaning of Section 2(h) of the Act...."

Respondent's Contention before CIC

The respondents case was that the DDCA is not enjoying Government land at concessional/minimal rates, it is paying Rs. 24,64,415/- per annum as yearly lease rent to the Central Government and it does not enjoy exemption from Income Tax. The land allotment is also subject to the approval of lay out plan by ADG (Arch), CPWD and it is required to use the land only for the purpose for which it has been allotted and not for any other purpose.

Learned Counsel for DDCA presented following points: a) DDCA has been registered as an Association under the Companies Act, which has its office at Willington Pavilion, Kotla Ferozshah, New Delhi. b) The object of this Association is to encourage and promote the game of cricket in the Province of Delhi and districts of Karnal, Meerut, Aligarh, Bulandshahr, Gurgaon etc. c) The other objects of the Association are to finance or assist in the organization or promotion of Provincial Cricket and of Inter Provincial Tournaments as also to promote and hold/organize, either singly or jointly with other Associations, Clubs or persons, cricket matches and competitions etc. d) DDCA is not an authority of self Government established or constituted either by or under the constitution or by any other law made by the Parliament or State Legislature. e) DDCA is neither owned nor controlled by the Government. f) DDCA is not a body or institution which is essentially financed by the Government. Importantly, g) DDCA is not in receipt of any grants from the Government or any of its instrumentalities and that its affairs are managed by self generated funds and the grants of BCCI alone.

Respondents raised certain preliminary objection: It is not disputed that this Hon'ble Commission has jurisdiction to adjudicate upon claims of RTI Applicants under the R.T.I. Act, 2005 in so far as such claims pertain to "Public Authorities" under the ambit and purview of the R.T.I. Act, 2005. However, problem arises if the very jurisdiction of this Hon'ble Commission is challenged at the threshold by the DDCA, on the ground that it is not a "Public Authority" under section 2(h) of the R.T.I. Act, 2005. In such cases, the issue essentially becomes an issue of fact which can only be determined on the basis of evidence lead by the parties to the dispute. It is again a settled principle of law of evidence that the onus to prove the existence of any fact lies on the party alleging that fact.

Respondents counsel contended that, not only has the complainant miserably failed to discharge that onus to support his averments and allegations but has further, miserably failed in bringing home necessary documentary evidence to prove that DDCA is either owned, controlled or substantially financed by any Government. In the absence of any coherent and probable evidence led by the complainant before this Hon'ble Commission in support of his averments, it will be unjust, improper and erroneous for this Hon'ble Commission to decide the issue of fact (i.e. whether or not DDCA is 'Public Authority' under Section 2(h) of the R.T.I. Act, 2005) against the Respondent - DDCA.

Respondent further submitted that this Hon'ble Commission lacks the statutory mandate of the R.T.I. Act, 2005 to declare anybody "Public Authority". The powers and functions of this Hon'ble Commission are set out distinctly under Chapter V of the R.T.I. Act, 2005 (Sections 18 and 19) and none of the provisions contained therein confer any power on this Hon'ble Commission to determine the issue as to whether a particular association (such as DDCA in the present case) is a 'Public Authority' under section 2(h) of the R.T.I. Act, 2005 or not.

Respondent contended that the Hon'ble Commission lacks the plenary inherent powers to determine issues which it is not statutorily empowered to determine or which are beyond the scope and ambit of Chapter V of the R.T.I. Act, 2005.

Question before CIC

'Whether the DDCA is a public authority as per Section 2(h) of R.T.I. Act, 2005'.

What is 'Public Authority' for RTI?

The "public authority" is defined in section 2(h) of the R.T.I. Act, saying:

Section 2(h) "public authority means any authority or body or institution of self government established or constituted -

(a) by or under the Constitution;

(b) by any other law made by Parliament;

(c) by any other law made by State Legislature;

(d) by notification issued or order made by the appropriate Government, and includes any

(i) body owned, controlled or substantially financed;

(ii) non-Government organization substantially financed, directly or indirectly by funds provided by the appropriate Government."

Test of 'Substantial Funding'

Hon'ble Supreme Court of India in Thalappalam Service Cooperative Bank Ltd. & others v. State of Kerala & others [2013 AIR SCW 5683] stated:—

"37.. In Black's Law Dictionary (6th Edn.), the word 'substantial' is defined as 'of real worth and importance; of considerable value; valuable. Belonging to substance; actually existing; real: not seeming or imaginary; not illusive; solid; true; veritable. Something worthwhile as distinguished from something without value or merely nominal. Synonymous with material.' The word 'substantially' has been defined to mean 'essentially; without material qualification; in the main; in substance; materially.' In the Shorter Oxford English Dictionary (5th Edn.), the word 'substantial' means 'of ample or considerable amount of size; sizeable, fairly large; having solid worth or value, of real significance; solid; weighty; important, worthwhile; of an act, measure etc. having force or effect, effective, thorough.' The word 'substantially' has been defined to mean 'in substance; as a substantial thing or being; essentially, intrinsically.' Therefore the word 'substantial' is not synonymous with 'dominant' or 'majority'. It is closer to 'material' or 'important' or 'of considerable value.' 'Substantially' is closer to 'essentially'. Both words can signify varying degrees depending on the context.

38. Merely providing subsidiaries, grants, exemptions, privileges etc., as such, cannot be said to be providing funding to a substantial extent, unless the record shows that the funding was so substantial to the body which practically runs by such funding and but for such funding, it would struggle to exist."

Whether a body is public authority or not the Hon'ble Supreme Court stated in Talappalam case in para 39 that the question whether a non-government

Organization is substantially funded or not may be question of fact to be examined by the authorities concerned under the R.T.I. Act. The Supreme Court said in Para 40: "the burden to show that a body is owned, controlled or substantially financed or that a non-government organization is substantially financed, directly or indirectly by the funds provided by the appropriate Government is on the applicant who seeks information or the appropriate Government and can be examined by the State Public Information Officer, State Chief Information Officer, State Chief Information Commission, Central Public Information Officer etc when the question comes up for consideration" ("etc"=. here includes CIC). In this case the SC in Para 51 very specifically stated: "All the same, if there is any dispute on facts as to whether a particular Society is a public authority or not, the State Information Commission can examine the same and find out whether the Society in question satisfies the test laid in this judgment".

DDCA and Need for Transparency

It is pertinent to mention here about the Serious Fraud Investigation report against DDCA as prominently reported in Media during 2013 (DNA Exclusive: Serious Fraud Investigation Office hauls up DDCA for irregularities) 1 November 2013) explaining the serious financial and election frauds between 2006 and 2012. In its report to the ministry of corporate affairs and a written communication to the Ministry of Urban Development, the SFIO has asked the ministries to initiate action against the DDCA in connection with several matters. The most serious objection raised by the SFIO has been regarding the lease of the Ferozeshah Kotla stadium. The DDCA has also been castigated for not ensuring transparency in doling out contracts for non-routine, big-ticket items like generators. "It is clear that every year, crores of rupees have been siphoned off without caring to go through the transparent system of inviting tenders even for non-routine items like generators, stadium-building, etc. Most of the big-ticket purchases have been through 'front companies' of key DDCA office-bearers and their supporters," former Delhi skipper and M.P. Kirti Azad alleged. The ROC has confirmed that action under sections 209, 150, 211, 314, 309 and 299 is proposed to be taken against the DDCA management for various infractions of the Companies Act. The news report also included a comment by former Delhi skipper Surinder

Khanna regarding proxy elections in DDCA: "The DDCA elections are nothing but a farce. All the 4,294 proxies are controlled by DDCA office-bearers and their cohorts. Twenty-four DDCA members are residing at the residence of its vice-president C.K. Khanna. If you look at the electoral roll, you will find practically all office-bearers having multiple members staying with them. This is the reason why these corrupt officials keep cricketers at a distance". [84]

Recently a news item published in the DNA on December 28, 2014 saying that an internal audit of DDCA books has opened a can of worms. The issue was transfer of a sum of Rs. 1.55 crore to three fictitious infrastructure companies that led to serious action of stripping of President of all functioning powers including right to vote. Media Manager of the DDCA was also sacked for holding onto DDCA's cash[85]. All this show that everything is not well with DDCA. There is a strong necessity of public scrutiny for protecting public interest, and the way the DDCA is indiscriminately spending the public money.

Decision by CIC

The complainant discharged his burden showing that 'DDCA was substantially funded indirectly' by the appropriate Government. The documents provided and official websites maintained by the concerned Government departments also proved that DDCA was indirectly and substantially financed. As mandated by R.T.I. Act, as rightly explained by the Hon'ble Supreme Court and also by Punjab High Court, it is the duty of Central Information Commission under Sections 18 & 19 to decide whether a authority is public authority or not.

CIC declared that the DDCA, though an NGO, is being substantially financed by appropriate Government indirectly through allocation of huge land in heart of New Delhi with substantial concession worth thousands of crores of rupees and monopoly of unlimited value, is the Public Authority as defined under section 2(h) of R.T.I. Act, on both questions of law and facts.

---

[84] (http://www.dnaindia.com/india/report-dna-exclusive-serious-fraud-investig ation-office-hauls-up-ddca-for-irregularities-1912049)

[85] (News clip of DNA newspaper -http://www.dnaindia.com/sport/report-jolt-to-n-srinivasan-as-ddca-sacks-president-sneh-bansal-for-committing-fraud-2047487 accessed on 6th Jan 2015 and also the FIR was Registered by former star cricketer Bishan Singh Bedi)

Therefore, CIC directed -

"(a) the DDCA to designate PIO and create necessary infrastructure to receive and respond the RTI applications, in compliance of legal duties under R.T.I. Act as public authority

(b) to comply with Section 4 of R.T.I. Act within one month from date of receipt of this order."

Chapter - 18

INFORMATION REGARDING THE CONSTITUTION CLUB OF INDIA[86]

Facts in Nutshell

Complainant filed RTI application seeking information regarding a news clipping "Constitution Club: 50 MPs slam management". He sought information on following points :

"i. Whether it is true that Lok Sabha is ex-officio President of Constitution Club?

ii. When was the Constitution Club constituted/opened for the first time and purpose of its Constitution?

iii. Was its Constitution ever changed to make it an association?

iv. If, yes, when was it changed?

v. If yes to (3), give copies of the file noting/documents/correspondence etc on change of Constitution of Constitution Club of India.

vi. Was there any funding from public-exchequer even after Constitution Club was changed into an association?

vii. Was a No-Objection-Certificate obtained from Union Ministry of Urban Development (owner of the building) before handing over Constitution Club to an association?

viii. Who owned property, assets, land, building and other belongings etc of Constitution Club (at the time of its first ever Constitution) ?

---

86 Appellants: Subhash Chandra Agrawal
Vs.
Respondent: Constitution Club of India (CCI)
Hon'ble Judges/Coram:
M. Sridhar Acharyulu and Sudhir Bhargava, Central Information Commissioners
Subhash Chandra Agrawal vs. Constitution Club of India (CCI) (14.10.2016 - CIC), CIC/SM/C/2011/000097/SS

ix. Who presently owns property, assets, lands, buildings and other belongings etc of Constitution Club presently etc?."

Deputy Secretary at Lok Sabha secretariat, on 10.06.2010 transferred the RTI application to the Manager, Constitution Club under section 6 (3) of the RTI Act. Complainant approached the Commission on 19.07.2010 against the non-receipt of information by CPIO. In his complaint, he claimed that the RTI petition was transferred to the manager, Constitution Club by Lok Sabha secretariat vide letter dated 10.06.2010. But since no further response has been there from Constitution Club of India, he approached the Commission (CIC).

Submission of Constitution Club of India to CIC

a. The Constitution Club of India was formed as an unregistered body in February 1947 with the objective and purpose of fostering social contacts and providing usual amenities of a Club for benefit of the members of the Constituent Assembly of India. It was later found expedient to constitute a society for the furtherance of its aims and objectives. Consequently a society was registered under the Societies Registration Act, 1860 by the name Constitution Club of India. The Club is therefore a society registered under the said Act.

b. The aims and objects of the Club were akin to the usual functions of any other Club or academic society. That there is nothing in the aims and objects of the Club which suggests, even remotely, that the Club performs any public functions or any activity which in ordinary course ought to be performed by the state or any of its machineries. The Club is a private body constituted for the benefit of private person. Membership of the Club, subject to its rules and regulations is open to all people's associated with or interested in the furtherance of the aims and objectives of the Club.

c. The Club is controlled by and the management of its affairs is entrusted to the governing council which consists of the President, Vice-President, General Secretary of the Club, Secretary (Administration), Secretary (Culture), Secretary (Sports), Treasurer and other elected members.

d. The Speaker, Lok Sabha is the ex-officio President of the Club, the Deputy Speaker, Lok Sabha is the ex-officio General Secretary and the Union Minister for Urban Development and the Deputy Chairperson, Rajya Sabha are the ex-officio Vice Presidents of the Club. However, the said positions are the honorary and ceremonial.

e. That there is no control of any nature or to any degree exercised by any Government over the Club or its management of activities. Merely because certain ceremonial positions in the Governing Council of the Club have been reserved for certain state-dignitaries, it does not make the Club a Government-controlled body. The respective official duties of these dignitaries as Speaker or Deputy Speaker or Union Minister do not include being members or office bearers of the Governing Council of the Club. Neither they gave any instructions by the Government in respect of the management of the Club nor do they have to report in this regard to the Government.

f. The Club is completely self-funded. The funds of the Club are constituted by membership subscriptions and tariff/charges received by the Club from members or outsiders who use the Club-auditorium etc. the Club does not received any fund, grant or financial support whatsoever from any Government or state or public entity or from any source other than membership subscriptions or charges. The day to day activities of the Club are performed with monies received in the aforesaid manner and through no other source.

g. The Club has movable assets including furniture, office-ware, computers and other equipments which have been and are purchased by the funds of the Club only. No assets have been provided to the Club by any Government or state or public authority.

h. The Club pays regular electricity and water charges as per market rates to the respective authorities. No subsidy or concession whatsoever has been given to the Club in this regard.

i. The Club does not enjoy any tax exemption granted by any tax authority and is assessed to and pays income tax and service tax as applicable to all societies.

j. The land and building in which the Club is housed has not been allotted by any Government to the Club. It is the property of the Ministry of Urban Development, Government of India. The Club is a licensee of the Government in the said building and is paying licensee fee to the Government.

k. The Club never applied to the Government/lessor for or sought any concession or subsidy in the rate of licensee fee. The Club has been paying to the Government/lessor whatever license fee has been demanded by them.

Manager of the Constitution Club reiterated that CCI was not public authority as per RTI Act, 2005.

Contentions by the Constitution Club of India (CCI) before CIC

Constitution Club of India is constituted by, consisting of all public authorities constituted under the Constitution of India like Speaker and Deputy Speaker, and other officers as ex-officio members. It is meant for the present and former members of Parliament. The Constitution Club of India is paying a very nominal amount of money as license fee and making profitable use of the highly valuable property. The Government of India is spending crores of rupees for repairs and renovation of the buildings under control of CCI. He said that these facts by themselves establish that the CCI is a public authority under Section 2(h) of Right to Information Act, 2005.

The Constitution Club of India has a historic background. It has a pre-Constitution existence, started for members of Indian Constituent Assembly. It is claimed to be acting as platform for interaction amongst the Past and Present Members of Parliament. It was established in 1947 housed at Curzon Road, formally inaugurated by the then President Sarvepalli Radhakrishnan on February 1965 at present location of Vitalbhai Patel House. It has partnership with Swaniti Initiative which runs Research and Development Advisory (RADA)cell to assist the Members of Parliament. The Constitution club spends public money for public representatives. The Constitution, common sense, provisions of RTI Act, Parliamentary control through Speaker, Deputy Speaker and Secretary demand that it should be public authority and its information be accessible under RTI law.

Decision by CIC

Central Information Commissio held that the CCI makes income of more than Rs. 2 crore on rent by using the land and buildings of Union Government, repaired and maintained by the Government, in the heart of national capital by paying nominal amount of Rs. 100 or 250. Besides this they have monopoly over 'assistance' to MPs relating to the research, academic, sports, conferences and entertainment needs of MPs, former MPs and others The submissions by various authorities reveal that the MoUD, office of Speaker, CPWD, etc are wielding complete control. Their claim about absence of control is not correct.

The Government spends hundreds of crores of Rupees for CCI, even plans to build a new building with Rs. 140 crore for CCI, but does not make it accountable. It is absolutely not reasonable on the part of MoUD to leave highly valuable land and buildings in the hands of a society, without even auditing or questioning the way resources are used by it. Such a kind of attitude of state towards public wealth does not go well with governance, let alone the 'good governance'.

The CCI is enjoying enormous concessions and manages valuable immovable properties, besides getting a new building and possession of suites etc. This substantial funding, if withdrawn, the CCI cannot function even for a minute. The test laid down by the Supreme Court in Thalappalam Ser. Coop. Bank Ltd. and others v. State of Kerala and others [SLP (C) No. 24290 of 2012]that "the funding was so substantial to the body which practically runs by such funding and but for such funding, it would struggle to exist" is met.

The CCI is surviving on the lands and properties of the Union Government. It is absolutely dependent upon the state property. It has no source of income of its own. The CCI makes income only with the land and buildings in the heart of national capital. Ownership in case of CCI is not clear because as per the respondent, the CCI is a lessee of the MoUD (leasor). However, no lease deed was produced before the Commission, despite a specific direction by the Commission in this regard.

CIC held that People should have a right to ask about functioning of CCI and spending on it to create facilities for their elected representatives and others.

Government does not control the affairs of the CCI In the above described circumstances. However the members of CCI are not mere officers or government employees but Constitutional Authorities like the Speaker and the Union Minister, etc, whose decisions are substantial enough to dictate terms to the CCI.

The three conditions mentioned in Section 2(h)(d)(i) of the RTI Act are distinct and not cumulative, therefore, even if one of the three is satisfied as per the facts of the case, it would be sufficient and there is no need for all three to be satisfied. The same was held by the Hon'ble Delhi High Court in the case of National Stock Exchange of India Limited v. Central Information Commission and Ors., W.P. (C) No. 4748/2007 dated 15.04.2010:

a. "17....The three conditions, i.e. owned, controlled, substantially financed are distinct in alternative and not cumulative.....If a body satisfies requirements of Clause (i) or (ii), conditions (a) to (d) need not be satisfied....."

Thus, it is clear that there is an indirect funding of the appropriate Government to the CCI and therefore, the CCI is held to be a Public Authority in terms of Section 2(h)(d)(i) of the RTI Act.

The Constitutional Club of India was thus declared as "public authority" under Section 2(h), it has to supply the information sought and it also required as per Section 19(8)(a)(ii) of RTI Act, 2005, the CCI to appoint a Central Public Information Officer, and put in place a RTI response cell.

Chapter - 19

RESERVE BANK OF INDIA IS BOUND TO DISCLOSE INFORMATION UNDER RTI ACT, 2005[87]

Facts in Nutshell

It was contended by the RBI/Appellant[88] that it carries out inspections of banks and financial institutions on regular basis and the inspection reports prepared by it contain a wide range of information that was collected in a fiduciary[89] capacity. During May-June, 2010 the statutory inspection of Makarpura Industrial Estate Cooperative Bank Ltd. was conducted by RBI under the Banking Regulation Act, 1949. Thereafter, in October 2010, the Respondent[90]— Jayantilal N. Mistry and Ors. asked information from the CPIO of RBI under the Act of 2005.

On 30.3.2011, the First Appellate Authority disposed of the appeal of the Respondent — Jayantilal N. Mistry and Ors. agreeing with the reply given by CPIO in query No. 2 to 6, relying on the decision of the Full Bench of CIC passed in the case of *Ravin Ranchochodlal Patel and Anr. v. Reserve Bank of India*. Thereafter, in the second appeal[91] preferred by the aggrieved

---

[87] Appellants: Reserve Bank of India and Ors. Vs. Respondent: Jayantilal N. Mistry and Ors.
Hon'ble Judges/Coram: M. Yusuf Eqbal and C. Nagappan, JJ., Supreme Court of India
Subject: Right to Information
Decided On: 16.12.2015, MANU/SC/1463/2015

[88] Meaning of Appellant:
One who appeals a court decision.

[89] Meaning of fiduciary:
a. Of or relating to a duty of acting in good faith with regard to the interests of another
b. Of or being a trustee or trusteeship.
c. Held in trust.

[90] Meaning of respondent:
The defending party in certain legal proceedings, as in a case brought by petition.

[91] Section 19 in The Right To Information Act, 2005
19. Appeal.—
(1) Any person who, does not receive a decision within the time specified in sub-section (1) or clause (a) of sub-section (3) of section 7, or is aggrieved by a decision of the Central Public

Respondent, the Central Information Commission directed RBI to provide information as per records to the Respondent in relation to queries Nos. 2 to 6.

Information Officer or the State Public Information Officer, as the case may be, may within thirty days from the expiry of such period or from the receipt of such a decision prefer an appeal to such officer who is senior in rank to the Central Public Information Officer or the State Public Information Officer, as the case may be, in each public authority: Provided that such officer may admit the appeal after the expiry of the period of thirty days if he or she is satisfied that the appellant was prevented by sufficient cause from filing the appeal in time.

(2) Where an appeal is preferred against an order made by a Central Public Information Officer or a State Public Information Officer, as the case may be, under section 11 to disclose third party information, the appeal by the concerned third party shall be made within thirty days from the date of the order.

(3) A second appeal against the decision under sub-section (1) shall lie within ninety days from the date on which the decision should have been made or was actually received, with the Central Information Commission or the State Information Commission: Provided that the Central Information Commission or the State Information Commission, as the case may be, may admit the appeal after the expiry of the period of ninety days if it is satisfied that the appellant was prevented by sufficient cause from filing the appeal in time.

(4) If the decision of the Central Public Information Officer or State Public Information Officer, as the case may be, against which an appeal is preferred relates to information of a third party, the Central Information Commission or State Information Commission, as the case may be shall give a reasonable opportunity of being heard to that third party.

(5) In any appeal proceedings, the onus to prove that a denial of a request was justified shall be on the Central Public Information Officer or State Public Information Officer, as the case may be, who denied the request.

(6) An appeal under sub-section (1) or sub-section (2) shall be disposed of within thirty days of the receipt of the appeal or within such extended period not exceeding a total of forty-five days from the date of filing thereof, as the case may be, for reasons to be recorded in writing.

(7) The decision of the Central Information Commission or State Information Commission, as the case may be, shall be binding.

(8) In its decision, the Central Information Commission or State Information Commission, as the case may be, has the power to,—

   (a) require the public authority to take any such steps as may be necessary to secure compliance with the provisions of this Act, including—

      (i) by providing access to information, if so requested, in a particular form;

      (ii) by appointing a Central Public Information Officer or State Public Information Officer, as the case may be;

      (iii) by publishing certain information or categories of information;

      (iv) by making necessary changes to its practices in relation to the maintenance, management and destruction of records;

      (v) by enhancing the provision of training on the right to information for its officials;

      (vi) by providing it with an annual report in compliance with clause (b) of sub-section (1) of section 4;

   (b) require the public authority to compensate the complainant for any loss or other detriment suffered;

   (c) impose any of the penalties provided under this Act;

   (d) reject the application.

Aggrieved by the decision of the Central Information Commission (CIC), RBI moved the Delhi High Court by way of a Writ Petition[92] inter alia[93] praying for quashing of the order of the CIC. The High Court, while issuing notice, stayed the operation of the aforesaid order of CIC.

---

(9) The Central Information Commission or State Information Commission, as the case may be, shall give notice of its decision, including any right of appeal, to the complainant and the public authority.

(10) The Central Information Commission or State Information Commission, as the case may be, shall decide the appeal in accordance with such procedure as may be prescribed.

92 Writ Petition

A petition seeking issuance of a writ is a writ petition. Pits in the first instance in the High Courts and the Supreme Court are writ petitions.

A writ of habeas corpus is issued to an authority or person to produce in court a person who is either missing or kept in illegal custody. Where the detention is found to be without authority of law, the Court may order compensation to the person illegally detained.

A writ of mandamus is a direction to an authority to either do or refrain from doing a particular act. For instance, a writ to the Pollution Control Board to strictly enforce the Pollution Control Acts. For a mandamus to be issued, it must be shown:

(a) That the authority was under obligation, statutory or otherwise to act in a particular manner;

(b) that the said authority failed in performing such obligation;

(c) that such failure has resulted in some specific violation of a fundamental right of either the petitioner or an indeterminate class of persons.

A writ of certiorari is a direction to an authority to produce before the Court the records on the basis of which a decision under challenge in the writ petition has been taken. By looking into those records, the Court will examine whether the authority applied its mind to the relevant materials before it took the decision. If the Court finds that no reasonable person could come to the decision in question, it will set aside (quash) that decision and give a further direction to the authority to consider the matter afresh.

For instance, the permission given by an authority to operate a distillery next to a school can be challenged by filing a petition asking for a writ of certiorari.

A writ of prohibition issues to prevent a judicial authority subordinate to the High Court from exercising jurisdiction over a matter pending before it. This could be on the ground that the authority lacks jurisdiction and further that prejudice would be caused if the authority proceeds to decide the matter. Where the authority is found to be biased and refuses to rescue, a writ of prohibition may issue.

A petition seeking a writ of quo warranto questions the legal basis and authority of a person appointed to public office. For instance, the appointment of a member of a Public Service Commission not qualified to hold the post can be questioned by a writ of quo warranto and appointment nullified if found to be illegal.

A writ of declaration issues to declare an executive, legislative or quasi- judicial act to be invalid in law. For instance, a court could declare S. 81 of the Mental Health Act, 1987 that permits use of mentally ill patients for experimentation to be violative of the fundamental rights of the mentally ill and therefore illegal and void. A petition seeking such declaratory relief must also necessarily seek certain consequential reliefs. For instance, immediate discontinuance of the illegal practice and appropriate remedial compensation.

93 Meaning of inter-alia: Among other things.

Similarly in other RTI matter, the Respondent— Jayantilal N. Mistry and Ors. sought information from the CPIO of National Bank for Agriculture and Rural Development[94]. The CPIO gave the reply that the inspection report of National Bank for Agriculture and Rural Development conducted by RBI cannot be supplied to respondent.

The First Appellate Authority concurred with the CPIO and held that inspection report cannot be supplied in terms of Section 8(1)(a) of the RTI Act, 2005. The Respondent filed Second Appeal before the Central Information Commission, which was allowed. The RBI filed writ petition before the High Court challenging the order of the CIC on identical issue and the High Court stayed the operation of the order of the CIC.

The information sought for by the Respondents from the Appellant-Bank have been denied mainly on the ground that such information was exempted from disclosure Under Section 8(1)(a)(d) and (e) of the RTI Act, 2005.

Contentions by the Learned Counsel of the Appellant before the Supreme Court

The learned senior Counsel appearing for the Appellant- Reserve Bank of India, assailed[95] the impugned orders passed by the Central Information Commissioner as illegal and without jurisdiction. Learned Counsel referred various provisions of The Reserve Bank of India Act, 1934; The Banking Regulation Act, 1949 and The Credit Information Companies (Regulation) Act, 2005 and made the following submissions:

(I) The Reserve Bank of India being the statutory authority has been constituted under the Reserve Bank of India Act, 1934 for the purpose of regulating and controlling the money supply in the country. It also acts as statutory banker with the Government of India and State Governments

---

[94] National Bank for Agriculture and Rural Development (NABARD) is an apex development bank in India, having headquarters in Mumbai (Maharashtra) and other branches are all over the country.

[95] Meaning of assail:

1. To attack violently, as with blows or military force; assault.
2. To attack verbally, as with ridicule or censure

and manages their public debts. In addition, it regulates and supervises Commercial Banks and Cooperative Banks in the country. The RBI exercises control over the volume of credit, the rate of interest chargeable on loan and advances and deposits in order to ensure the economic stability. The RBI is also vested with the powers to determine "Banking Policy" in the interest of banking system, monetary stability and sound economic growth.

The RBI in exercise of powers of powers conferred Under Section 35[96] of the Banking Regulation Act, 1949 conducts inspection of the banks in the country.

---

[96] Section 35 in BANKING REGULATION ACT,1949

35. Inspection.—

(1) Notwithstanding anything to the contrary contained in 1[section 235 of the Companies Act, 1956 (1 of 1956)], the Reserve Bank at any time may, and on being directed so to do by the Central Government shall, cause an inspection to be made by one or more of its officers of any banking company and its books and accounts; and the Reserve Bank shall supply to the banking company a copy of its report on such inspection. [(1A) (a) Notwithstanding anything to the contrary contained in any law for the time being in force and without prejudice to the provisions of sub-section (1), the Reserve Bank, at any time, may also cause a scrutiny to be made by any one or more of its officers, of the affairs of any banking company and its books and accounts; and (b) A copy of the report of the scrutiny shall be furnished to the banking company if the banking company makes a request for the same or if any adverse action is contemplated against the banking company on the basis of the scrutiny.]

(2) It shall be the duty of every director or other officer [or employee] of the banking company to produce to any officer making an inspection under sub-section (1) [or a scrutiny under sub-section (1A)] all such books, accounts and other documents in his custody or power and to furnish him with any statements and information relating to the affairs of the banking company as the said officer may require of him within such time as the said officer may specify.

(3) Any person making an inspection under sub-section (1) [or a scrutiny under sub-section (1A)] may examine on oath any director or other officer [or employee] of the banking company in relation to its business, and may administer an oath accordingly.

(4) The Reserve Bank shall, if it has been directed by the Central Government to cause an inspection to be made, and may, in any other case, report to the Central Government on any inspection [or scrutiny] made under this section, and the Central Government, if it is of opinion after considering the report that the affairs of the banking company are being conducted to the detriment of the interests of its depositors, may, after giving such opportunity to the banking company to make a representation in connection with the report as, in the opinion of the Central Government, seems reasonable, by order in writing—

(a) prohibit the banking company from receiving fresh deposits;

(b) direct the Reserve Bank to apply under section 38 for the winding up of the banking company: Provided that the Central Government may defer, for such period as it may think fit, the passing of an order under this sub-section, or cancel or modify any such order, upon such terms and conditions as it may think fit to impose.

(II) The RBI in its capacity as the regulator and supervisor of the banking system of the country access to various information collected and kept by the banks. The inspecting team and the officers carry out inspections of different banks and much of the information accessed by the inspecting officers of RBI would be confidential. Referring Section 28[97] of the Banking Regulation Act, it was submitted by the learned counsel that the RBI in the public interest may publish the information obtained by it, in a consolidated form but not otherwise.

(III) The role of RBI is to safeguard the economic and financial stability of the country and it has large contingent of expert advisors relating to matters deciding the economy of the entire country and nobody can doubt the bona fide of the bank.

(IV) That the RBI is vested with the responsibility of Regulation and supervision of the banking system. As part of its supervisory role, RBI supervises and monitors the banks under its jurisdiction through on-site inspection conducted on annual basis under the statutory powers derived by it Under Section 35 of the Banking Regulation Act 1949, off-site

---

(5) The Central Government may, after giving reasonable notice to the banking company, publish the report submitted by the Reserve Bank or such portion thereof as may appear necessary. [Explanation.—For the purpose of this section, the expression "banking company" shall include—

(i) in the case of a banking company incorporated outside India, all its branches in India; and

(ii) in the case of a banking company incorporated in India—

(a) all its subsidiaries formed for the purpose of carrying on the business of banking exclusively outside India; and

(b) all its branches whether situated in India or outside India.] [(6) The powers exercisable by the Reserve Bank under this section in relation to regional rural banks may (without prejudice to the exercise of such powers by the Reserve Bank in relation to any regional rural bank whenever it considers necessary so to do) be exercised by the National Bank in relation to the regional rural banks, and accordingly, sub-sections (1) to (5) shall apply in relation to regional rural banks as if every reference therein to the Reserve Bank included also a reference to the National Bank.]

[97] Section 28 in BANKING REGULATION ACT, 1949

28. Power to publish information.—The Reserve Bank or the National Bank, or both, if they consider it in the public interest so to do, may publish—

(a) any information obtained by them under this Act in such consolidated form as they think fit;

(b) in such manner as they may consider proper, any credit information disclosed under the Credit Information Companies (Regulation) Act, 2005.

returns on key financial parameters and engaging banks in dialogue through periodical meetings. RBI may take supervisory actions where warranted for violations of its guidelines/directives. The supervisory actions would depend on the seriousness of the offence, systemic implications and may range from imposition of penalty, to issue of strictures or letters of warning. While RBI recognizes and promotes enhanced transparency in banks disclosures to the public, as transparency strengthens market discipline, a bank may not be able to disclose all data that may be relevant to assess its risk profile, due to the inherent need to preserve confidentially in relation to its customers. In this light, while mandatory disclosures include certain prudential parameters such as capital adequacy, level of Non Performing Assets etc., the supervisors themselves may not disclose all or some information obtained on-site or off-site. In some countries, wherever there are supervisory concerns, "prompt corrective action" programmes are normally put in place, which may or may not be publicly disclosed. Circumspection in disclosures by the supervisors arises from the potential market reaction that such disclosure might trigger, which may not be desirable. Thus, in any policy of transparency, there is a need to build processes which ensure that the benefits of supervisory disclosure are appropriately weighed against the risk to stakeholders, such as depositors.

(V) As per the RBI policy, the reports of the annual financial inspection, scrutiny of all banks/financial institutions are confidential document cannot be disclosed. As a matter of fact, the annual financial inspection/scrutiny report reflect the supervisor's critical assessment of banks and financial institutions and their functions. Disclosure of these scrutiny and information would create misunderstanding/misinterpretation in the minds of the public. That apart, this may prove significantly counter productive. Learned Counsel submitted that the disclosure of information sought for by the applicant would not serve the public interest as it will give adverse impact in public confidence on the bank. This has serious implication for financial stability which rests on public confidence. This will also adversely affect the economic interest of the State and would not serve the larger public interest.

The specific stand of Appellant- Reserve Bank of India was that the information sought for was exempted Under Section 8(1)(a), (d) and (e) of the Right to Information Act, 2005. As the regulator and supervisor of the banking system, the RBI has discretion in the disclosure of such information in public interest.

Question before the Supreme Court

- Whether all the information sought by the Respondent[98]— Jayantilal N. Mistry and Ors. under the Right to Information Act, 2005 can be denied by the Reserve Bank of India/Appellant and other Banks to the public at large on the ground of economic interest, commercial confidence, fiduciary relationship with other Bank on the one hand and the public interest on the other.
- Whether the Reserve Bank of India has rightly refused to disclose information on the ground of its fiduciary relationship with the banks.

Contentions by the Learned Counsel for the Respondents before the Supreme Court

Learned Counsel appearing for the Respondents submitted that the right to information regarding the functioning of public institutions is a fundamental right[99]

---

98 Meaning of Respondent:
The defending party in certain legal proceedings, as in a case brought by petition.

99 Fundamental Rights is a charter of rights contained in the Constitution of India. It guarantees civil liberties such that all Indians can lead their lives in peace and harmony as citizens of India. These include individual rights common to most liberal democracies, such as equality before law, freedom of speech and expression, and peaceful assembly,freedom to practice religion, and the right to constitutional remedies for the protection of civil rights by means of writssuch as habeas corpus. Violation of these rights result in punishments as prescribed in the Indian Penal Code or other special laws, subject to discretion of the judiciary. The Fundamental Rights are defined as basic human freedoms that every Indian citizen has the right to enjoy for a proper and harmonious development of personality. These rights universally apply to all citizens, irrespective of race, place of birth, religion, caste or gender. Aliens (persons who are not citizens) are also considered in matters like equality before law. They are enforceable by the courts, subject to certain restrictions. The Rights have their origins in many sources, including England's Bill of Rights, the United States Bill of Rights and France's Declaration of the Rights of Man.

as enshrined in Article 19[100] of the Constitution of India. This Hon'ble Court has declared in a plethora of cases that the most important value for the functioning of a healthy and well informed democracy is transparency. In the case of *State of U.P. v. Raj Narain*[101], it was held by the court that is a Government's responsibility like ours, where all the agents of the public must be responsible for their conduct, there can be but few secrets. The people of this country have a right to know every public act, everything that is done in a public way, by their

---

[100] Article 19 in The Constitution Of India 1949

19. Protection of certain rights regarding freedom of speech etc

(1) All citizens shall have the right
   (a) to freedom of speech and expression;
   (b) to assemble peaceably and without arms;
   (c) to form associations or unions;
   (d) to move freely throughout the territory of India;
   (e) to reside and settle in any part of the territory of India; and
   (f) omitted
   (g) to practise any profession, or to carry on any occupation, trade or business

(2) Nothing in sub clause (a) of clause (1) shall affect the operation of any existing law, or prevent the State from making any law, in so far as such law imposes reasonable restrictions on the exercise of the right conferred by the said sub clause in the interests of the sovereignty and integrity of India, the security of the State, friendly relations with foreign States, public order, decency or morality or in relation to contempt of court, defamation or incitement to an offence

(3) Nothing in sub clause (b) of the said clause shall affect the operation of any existing law in so far as it imposes, or prevent the State from making any law imposing, in the interests of the sovereignty and integrity of India or public order, reasonable restrictions on the exercise of the right conferred by the said sub clause

(4) Nothing in sub clause (c) of the said clause shall affect the operation of any existing law in so far as it imposes, or prevent the State from making any law imposing, in the interests of the sovereignty and integrity of India or public order or morality, reasonable restrictions on the exercise of the right conferred by the said sub clause

(5) Nothing in sub clauses (d) and (e) of the said clause shall affect the operation of any existing law in so far as it imposes, or prevent the State from making any law imposing, reasonable restrictions on the exercise of any of the rights conferred by the said sub clauses either in the interests of the general public or for the protection of the interests of any Scheduled Tribe

(6) Nothing in sub clause (g) of the said clause shall affect the operation of any existing law in so far as it imposes, or prevent the State from making any law imposing, in the interests of the general public, reasonable restrictions on the exercise of the right conferred by the said sub clause, and, in particular, nothing in the said sub clause shall affect the operation of any existing law in so far as it relates to, or prevent the State from making any law relating to,

(i) the professional or technical qualifications necessary for practising any profession or carrying on any occupation, trade or business, or

(ii) the carrying on by the State, or by a corporation owned or controlled by the State, of any trade, business, industry or service, whether to the exclusion, complete or partial, of citizens or otherwise

[101] AIR 1975 SC 865

functionaries. The right to know, which is derived from the concept of freedom of speech, though not absolute, is a factor which should make one wary, when secrecy is claimed for transactions which can, at any rate, have no repercussion on public security. To cover with veil[102] of secrecy, the common routine business is not in the interest of public.

In the case of *S.P. Gupta v. President of India and Ors.*[103] a seven Judge Bench of Supreme Court made the following observations regarding the right to information:

There is also in every democracy a certain amount of public suspicion and distrust of Government, varying of course from time to time according to its performance, which prompts people to insist upon maximum exposure of its functioning. It is axiomatic that every action of the Government must be actuated by public interest but even so we find cases, though not many, where Governmental action is taken not for public good but for personal gain or other extraneous considerations. Sometimes Governmental action is influenced by political and other motivations and pressures and at times, there are also instances of misuse or abuse of authority on the part of the executive. Now, if secrecy were to be observed in the functioning of Government and the processes of Government were to be kept hidden from public scrutiny, it would tend to promote and encourage oppression, corruption and misuse or abuse of authority, for it would all be shrouded in the veil of secrecy without any public accountability. But if there is an open Government with means of information available to the public, there would be greater exposure of the functioning of Government and it would help to assure the people a better and more efficient administration. There can be little doubt that exposure to public gaze and scrutiny is one of the surest means of achieving a clean and healthy administration. It has been truly said that an open Government is clean Government and a powerful safeguard against political and administrative aberration and inefficiency.

In the case of the *Union of India v. Association for Democratic Reforms*[104] while declaring that it is part of the fundamental right of citizens Under

[102] Meaning of veil: Something that conceals, separates, or screens like a curtain
[103] AIR 1982 SC 149
[104] AIR 2002 SC 2112

Article 19(1)(a) to know the assets and liabilities of candidates contesting election to the Parliament or the State Legislatures, a three Judge Bench of Supreme Court held unequivocally that: "The right to get information in a democracy is recognized all throughout and is a natural right flowing from the concept of democracy." Thereafter, legislation was passed amending the Representation of People Act, 1951 that candidates need not provide such information.

The RTI Act, 2005, in its very preamble, does not create any new right but only provides machinery to effectuate[105] the fundamental right to information. The institution of the CIC and the SICs are part of that machinery. The preamble also inter-alia states "... democracy requires an informed citizenry and transparency of information which are vital to its functioning and also to contain corruption and to hold Governments and their instrumentalities accountable to the governed."

The Making of the RTI Act, 2005

While introducing the Right to Information Bill, 2004 a serious debate and discussion took place. The then Prime Minister while addressing the House informed that the RTI Bill is to provide for setting out practical regime of right to information for people, to secure access to information under the control of public authorities in order to promote transparency and accountability in the working of every public authority. The new legislation would radically alter the ethos and culture of secrecy through ready sharing of information by the State and its agencies with the people. An era of transparency and accountability in governance is on the anvil. Information, and more appropriately access to information would empower and enable people not only to make informed choices but also participate effectively in decision making processes. Tracing the origin of the idea of the then Prime Minister who had stated, "Modern societies are information societies. Citizens tend to get interested in all fields of life and demand information that is as comprehensive, accurate and fair as possible." In the Bill, reference has also been made to the decision of the Supreme Court to the effect that Right to Information has been held as inherent in Article 19 of our Constitution, thereby,

---

105 Meaning of effectuate: To bring about; effect.

elevating it to a fundamental right of the citizen. The Bill, which sought to create an effective mechanism for easy exercise of this Right, was held to have been properly titled as "Right to Information Act". The Bill further states that a citizen has to merely make a request to the concerned Public Information Officer specifying the particulars of the information sought by him. He is not required to give any reason for seeking information, or any other personal details except those necessary for contacting him. Further, the Bill states:

The categories of information exempted from disclosure are a bare minimum and are contained in Clause 8 of the Bill. Even these exemptions are not absolute and access can be allowed to them in public interest if disclosure of the information outweighs the harm to the public authorities. Such disclosure has been permitted even if it is in conflict with the provisions of the Official Secrets Act, 1923. Moreover, barring two categories that relate to information disclosure-which may affect sovereignty and integrity of India etc., or information relating to Cabinet papers etc.-all other categories of exempted information would be disclosed after twenty years.

There is another aspect about which information is to be made public. We had a lengthy discussion and it is correctly provided in the amendment Under Clause 8 of the Bill. The following information shall be exempted from disclosure which would prejudicially affect the sovereignty and integrity of India; which has been expressly forbidden; which may result in a breach of privileges of Parliament or the Legislature; and also information pertaining to defence matters. They are listed in Clause 8 (a) to (g). There are exceptions to this clause. Where it is considered necessary that the information will be divulged in the interest of the State, that will be done. There must be transparency in public life. There must be transparency in administration and people must have a right to know what has actually transpired in the secretariat of the State as well as the Union Ministry. A citizen will have a right because it will be safe to prevent corruption. Many things are done behind the curtain. Many shoddy deals take place in the secretariats of the Central and State Governments and the information will always be kept hidden. Such practice should not be allowed in a democratic country like ours. Ours is a republic. The citizenry should have a right to know what transpired in the secretariat. Even Cabinet papers, after a decision has been taken, must be divulged as per the provisions of this amendment. It cannot be hidden from the knowledge of others.

Addressing the House, it was pointed out by the then Prime Minister that in our country, Government expenditure both at the Central and at the level of the States and local bodies, account for nearly 33% of our Gross National Product. At the same time, the socio-economic imperatives require our Government to intervene extensively in economic and social affairs. Therefore, the efficiency and effectiveness of the government processes are critical variables, which will determine how our Government functions and to what extent it is able to discharge the responsibilities entrusted. It was pointed out that there are widespread complaints in our country about wastefulness of expenditure, about corruption, and matter which have relations with the functioning of the Government. Therefore, it was very important to explore new effective mechanism to ensure that the Government will purposefully and effectively discharge the responsibilities entrusted to it.

Finally the Right to Information Act was passed by the Parliament called "The Right to Information Act, 2005". The Preamble states:

An Act to provide for setting out the practical regime of right to information for citizens to secure access to information under the control of public authorities, in order to promote transparency and accountability in the working of every public authority, the constitution of a Central Information Commission and State Information Commissions and for matters connected therewith or incidental thereto.

WHEREAS the Constitution of India has established democratic Republic;

AND WHEREAS democracy requires an informed citizenry and transparency of information which are vital to its functioning and also to contain corruption and to hold Governments and their instrumentalities accountable to the governed;

AND WHEREAS revelation of information in actual practice is likely to conflict with other public interests including efficient operations of the Governments, optimum use of limited fiscal resources and the preservation of confidentiality of sensitive information;

AND WHEREAS it is necessary to harmonise these conflicting interest while preserving the paramountcy of the democratic ideal;

NOW, THEREFORE, it is expedient to provide for furnishing certain information to citizens who desire to have it.

Section 2 of the Act defines various authorities and the words. Section 2(j) defines right to information as under:

2(j) "right to information" means the right to information accessible under this Act which is held by or under the control of any public authority and includes the right to-

(i) inspection of work, documents, records;

(ii) taking notes, extracts, or certified copies of documents or records;

(iii) taking certified samples of material;

(iv) obtaining information in the form of diskettes, floppies, tapes, video cassettes or in any other electronic mode or through printouts where such information is stored in a computer or in any other device;

Section 3[106] provides that all citizens shall have the right to information subject to the provisions of this Act. Section 4[107] makes it obligatory on all public authorities to maintain records in the manner provided therein. According to

---

[106] 3. Right to information.—Subject to the provisions of this Act, all citizens shall have the right to information.

[107] 4. Obligations of public authorities.—

(1) Every public authority shall—

(a) maintain all its records duly catalogued and indexed in a manner and the form which facilitates the right to information under this Act and ensure that all records that are appropriate to be computerised are, within a reasonable time and subject to availability of resources, computerised and connected through a network all over the country on different systems so that access to such records is facilitated;

(b) publish within one hundred and twenty days from the enactment of this Act,—

(i) the particulars of its organisation, functions and duties;

(ii) the powers and duties of its officers and employees;

(iii) the procedure followed in the decision making process, including channels of supervision and accountability;

(iv) the norms set by it for the discharge of its functions;

(v) the rules, regulations, instructions, manuals and records, held by it or under its control or used by its employees for discharging its functions;

(vi) a statement of the categories of documents that are held by it or under its control;

Section 6[108], a person who desires to obtain any information under the Act shall make a request in writing or through electronic means in English or Hindi in the

---

(vii) the particulars of any arrangement that exists for consultation with, or representation by, the members of the public in relation to the formulation of its policy or implementation thereof;

(viii) a statement of the boards, councils, committees and other bodies consisting of two or more persons constituted as its part or for the purpose of its advice, and as to whether meetings of those boards, councils, committees and other bodies are open to the public, or the minutes of such meetings are accessible for public;

(ix) a directory of its officers and employees;

(x) the monthly remuneration received by each of its officers and employees, including the system of compensation as provided in its regulations;

(xi) the budget allocated to each of its agency, indicating the particulars of all plans, proposed expenditures and reports on disbursements made;

(xii) the manner of execution of subsidy programmes, including the amounts allocated and the detailsof beneficiaries of such programmes;

(xiii) particulars of recipients of concessions, permits or authorisations granted by it;

(xiv) details in respect of the information, available to or held by it, reduced in an electronic form;

(xv) the particulars of facilities available to citizens for obtaining information, including the working hours of a library or reading room, if maintained for public use;

(xvi) the names, designations and other particulars of the Public Information Officers;

(xvii) such other information as may be prescribed, and thereafter update these publications every year;

(c) publish all relevant facts while formulating important policies or announcing the decisions which affect public;

(d) provide reasons for its administrative or quasi judicial decisions to affected persons.

(2) It shall be a constant endeavour of every public authority to take steps in accordance with the requirements of clause (b) of sub-section (1) to provide as much information suo motu to the public at regular intervals through various means of communications, including internet, so that the public have minimum resort to the use of this Act to obtain information.

(3) For the purpose of sub-section (1), every information shall be disseminated widely and in such form and manner which is easily accessible to the public.

(4) All materials shall be disseminated taking into consideration the cost effectiveness, local language and the most effective method of communication in that local area and the information should be easily accessible, to the extent possible in electronic format with the Central Public Information Officer or State Public Information Officer, as the case may be, available free or at such cost of the medium or the print cost price as may be prescribed. Explanation.—For the purposes of sub-sections (3) and (4), "disseminated" means making known or communicated the information to the public through notice boards, newspapers, public announcements, media broadcasts, the internet or any other means, including inspection of offices of any public authority.

[108] 6. Request for obtaining information.—

(1) A person, who desires to obtain any information under this Act, shall make a request in writing or through electronic means in English or Hindi in the official language of the area in which the application is being made, accompanying such fee as may be prescribed, to—

(a) the Central Public Information Officer or State Public Information Officer, as the case may be, of the concerned public authority;

official language of the area in which the application is being made to the competent authority specifying the particulars of information sought by him or her. Sub-section (ii) of Section 6 provides that the applicant making request for information shall not be required to give any reason for requesting the information or any other personal details except those that may be necessary for contacting him. Section 7[109] lays down the procedure for disposal of the request so made

---

(b) the Central Assistant Public Information Officer or State Assistant Public Information Officer, as the case may be, specifying the particulars of the information sought by him or her: Provided that where such request cannot be made in writing, the Central Public Information Officer or State Public Information Officer, as the case may be, shall render all reasonable assistance to the person making the request orally to reduce the same in writing.

(2) An applicant making request for information shall not be required to give any reason for requesting the information or any other personal details except those that may be necessary for contacting him.

(3) Where an application is made to a public authority requesting for an information,—

(i) which is held by another public authority; or

(ii) the subject matter of which is more closely connected with the functions of another public authority, the public authority, to which such application is made, shall transfer the application or such part of it as may be appropriate to that other public authority and inform the applicant immediately about such transfer: Provided that the transfer of an application pursuant to this sub-section shall be made as soon as practicable but in no case later than five days from the date of receipt of the application.

[109] 7. Disposal of request.—

(1) Subject to the proviso to sub-section (2) of section 5 or the proviso to sub-section (3) of section 6, the Central Public Information Officer or State Public Information Officer, as the case may be on receipt of a request under section 6 shall, as expeditiously as possible, and in any case within thirty days of the receipt of the request, either provide the information on payment of such fee as may be prescribed or reject the request for any of the reasons specified in sections 8 and 9: Provided that where the information sought for concerns the life or liberty of a person, the same shall be provided within forty-eight hours of the receipt of the request.

(2) If the Central Public Information Officer or State Public Information Officer, as the case may be fails to give decision on the request for information within the period specified under sub-section (1), the Central Public Information Officer or State Public Information Officer, as the case may be shall be deemed to have refused the request.

(3) Where a decision is taken to provide the information on payment of any further fee representing the cost of providing the information, the Central Public Information Officer or State Public Information Officer, as the case may be shall send an intimation to the person making the request, giving—

(a) the details of further fees representing the cost of providing the information as determined by him, together with the calculations made to arrive at the amount in accordance with fee prescribed under sub-section (1), requesting him to deposit that fees, and the period intervening between the despatch of the said intimation and payment of fees shall be excluded for the purpose of calculating the period of thirty days referred to in that sub-section;

by the person Under Section 6 of the Act. Section 8, however, provides certain exemption from disclosure of information. For better appreciation Section 8 is quoted hereinbelow:

> 8. Exemption from disclosure of information.—
>
> (1) Notwithstanding anything contained in this Act, there shall be no obligation to give any citizen,—
>
> (a) information, disclosure of which would prejudicially affect the sovereignty and integrity of India, the security, strategic, scientific or economic interests of the State, relation with foreign State or lead to incitement of an offence;
>
> (b) information which has been expressly forbidden to be published by any court of law or tribunal or the disclosure of which may constitute contempt of court;

(b) information concerning his or her right with respect to review the decision as to the amount of fees charged or the form of access provided, including the particulars of the appellate authority, time limit, process and any other forms.

(4) Where access to the record or a part thereof is required to be provided under this Act and the person to whom access is to be provided is sensorily disabled, the Central Public Information Officer or State Public Information Officer, as the case may be shall provide assistance to enable access to the information, including providing such assistance as may be appropriate for the inspection.

(5) Where access to information is to be provided in the printed or in any electronic format, the applicant shall, subject to the provisions of sub-section (6), pay such fee as may be prescribed: Provided that the fee prescribed under sub-section (1) of section 6 and sub-sections (1) and (5) of section 7 shall be reasonable and no such fee shall be charged from the persons who are of below poverty line as may be determined by the appropriate Government.

(6) Notwithstanding anything contained in sub-section (5), the person making request for the information shall be provided the information free of charge where a public authority fails to comply with the time limits specified in sub-section (1).

(7) Before taking any decision under sub-section (1), the Central Public Information Officer or State Public Information Officer, as the case may be shall take into consideration the representation made by a third party under section 11.

(8) Where a request has been rejected under sub-section (1), the Central Public Information Officer or State Public Information Officer, as the case may be shall communicate to the person making the request,—

(i) the reasons for such rejection;

(ii) the period within which an appeal against such rejection may be preferred; and

(iii) the particulars of the appellate authority.

(9) An information shall ordinarily be provided in the form in which it is sought unless it would disproportionately divert the resources of the public authority or would be detrimental to the safety or preservation of the record in question.

(c) information, the disclosure of which would cause a breach of privilege of Parliament or the State Legislature;

(d) information including commercial confidence, trade secrets or intellectual property, the disclosure of which would harm the competitive position of a third party, unless the competent authority is satisfied that larger public interest warrants the disclosure of such information;

(e) information available to a person in his fiduciary relationship, unless the competent authority is satisfied that the larger public interest warrants the disclosure of such information;

(f) information received in confidence from foreign government;

(g) information, the disclosure of which would endanger the life or physical safety of any person or identify the source of information or assistance given in confidence for law enforcement or security purposes;

(h) information which would impede the process of investigation or apprehension or prosecution of offenders;

(i) cabinet papers including records of deliberations of the Council of Ministers, Secretaries and other officers: Provided that the decisions of Council of Ministers, the reasons thereof, and the material on the basis of which the decisions were taken shall be made public after the decision has been taken, and the matter is complete, or over: Provided further that those matters which come under the exemptions specified in this section shall not be disclosed;

(j) information which relates to personal information the disclosure of which has not relationship to any public activity or interest, or which would cause unwarranted invasion of the privacy of the individual unless the Central Public Information Officer or the State Public Information Officer or the appellate authority, as the case may be, is satisfied that the larger public interest justifies the disclosure of such information: Provided that the information, which cannot be denied to the Parliament or a State Legislature shall not be denied to any person.

(2) Notwithstanding anything in the Official Secrets Act, 1923 (19 of 1923) nor any of the exemptions permissible in accordance with Sub-section (1), a public authority may allow access to information, if public interest in disclosure outweighs the harm to the protected interests.

(3) Subject to the provisions of Clauses (a), (c) and (i) of Sub-section (1), any information relating to any occurrence, event or matter which has taken place, occurred or happened twenty years before the date on which any request is made Under Section 6 shall be provided to any person making a request under that section: Provided that where any question arises as to the date from which the said period of twenty years has to be computed, the decision of the Central Government shall be final, subject to the usual appeals provided for in this Act.

Meaning of Fiduciary Relationship

The Advanced Law Lexicon, 3rd Edition, 2005, defines fiduciary relationship as "a relationship in which one person is under a duty to act for the benefit of the other on the matters within the scope of the fiduciary relationship. Fiduciary relationship usually arise in one of the four situations (1) when one person places trust in the faithful integrity of another, who as a result gains superiority or influence over the first, (2) when one person assumes control and responsibility over another, (3) when one person has a duty to act or give advice to another on matters falling within the scope of the relationship, or (4) when there is specific relationship that has traditionally be recognized as involving fiduciary duties, as with a lawyer and a client, or a stockbroker and a customer."

The Scope of the Fiduciary Relationship Consists of the Following Rules:

(i) No Conflict rule-A fiduciary must not place himself in a position where his own interests conflicts with that of his customer or the beneficiary. There must be "real sensible possibility of conflict.

(ii) No profit rule-a fiduciary must not profit from his position at the expense of his customer, the beneficiary;

(iii) Undivided loyalty rule-a fiduciary owes undivided loyalty to the beneficiary, not to place himself in a position where his duty towards one person conflicts with a duty that he owes to another customer. A consequence of this duty is that a fiduciary must make available to a customer all the information that is relevant to the customer's affairs

(iv) Duty of confidentiality-a fiduciary must only use information obtained in confidence and must not use it for his own advantage, or for the benefit of another person.

Black's Law Dictionary (7th Edition, Page 640) defines 'Fiduciary Relationship' thus:

A relationship in which one person is under a duty to act for the benefit of the other on matters within the scope of the relationship. Fiduciary relationships-such as trustee-beneficiary, guardian-ward, agent-principal, and attorney-client-require the highest duty of care. Fiduciary relationships usually arise in one of four situations: (1) when one person places trust in the faithful integrity of another, who as a result gains superiority or influence over the first, (2) when one person assumes control and responsibility over another, (3) when one person has a duty to act for or give advice to another on matters falling within the scope of the relationship, or (4) when there is a specific relationship that has traditionally been recognized as involving fiduciary duties, as with a lawyer and a client or a stockbroker and a customer.

The American Restatements (Trusts and Agency) define 'fiduciary' as one whose intention is to act for the benefit of another as to matters relevant to the relation between them.

The Corpus Juris Secundum (Vol. 36A Page 381) Attempts To Define Fiduciary Thus:

A general definition of the word which is sufficiently comprehensive to embrace all cases cannot well be given. The term is derived from the civil, or Roman, law. It connotes the idea of trust or confidence, contemplates good faith, rather than legal obligation, as the basis of the transaction, refers to the integrity, the fidelity, of the party trusted, rather than his credit or ability, and has been held to apply to all persons who occupy a position of peculiar confidence toward others, and to include those informal relations which exist whenever one party trusts and relies on another, as well as technical fiduciary relations.

The word 'fiduciary,' as a noun, means one who holds a thing in trust for another, a trustee, a person holding the character of a trustee, or a character analogous to that of a trustee, with respect to the trust and confidence involved in it and the scrupulous good faith and candor which it requires; a person having the duty, created by his undertaking, to act primarily for another's benefit in matters connected with such undertaking. Also more specifically, in a statute, a guardian, trustee, executor, administrator, receiver, conservator, or any person acting in any fiduciary capacity for any person, trust, or estate. Some examples of what, in particular connections, the term has been held to include and not to include are set out in the note.

Words and Phrases, Permanent Edition (Vol. 16A, Page 41) Defines 'Fiducial Relation' Thus:

There is a technical distinction between a 'fiducial relation' which is more correctly applicable to legal relationships between parties, such as guardian and ward, administrator and heirs, and other similar relationships, and 'confidential relation' which includes the legal relationships, and also every other relationship wherein confidence is rightly reposed and is exercised.

Generally, the term 'fiduciary' applies to any person who occupies a position of peculiar confidence towards another. It refers to integrity and fidelity. It contemplates fair dealing and good faith, rather than legal obligation, as the basis of the transaction. The term includes those informal relations which exist whenever one party trusts and relies upon another, as well as technical fiduciary relations.

In Bristol and West Building Society v. Mothew [1998 Ch. 1] the Term Fiduciary Was Defined Thus:

A fiduciary is someone who has undertaken to act for and on behalf of another in a particular matter in circumstances which give rise to a relationship of trust and confidence. The distinguishing obligation of a fiduciary is the obligation of loyalty..... A fiduciary must act in good faith; he must not make a profit out of his trust; he must not place himself in a position where his duty and his interest may conflict; he may not act for his own benefit or the benefit of a third person without the informed consent of his principal.

In Wolf v. Superior Court [2003 (107) California Appeals, 4th 25] the California Court of Appeals Defined Fiduciary Relationship As Under:

any relationship existing between the parties to the transaction where one of the parties is duty bound to act with utmost good faith for the benefit of the other party. Such a relationship ordinarily arises where confidence is reposed by one person in the integrity of another, and in such a relation the party in whom the confidence is reposed, if he voluntarily accepts or assumes to accept the confidence, can take no advantage from his acts relating to the interests of the other party without the latter's knowledge and consent.

The term 'fiduciary' refers to a person having a duty to act for the benefit of another, showing good faith and condour, where such other person reposes trust and special confidence in the person owing or discharging the duty. The term 'fiduciary relationship' is used to describe a situation or transaction where one person (beneficiary) places complete confidence in another person (fiduciary) in regard to his affairs, business or transaction/s. The term also refers to a person who holds a thing in trust for another (beneficiary). The fiduciary is expected to act in confidence and for the benefit and advantage of the beneficiary, and use good faith and fairness in dealing with the beneficiary or the things belonging to the beneficiary. If the beneficiary has entrusted anything to the fiduciary, to hold the thing in trust or to execute certain acts in regard to or with reference to the entrusted thing, the fiduciary has to act in confidence and expected not to disclose the thing or information to any third party. There are also certain relationships where both the parties have to act in a fiduciary capacity treating the other as the beneficiary. Examples of these are: a partner vis-a-vis another partner and an employer vis-a-vis employee. An employee who comes into possession of business or trade secrets or confidential information relating to the employer in the course of his employment, is expected to act as a fiduciary and cannot disclose it to others. Similarly, if on the request of the employer or official superior or the head of a department, an employee furnishes his personal details and information, to be retained in confidence, the employer, the official superior or departmental head is expected to hold such personal information in confidence as a fiduciary, to be made use of or disclosed only if the employee's conduct or acts are found to be prejudicial to the employer.

Decision by the Supreme Court

Court observed that In the instant case, the RBI does not place itself in a fiduciary relationship with the Financial institutions (though, in word it puts itself to be in that position) because, the reports of the inspections, statements of the bank, information related to the business obtained by the RBI are not under the pretext of confidence or trust. In this case neither the RBI nor the Banks act in the interest of each other. By attaching an additional "fiduciary" label to the statutory duty, the Regulatory authorities have intentionally or unintentionally created an in terrorem[110] effect.

RBI is a statutory body set up by the RBI Act as India's Central Bank. It is a statutory regulatory authority to oversee the functioning of the banks and the country's banking sector. Under Section 35A[111] of the Banking Regulation Act, RBI has been given powers to issue any direction to the banks in public interest, in the interest of banking policy and to secure proper management of a banking company. It has several other far-reaching statutory powers.

RBI is supposed to uphold public interest and not the interest of individual banks. RBI is clearly not in any fiduciary relationship with any bank. RBI has no legal duty to maximize the benefit of any public sector or private sector bank,

---

[110] Meaning of terrorem:

In terrorem, Latin for "into/about fear", is a legal threat, usually one given in hope of compelling someone to act without resorting to a lawsuit or criminal prosecution.

[111] Section 35A in BANKING REGULATION ACT, 1949

35A Power of the Reserve Bank to give directions. —

(1) Where the Reserve Bank is satisfied that—

(a) in the public interest; or

(aa) in the interest of banking policy; or

(b) to prevent the affairs of any banking company being conducted in a manner detrimental to the interests of the depositors or in a manner prejudicial to the interests of the banking company; or

(c) to secure the proper management of any banking company generally,

it is necessary to issue directions to banking companies generally or to any banking company in particular, it may, from time to time, issue such directions as it deems fit, and the banking companies or the banking company, as the case may be, shall be bound to comply with such directions.

(2) The Reserve Bank may, on representation made to it or on its own motion, modify or cancel any direction issued under sub-section (1), and in so modifying or cancelling any direction may impose such conditions as it thinks fit, subject to which the modification or cancellation shall have effect.

and thus there is no relationship of 'trust' between them. RBI has a statutory duty to uphold the interest of the public at large, the depositors, the country's economy and the banking sector. Thus, RBI ought to act with transparency and not hide information that might embarrass individual banks. It is duty bound to comply with the provisions of the RTI Act and disclose the information sought by the Respondents.

As per court the baseless and unsubstantiated argument of the RBI that the disclosure would hurt the economic interest of the country was totally misconceived.

The exemption contained in Section 8(1)(e) applies to exceptional cases and only with regard to certain pieces of information, for which disclosure is unwarranted or undesirable. If information is available with a regulatory agency not in fiduciary relationship, there is no reason to withhold the disclosure of the same. However, where information is required by mandate of law to be provided to an authority, it cannot be said that such information is being provided in a fiduciary relationship. The Financial institutions have an obligation to provide all the information to the RBI and such an information shared under an obligation/ duty cannot be considered to come under the purview of being shared in fiduciary relationship. One of the main characteristic of a Fiduciary relationship is "Trust and Confidence". Something that RBI and the Banks lack between them.

Since, RTI Act is enacted to empower the common people, the test to determine limits of Section 8 of RTI Act is whether giving information to the general public would be detrimental to the economic interests of the country? To what extent the public should be allowed to get information?

The Public Information Officers (PIO) under the guise of one of the exceptions given Under Section 8 of RTI Act, have evaded the general public from getting their hands on the rightful information that they are entitled to.

And in this case the RBI and the Banks have sidestepped the General public's demand to give the requisite information on the pretext of "Fiduciary relationship" and "Economic Interest". This attitude of the RBI will only attract more suspicion and disbelief in them. RBI as a regulatory authority should work to make the Banks accountable to their actions.

Furthermore, the RTI Act Under Section 2(f) clearly provides that the inspection reports, documents etc. fall under the purview of "Information" which is obtained by the public authority (RBI) from a private body. Section 2(f), reads thus:

"information" means any material in any form, including records, documents, memos, e-mails, opinions, advices, press releases, circulars, orders, logbooks, contracts, reports, papers, samples, models, data material held in any electronic form and information relating to any private body which can be accessed by a public authority under any other law for the time being in force;

From reading of the above section it can be inferred that the Legislature's intent was to make available to the general public such information which had been obtained by the public authorities from the private body. Had it been the case where only information related to public authorities was to be provided, the Legislature would not have included the word "private body". Therefore, the court held that the RBI was liable to provide information regarding inspection report and other documents to the general public.

Chapter - 20

OFFICE OF ATTORNEY GENERAL OF INDIA[112] NOT UNDER RTI ACT, 2005[113]

Facts in Nutshell

By Common order dated 10.03.2015 in Writ Petition[114] (Civil) No. 1041/ 2013 and Writ Petition (Civil) No. 1665/2013, the learned Single Judge of Delhi High Court held that the office of Attorney General of India (AGI) is a ''public authority'' within the meaning of Section 2(h)[115] of the Right to Information Act, 2005 (for short 'the RTI Act').

---

[112] The Attorney General for India is the Indian government's chief legal advisor, and is primary lawyer in the Supreme Court of India. He can be said to be the lawyer from government's side. He is appointed by the President of India under Article 76(1) of the Constitutionand holds office during the pleasure of the President. He must be a person qualified to be appointed as a Judge of the Supreme Court (He must have been a judge of some high court for five years or an advocate of some high court for ten years or an eminent jurist, in the opinion of the President and must be a citizen of India.)

[113] Appellants: Union of India Vs. Respondent: Subhash Chandra Aggarwal and Ors.
Hon'ble Judges/Coram: G. Rohini, C.J. and Jayant Nath, Judge, High Court of Delhi
Decided On: 03.02.2017, MANU/DE/0250/2017
Subject: Right to Information

[114] A writ is a formal written order issued by a Court. Any warrant, orders, directions, and so on, issued by the Supreme Court or the High court are called writs.
A writ petition can be filed in the High Court (Article 226) or the Supreme Court (Article 32) of India when any of your fundamental rights are violated. The jurisdiction with the High Courts (Article 226) with regards to a writ petition is wider and extends to constitutional rights too.

[115] (h) "public authority" means any authority or body or institution of self-government established or constituted,—

(a) by or under the Constitution;
(b) by any other law made by Parliament;
(c) by any other law made by State Legislature;
(d) by notification issued or order made by the appropriate Government, and includes any—
(i) body owned, controlled or substantially financed;
(ii) non-Government Organisation substantially financed, directly or indirectly by funds provided by the appropriate Government

Aggrieved by the same, two appeals[116] were filed by the Union of India before Division bench[117] of the High Court.

Facts

The application was made by the respondent[118] to provide certain information relating to the office of AGI was returned by the office of the AGI on the ground that AGI is not a public authority and there is no CPIO in the office of AGI.

Decision by CIC[119]

On a complaint by the respondent under Section 18[120] of RTI Act, the Central Information Commission (CIC) had also held that AGI is not a public authority within the meaning of Section 2(h) of the RTI Act. The application dated

116 Meaning of appeal:

a. A higher court's review of the correctness of a decision by a lower court.

b. A case so reviewed.

117 A Division Bench is a term in judicial system in India in which a case is heard and judged by at least 2 judges. However, if the bench during the hearing of any matter feels that the matter needs to be considered by a larger bench, such a matter is referred to a larger bench.

118 Meaning of respondent:

The defending party in certain legal proceedings, as in a case brought by petition.

119 The Central Information Commission (CIC) set up under the Right to Information Act is the authorised body, established in 2005, under the Government of India to act upon complaints from those individuals who have not been able to submit information requests to a Central Public Information Officer or State Public Information Officer due to either the officer not have been appointed, or because the respective Central Assistant Public Information Officer or State Assistant Public Information Officer refused to receive the application for information under the RTI Act.

120 Section 18 in The Right To Information Act, 2005

18. Powers and functions of Information Commission.—

(1) Subject to the provisions of this Act, it shall be the duty of the Central Information Commission or State Information Commission as the case may be to receive and inquire into a complaint from any person,—

(a) who has been unable to submit a request to a Central Public Information Officer, or State Public Information Officer as the case may be, either by reason that no such officer has been appointed under this Act, or because the Central Assistant Public Information Officer or State Assistant Public Information Officer, as the case may be, has refused to accept his or her application for information or appeal under this Act for forwarding the same to the Central Public Information Officer or State Public Information Officer or Senior Officer specified in sub-section (1) of section 19 or the Central Information Commission or the State Information Commission, as the case may be;

(b) who has been refused access to any information requested under this Act;

(c) who has not been given a response to a request for information or access to information within the time limits specified under this Act;

07.01.2013 made by the respondent seeking information regarding the representation/petition[121] received from Indirect Tax Practitioners Association, Bangalore was also rejected on the same ground.

Contention of the Writ Petitioner before Learned Single Judge

The contention of the writ petitioners was that AGI being an authority under the Constitution, falls within the definition of "public authority" under Section 2(h) of the RTI Act.

Contention of the Union of India before Learned Single Judge

Per contra, it was contended on behalf of the Union of India in the writ petitions that AGI having been appointed under Article 76[122] of the Constitution

---

(d) who has been required to pay an amount of fee which he or she considers unreasonable;

(e) who believes that he or she has been given incomplete, misleading or false information under this Act; and

(f) in respect of any other matter relating to requesting or obtaining access to records under this Act.

(2) Where the Central Information Commission or State Information Commission, as the case may be, is satisfied that there are reasonable grounds to inquire into the matter, it may initiate an inquiry in respect thereof.

(3) The Central Information Commission or State Information Commission, as the case may be shall, while inquiring into any matter under this section, have the same powers as are vested in a civil court while trying a suit under the Code of Civil Procedure, 1908, in respect of the following matters, namely:—

(a) summoning and enforcing the attendance of persons and compel them to give oral or written evidence on oath and to produce the documents or things;

(b) requiring the discovery and inspection of documents;

(c) receiving evidence on affidavit;

(d) requisitioning any public record or copies thereof from any court or office;

(e) issuing summons for examination of witnesses or documents; and

(f) any other matter which may be prescribed.

(4) Notwithstanding anything inconsistent contained in any other Act of Parliament, or the State Legislature, as the case may be, the Central Information Commission or the State Information Commission, as the case may be, may, during the inquiry of any complaint under this Act, examine any record to which this Act applies which is under the control of the public authority, and no such record may be withheld from it on any grounds.

121 Meaning of petition:
A formal written application seeking a court's intervention and action on a matter.

122 Article 76 in The Constitution Of India 1949
76. Attorney General for India
(1) The President shall appoint a person who is qualified to be appointed a Judge of the Supreme Court to be Attorney General for India

of India to give advice to the Government of India upon the legal matters, the relationship between AGI and the Government of India is that of a lawyer and client and therefore, the office of AGI does not fall within the definition of "public authority" under the RTI Act.

Decision by Learned Single Judge

While rejecting the contention on behalf of the Union of India, the learned Single Judge accepted the plea of the writ petitioners that the office of AGI is covered by the definition of "public authority" under Section 2(h) of the RTI Act. The relevant paragraphs from the order under appeal may be reproduced hereunder for ready reference:

"19. It is apparent from the above that the role of the AGI is not limited to merely acting as a lawyer for the Government of India as is contended by the respondent; the AGI is a constitutional functionary and is also obliged to discharge the functions under the Constitution as well as under any other law.

20. Although, it cannot be disputed that AGI is a constitutional functionary, the point in issue is whether he can be termed as an "authority". The term "authority" as used in the opening sentence of Section 2(h) of the Act cannot be interpreted in a restrictive sense. The expression "authority" would also include all persons or bodies that have been conferred a power to perform the functions entrusted to them. Merely because the bulk of the duties of the AGI are advisory, the same would not render the office of the AGI any less authoritative than other constitutional functionaries. There are various bodies, which are entrusted with 'staff functions' (i.e. which are advisory in nature) as distinct from 'line functions'.

---

(2) it shall be the duty of the Attorney General to give advice to the Government of India upon such legal matters, and to perform such other duties of a legal character, as may from time to time be referred or assigned to him by the President, and to discharge the functions conferred on him by or under this Constitution or any other law for the time being in force

(3) In the performance of his duties the Attorney General shall have right of audience in all courts in the territory of India

(4) The Attorney General shall hold office during the pleasure of the President, and shall receive such remuneration as the President may determine Conduct of Government Business

The expression authority" as used in Section 2(h) cannot be read as a term to exclude bodies or entities which are, essentially, performing advisory functions.

22. In my view, the expression "authority" as used in Section 2(h) of the Act would encompass any office that is conferred with any statutory or constitutional power. The office of the AGI is an office established under the Constitution of India; the incumbent appointed to that office discharges functions as provided under the Constitution. Article 76(2) of the Constitution expressly provides that the AGI would perform the duties of a legal character and also discharge the functions conferred on him under the Constitution or any other law in force. Indisputably, the appointee to that office is, by virtue the constitution, vested with the authority to discharge those functions.

It is not disputed that the functions of the AGI are also in the nature of public functions. The AGI performs the functions as are required by virtue of Article 76(2) of the Constitution of India."

The learned Single Judge by the order held that the office of AGI is a "public authority". Accordingly, the Union of India moved to the Division Bench of the High Court.

Contention by Union of India before Division Bench

Assailing[123] the order of single judge, it was contended by the learned ASG that AGI who maintains a fiduciary relationship with the Government of India and does not occupy an office of profit cannot be held to be a "public authority" within the meaning of Section 2(h) of the RTI Act. It was also contended that none of the functions of AGI involve authority/power to alter the relations or rights of others and therefore, the definition of "public authority" under Section 2(h) is not attracted at all. It was also submitted by the learned ASG that AGI who is appointed under the Constitution of India occupies a position of great importance

---

[123] Meaning of assail:

1. To attack violently, as with blows or military force; assault.
2. To attack verbally, as with ridicule or censure.

and relevance and in some respects acts as the friend, philosopher and guide of the Court and thus maintains only a fiduciary relationship.

Contention by Respondent before Division Bench

On the other hand, the learned counsel for the respondents/writ petitioners while supporting the conclusion of the learned Single Judge, contended that having regard to the admitted fact that AGI performs various important public functions apart from extending legal advice and appearing on behalf of the Government of India, whether AGI has acted in fiduciary capacity or not has to be decided in the facts and circumstances of a given case in the light of the information sought by the applicant, but he cannot be altogether excluded from the purview of definition under Section 2(h) of RTI Act. Though there is an element of lawyer - client relationship between the AGI and the Government of India, he holds a public office and thus falls within the definition of Section 2(h) of the RTI Act, 2005.

Question before the Division Bench of the High Court

Can the AGI be termed to be "Public authority" as defined in the RTI Act, 2005?

Right to Information Act, 2005[124]

The Right to Information Act, 2005 has been enacted to provide for setting out the practical regime of right to information for citizens to secure access to information under the control of public authorities in order to promote transparency and accountability in the working of every public authority. It is aimed at providing an effective framework for effectuating the right of information recognized under Article 19[125] of the Constitution of India.

---

[124] Right to Information (RTI) is act of the Parliament of India to provide for setting out the practical regime of the right to information for citizens and replaces the erstwhile Freedom of information Act, 2002. Under the provisions of the Act, any citizen of India may request information from a "public authority" (a body of Government or "instrumentality of State") which is required to reply expeditiously or within thirty days. The Act also requires every public authority to computerise their records for wide dissemination and to proactively certain categories of information so that the citizens need minimum recourse to request for information formally.

[125] Article 19 in The Constitution Of India 1949

19. Protection of certain rights regarding freedom of speech etc

Section 3 of the RTI Act Which Provides for Right to Information As Well As Section 2(H) and Section 2(J) Which Define "Public Authority" And "Right to Information" Respectively:

"Section 3. Right to Information - Subject to the provisions of this Act, all citizens shall have the right to information.

Section 2(h) - "public authority" means any authority or body or institution of self- government established or constituted-

(a) by or under the Constitution;

---

(1) All citizens shall have the right
   (a) to freedom of speech and expression;
   (b) to assemble peaceably and without arms;
   (c) to form associations or unions;
   (d) to move freely throughout the territory of India;
   (e) to reside and settle in any part of the territory of India; and
   (f) omitted
   (g) to practise any profession, or to carry on any occupation, trade or business

(2) Nothing in sub clause (a) of clause (1) shall affect the operation of any existing law, or prevent the State from making any law, in so far as such law imposes reasonable restrictions on the exercise of the right conferred by the said sub clause in the interests of the sovereignty and integrity of India, the security of the State, friendly relations with foreign States, public order, decency or morality or in relation to contempt of court, defamation or incitement to an offence

(3) Nothing in sub clause (b) of the said clause shall affect the operation of any existing law in so far as it imposes, or prevent the State from making any law imposing, in the interests of the sovereignty and integrity of India or public order, reasonable restrictions on the exercise of the right conferred by the said sub clause

(4) Nothing in sub clause (c) of the said clause shall affect the operation of any existing law in so far as it imposes, or prevent the State from making any law imposing, in the interests of the sovereignty and integrity of India or public order or morality, reasonable restrictions on the exercise of the right conferred by the said sub clause

(5) Nothing in sub clauses (d) and (e) of the said clause shall affect the operation of any existing law in so far as it imposes, or prevent the State from making any law imposing, reasonable restrictions on the exercise of any of the rights conferred by the said sub clauses either in the interests of the general public or for the protection of the interests of any Scheduled Tribe

(6) Nothing in sub clause (g) of the said clause shall affect the operation of any existing law in so far as it imposes, or prevent the State from making any law imposing, in the interests of the general public, reasonable restrictions on the exercise of the right conferred by the said sub clause, and, in particular, nothing in the said sub clause shall affect the operation of any existing law in so far as it relates to, or prevent the State from making any law relating to,
   (i) the professional or technical qualifications necessary for practising any profession or carrying on any occupation, trade or business, or
   (ii) the carrying on by the State, or by a corporation owned or controlled by the State, of any trade, business, industry or service, whether to the exclusion, complete or partial, of citizens or otherwise

(b) by any other law made by Parliament;

(c) by any other law made by State Legislature;

(d) by notification issued or order made by the appropriate Government, and includes any-

(i) body owned, controlled or substantially financed;

(ii) non-Government organization substantially financed, directly or indirectly by funds provided by the appropriate Government;"

Section 2(j) - "right to information" means the right to information accessible under this Act which is held by or under the control of any public authority and includes the right to-

(i) inspection of work, documents, records;

(ii) taking notes, extracts or certified copies of documents or records;

(iii) taking certified samples of material;

(iv) obtaining information in the form of diskettes, floppies, tapes, video cassettes or in any other electronic mode or through printouts where such information is stored in a computer or in any other device."

As is evident from the language of Section 3 of the RTI Act and as explained in Thalapalam Service Cooperative Bank Limited and Others, the right to information under the RTI Act is not an unlimited and unrestricted right but it is subject to the provisions of the Act itself. The expression "right to information" has been defined under Section 2(j) as the right to information accessible under the Act which is held by or under the control of any public authority. Thus, it is clear that the right to information provided to the citizens under the RTI Act is the right to secure access to information held by or under the control of public authorities. The expression "public authority" has also been specifically defined under Section 2(h) of the RTI Act thereby making it clear that only those categories which are specifically included under Section 2(h), answer the description of a "public authority" for the purpose of RTI Act.

The Apex Court in Thalapalam Service Cooperative Bank Limited and Others v. State of Kerala and Others[126] while reiterating the well-settled principle of law

[126] (2013) 16 SCC 82

that right to information is a facet of freedom of "speech and expression" contained in Article 19(1)(a) of the Constitution of Indian and thus right to information is a fundamental right, further explained as under:

"56. The Right to Information Act, 2005 is an Act which provides for setting up the practical regime of right to information for citizens to secure access to information under the control of public authorities in order to promote transparency and accountability in the working of every public authority. Preamble of the Act also states that the democracy requires an informed citizenry and transparency of information which are vital to its functioning and also to contain corruption and to hold Governments and their instrumentalities accountable to the governed. Citizens have, however, the right to secure access to information of only those matters which are "under the control of public authorities", the purpose is to hold "Government and its instrumentalities" accountable to the governed. Consequently, though right to get information is a fundamental right guaranteed under Article 19(1)(a) of the Constitution, limits are being prescribed under the Act itself, which are reasonable restrictions within the meaning of Article 19(2) of the Constitution of India."

The Duties of an the AGI are Stated in Article 76(2) of the Constitution. Article 76 of the Constitution Reads As Follows:-

"76. Attorney General for India -

(1) The President shall appoint a person who is qualified to be appointed a Judge of the Supreme Court to be Attorney General for India

(2) It shall be the duty of the Attorney General to give advice to the Government of India upon such legal matters, and to perform such other duties of a legal character, as may from time to time be referred or assigned to him by the President, and to discharge the functions conferred on him by or under this Constitution or any other law for the time being in force

(3) In the performance of his duties the Attorney General shall have right of audience in all courts in the territory of India

(4) The Attorney General shall hold office during the pleasure of the President, and shall receive such remuneration as the President may determine."

Union of India in exercise of powers conferred under the proviso to Article 309 read with Article 76 of the Constitution has framed the Law Officers (Condition of Service) Rules 1972. The duties of a law officer are stated in the said Rules as follows:-

"5. Duties- It shall be the duty of a Law Officer -

(a) to give advice to the Government of India upon such legal matters, and to perform such other duties of a legal character, as may from time to time, be referred or assigned to him by the Government of India.

(b) to appear, whenever required, in the Supreme Court or in any High Court on behalf of the Government of India in cases (including suits, writ petitions, appeal and other proceedings) in which the Government of India is concerned as a party or is otherwise interested;

(c) to represent the Government of India in any reference made by the President to the Supreme Court under Article 143[127] of the Constitution; and

(d) to discharge such other functions as are conferred on a Law Officer by or under the Constitution or any other Law for the time being in force."

The Rules state that the functions of the AGI are to advise the Government of India upon legal matters, to appear whenever required in the Supreme Court or in the High Court on behalf of the Government of India, to represent Government of India in any reference made by the President to the Supreme Court under Article 143 of the Constitution and to discharge such other functions as conferred on a law officer by or under the Constitution or any other law for the time being in force.

---

[127] Article 143 in The Constitution Of India 1949

143. Power of President to consult Supreme Court

(1) If at any time it appears to the President that a question of law or fact has arisen, or is likely to arise, which is of such a nature and of such public importance that it is expedient to obtain the opinion of the Supreme Court upon it, he may refer the question to that Court for consideration and the Court may, after such hearing as it thinks fit, report to the President its opinion thereon

(2) The President may, notwithstanding anything in the proviso to Article 131, refer a dispute of the kind mentioned in the said proviso to the Supreme Court for opinion and the Supreme Court shall, after such hearing as it thinks fit, report to the President its opinion thereon

A perusal of the above constitutional and statutory provision shows that essentially the AGI performs the duties of giving advice to the Government of India upon legal matters and also to appear before the Supreme Court or any High Court on behalf of the Government of India apart from other duties.

Decision by High Court

Court observed that the predominant function of the AGI is to give advice upon legal matters, to appear in court, i.e. perform the duties akin to an Advocate/ Senior Advocate. Essentially, the function being that akin to an Advocate of the Government of India, he is in a fiduciary relationship with the Government of India and cannot put in the public domain his opinions or the materials forwarded to him by the Government of India.

Reference in this context may be had to Section 126 of the Evidence Act which reads as follows:-

"126. Professional communications.-No barrister, attorney, pleader or vakil shall at any time be permitted, unless with his client's express consent, to disclose any communication made to him in the course and for the purpose of his employment as such barrister, pleader, attorney or vakil, by or on behalf of his client, or to state the contents or condition of any document with which he has become acquainted in the course and for the purpose of his professional employment, or to disclose any advice given by him to his client in the course and for the purpose of such employment:

Provided that nothing in this section shall protect from disclosure-

(1) Any such communication made in furtherance of any [illegal] purpose; [illegal] purpose;"

(2) Any fact observed by any barrister, pleader, attorney or vakil, in the course of his employment as such, showing that any crime or fraud has been committed since the commencement of his employment. It is immaterial whether the attention of such barrister, 2[pleader], attorney or vakil was or was not directed to such fact by or on behalf of his client.

Explanation.-The obligation stated in this section continues after the employment has ceased."

In a catena of judgments, the Supreme Court has reiterated that a lawyer acts in a fiduciary capacity with his client. Reference maybe had to the judgment of the Supreme Court in the case of Central Board of Secondary Education & Anr. v. Aditya Bandopadhyay & Ors.,[128]. That was a case where the petitioner in the writ petition had made an application for inspection and re-evaluation of the answer book. While dealing with the contention of the CBSE that the examining body holds the evaluated answer books in a fiduciary relationship, the Supreme Court held as follows:-

"41. In a philosophical and very wide sense, examining bodies can be said to act in a fiduciary capacity, with reference to students who participate in an examination, as a government does while governing its citizens or as the present generation does with reference to the future generation while preserving the environment. But the words 'information available to a person in his fiduciary relationship' are used in Section 8(1)(e)[129] *of RTI Act*

---

[128] (2011) 8 SCC 497

[129] Section 8 in The Right To Information Act, 2005

8. Exemption from disclosure of information.—

(1) Notwithstanding anything contained in this Act, there shall be no obligation to give any citizen,—

(a) information, disclosure of which would prejudicially affect the sovereignty and integrity of India, the security, strategic, scientific or economic interests of the State, relation with foreign State or lead to incitement of an offence;

(b) information which has been expressly forbidden to be published by any court of law or tribunal or the disclosure of which may constitute contempt of court;

(c) information, the disclosure of which would cause a breach of privilege of Parliament or the State Legislature;

(d) information including commercial confidence, trade secrets or intellectual property, the disclosure of which would harm the competitive position of a third party, unless the competent authority is satisfied that larger public interest warrants the disclosure of such information;

(e) information available to a person in his fiduciary relationship, unless the competent authority is satisfied that the larger public interest warrants the disclosure of such information;

(f) information received in confidence from foreign government;

(g) information, the disclosure of which would endanger the life or physical safety of any person or identify the source of information or assistance given in confidence for law enforcement or security purposes;

in its normal and well recognized sense, that is to refer to persons who act in a fiduciary capacity, with reference to a specific beneficiary or beneficiaries who are to be expected to be protected or benefited by the actions of the fiduciary - a trustee with reference to the beneficiary of the trust, a guardian with reference to a minor/physically/infirm/mentally challenged, a parent with reference to a child, a lawyer or a chartered accountant with reference to a client, a doctor or nurse with reference to a patient, an agent with reference to a principal, a partner with reference to another partner, a director of a company with reference to a share-holder, an executor with reference to a legatee, a receiver with reference to the parties to a lis, an employer with reference to the confidential information relating to the employee, and an employee with reference to business dealings/transaction of the employer. We do not find that kind of fiduciary relationship between the examining body and the examinee, with reference to the evaluated answer-books, that come into the custody of the examining body."

Similarly in the case of Kokkanda B. Poondacha & Ors. v. K.D. Ganapathi & Anr.,[130] the Supreme Court held as follows:-

"12. At this stage, we may also advert to the nature of relationship between a lawyer and his client, which is solely founded on trust and confidence. A lawyer

---

(h) information which would impede the process of investigation or apprehension or prosecution of offenders;

(i) cabinet papers including records of deliberations of the Council of Ministers, Secretaries and other officers: Provided that the decisions of Council of Ministers, the reasons thereof, and the material on the basis of which the decisions were taken shall be made public after the decision has been taken, and the matter is complete, or over: Provided further that those matters which come under the exemptions specified in this section shall not be disclosed;

(j) information which relates to personal information the disclosure of which has not relationship to any public activity or interest, or which would cause unwarranted invasion of the privacy of the individual unless the Central Public Information Officer or the State Public Information Officer or the appellate authority, as the case may be, is satisfied that the larger public interest justifies the disclosure of such information: Provided that the information, which cannot be denied to the Parliament or a State Legislature shall not be denied to any person.

(2) Notwithstanding anything in the Official Secrets Act, 1923 (19 of 1923) nor any of the exemptions permissible in accordance with sub-section (1), a public authority may allow access to information, if public interest in disclosure outweighs the harm to the protected interests.

cannot pass on the confidential information to anyone else. This is so because he is a fiduciary of his client, who reposes trust and confidence in the lawyer. Therefore, he has a duty to fulfil all his obligations towards his client with care and act in good faith. Since the client entrusts the whole obligation of handling legal proceedings to an advocate, he has to act according to the principles of uberrima fides, i.e., the utmost good faith, integrity, fairness and loyalty."

In the case of Superintendent and Remembrancer of Legal Affairs, West Bengal v. Satyen Bhowmick & Ors.[131]. That was a case in which the accused[132] was charged under the Official Secrets Act[133]. The Magistrate directed the lawyer to produce his notebook. The Magistrate permitted the defence lawyer to take copies of the statement of the witness[134] in order to be in a position to cross-examine[135] the witness. Subsequently, the Magistrate directed the lawyer to produce his notebook to examine that only a summary of the evidence has been taken by the lawyer not in extenso in violation of Section 14[136]. The lawyer

---

(3) Subject to the provisions of clauses (a), (c) and (i) of sub-section (1), any information relating to any occurrence, event or matter which has taken place, occurred or happened twenty years before the date on which any request is made under section 6 shall be provided to any person making a request under that section: Provided that where any question arises as to the date from which the said period of twenty years has to be computed, the decision of the Central Government shall be final, subject to the usual appeals provided for in this Act.

[130] (2011) 12 SCC 600

[131] AIR 1981 SCC 917

[132] Meaning of accused:
The defendant in a criminal case

[133] The Official Secret Act 1923 is India's anti-espionage act held over from the British colonial period. It states clearly that actions which involve helping an enemy state against India are strongly condemned. It also states that one cannot approach, inspect, or even pass over a prohibited government site or area. According to this Act, helping the enemy state can be in the form of communicating a sketch, plan, model of an official secret, or of official codes or passwords, to the enemy.

[134] Meaning of witness:
a. One who is called on to testify before a court.
b. One who is called on to be present at a transaction in order to attest to what takes place.
c. One who signs one's name to a document for the purpose of attesting to its authenticity.

[135] Meaning of cross examine:
Question closely, or question a witness that has already been questioned by the opposing side

[136] Section 14 in The Indian Evidence Act, 1872
14. Facts showing existence of state of mind, or of body or bodily feeling.—Facts showing the existence of any state of mind, such as intention, knowledge, good faith, negligence, rashness, ill-will or good-will towards any particular person, or showing the existence of any state of body or bodily feeling, are relevant, when the existence of any such state of mind or body or bodily

claimed privilege under Section 126 of the Act. The Supreme Court held as follows:-

That there was absolutely no impropriety on the part of the Magistrate in not taking action against the defence lawyer for his refusal to' show his register because the lawyer had rightly claimed privilege under Section 126 of the Evidence Act as the register contained instructions given by the client which being privileged could not be disclosed to the Court. On a parity of reasoning we find no impropriety on the conduct of the lawyer in refusing to show the statement of witnesses recorded by the Court in extenso in order to prepare himself for an effective cross-examination of the witnesses. Hence the strictures passed by the High Court on the Magistrate as also on the lawyer of the defence were, in our opinion, totally unwarranted.

In the case of Reserve Bank of India & Ors. v. Jayantilal N. Mistry & Ors.[137], the Supreme Court while dealing with the defence of RBI that it was in the fiduciary relationship with the Bank noted as follows:-

The Advanced Law Lexicon, 3rd Edition, 2005, defines fiduciary relationship as "a relationship in which one person is under a duty to act for the benefit of the other on the matters within the scope of the fiduciary relationship. Fiduciary relationship usually arise in one of the four situations (1) when one person places trust in the faithful integrity of another, who as a result gains superiority or influence over the first, (2) when one person assumes control and responsibility over another, (3) when one person has a duty to act or give advice to another on matters falling within the scope of the relationship, or (4) when there is specific relationship that has traditionally be recognized as involving fiduciary duties, as with a lawyer and a client, or a stockbroker and a customer.

---

feeling, is in issue or relevant. 1[Explanation 1.—A fact relevant as showing the existence of a relevant state of mind must show that the state of mind exists, not generally, but in reference to the particular matter in question.[Explanation 1.—A fact relevant as showing the existence of a relevant state of mind must show that the state of mind exists, not generally, but in reference to the particular matter in question." Explanation 2.—But where, upon the trial of a person accused of an offence, the previous commission by the accused of an offence is relevant within the meaning of this section, the previous conviction of such person shall also be a relevant fact.

[137] (2016) 3 SCC 525

The term fiduciary relationship has been well discussed by Court in the case of Central Board of Secondary Education and Anr. v. Aditya Bandopadhyay and Ors.. In the said decision, their Lordships referred various authorities to ascertain the meaning of the term fiduciary relationship and observed thus:

Black's Law Dictionary (7th Edition, Page 640) defines 'fiduciary relationship' thus:

A relationship in which one person is under a duty to act for the benefit of the other on matters within the scope of the relationship. Fiduciary relationships-such as trustee-beneficiary, guardian-ward, agent-principal, and attorney-client-require the highest duty of care. Fiduciary relationships usually arise in one of four situations: (1) when one person places trust in the faithful integrity of another, who as a result gains superiority or influence over the first, (2) when one person assumes control and responsibility over another, (3) when one person has a duty to act for or give advice to another on matters falling within the scope of the relationship, or (4) when there is a specific relationship that has traditionally been recognized as involving fiduciary duties, as with a lawyer and a client or a stockbroker and a customer."

Court held that the essential services provided by the AGI are to advice the Government upon legal matters and perform other duties such of a legal character as may be assigned. AGI is not a functionary reposed with any administrative or other authority which effect the rights or liabilities of persons. The objects of the RTI Act have been noted by the Supreme Court in the case of Instituted of Chartered Accountants of India v. Shaunak H. Satya & Ors.[138], as under:-

"23. The information to which RTI Act applies falls into two categories, namely, (i) information which promotes transparency and accountability in the working of every public authority, disclosure of which helps in containing or discouraging corruption, enumerated in Clauses (b) and (c) of Section 4(1) of RTI Act; and (ii) other information held by public authorities not falling under Section 4(1)(b) and (c) of RTI Act. In regard to information falling under the first category, the public authorities owe a duty to disseminate the information widely suo moto to the public so as to make it easily accessible to the public. In

138 (2011) 8 SCC 781

regard to information enumerated or required to be enumerated under Section 4(1)(b) and (c) of RTI Act, necessarily and naturally, the competent authorities under the RTI Act, will have to act in a pro-active manner so as to ensure accountability and ensure that the fight against corruption goes on relentlessly. But in regard to other information which do not fall under Section 4(1)(b) and (c) of the Act, there is a need to proceed with circumspection as it is necessary to find out whether they are exempted from disclosure.

24. One of the objects of democracy is to bring about transparency of information to contain corruption and bring about accountability. But achieving this object does not mean that other equally important public interests including efficient functioning of the governments and public authorities, optimum use of limited fiscal resources, preservation of confidentiality of sensitive information, etc. are to be ignored or sacrificed. The object of RTI Act is to harmonize the conflicting public interests, that is, ensuring transparency to bring in accountability and containing corruption on the one hand, and at the same time ensure that the revelation of information, in actual practice, does not harm or adversely affect other public interests which include efficient functioning of the governments, optimum use of limited fiscal resources and preservation of confidentiality of sensitive information, on the other hand. While Sections 3 and 4[139] seek to achieve

---

[139] Section 4 in The Right To Information Act, 2005

4. Obligations of public authorities.—

(1) Every public authority shall—

(a) maintain all its records duly catalogued and indexed in a manner and the form which facilitates the right to information under this Act and ensure that all records that are appropriate to be computerised are, within a reasonable time and subject to availability of resources, computerised and connected through a network all over the country on different systems so that access to such records is facilitated;

(b) publish within one hundred and twenty days from the enactment of this Act,—

(i) the particulars of its organisation, functions and duties;

(ii) the powers and duties of its officers and employees;

(iii) the procedure followed in the decision making process, including channels of supervision and accountability;

(iv) the norms set by it for the discharge of its functions;

(v) the rules, regulations, instructions, manuals and records, held by it or under its control or used by its employees for discharging its functions;

(vi) a statement of the categories of documents that are held by it or under its control;

(vii) the particulars of any arrangement that exists for consultation with, or representation by, the members of the public in relation to the formulation of its policy or implementation thereof;

the first objective, Sections 8, 9[140], 10[141] and 11[142] seek to achieve the second objective."

(viii) a statement of the boards, councils, committees and other bodies consisting of two or more persons constituted as its part or for the purpose of its advice, and as to whether meetings of those boards, councils, committees and other bodies are open to the public, or the minutes of such meetings are accessible for public;
(ix) a directory of its officers and employees;
(x) the monthly remuneration received by each of its officers and employees, including the system of compensation as provided in its regulations;
(xi) the budget allocated to each of its agency, indicating the particulars of all plans, proposed expenditures and reports on disbursements made;
(xii) the manner of execution of subsidy programmes, including the amounts allocated and the details of beneficiaries of such programmes;
(xiii) particulars of recipients of concessions, permits or authorisations granted by it;
(xiv) details in respect of the information, available to or held by it, reduced in an electronic form;
(xv) the particulars of facilities available to citizens for obtaining information, including the working hours of a library or reading room, if maintained for public use;
(xvi) the names, designations and other particulars of the Public Information Officers;
(xvii) such other information as may be prescribed, and thereafter update these publications every year;

(c) publish all relevant facts while formulating important policies or announcing the decisions which affect public;
(d) provide reasons for its administrative or quasi judicial decisions to affected persons.

(2) It shall be a constant endeavour of every public authority to take steps in accordance with the requirements of clause (b) of sub-section (1) to provide as much information suo motu to the public at regular intervals through various means of communications, including internet, so that the public have minimum resort to the use of this Act to obtain information.
(3) For the purpose of sub-section (1), every information shall be disseminated widely and in such form and manner which is easily accessible to the public.
(4) All materials shall be disseminated taking into consideration the cost effectiveness, local language and the most effective method of communication in that local area and the information should be easily accessible, to the extent possible in electronic format with the Central Public Information Officer or State Public Information Officer, as the case may be, available free or at such cost of the medium or the print cost price as may be prescribed. Explanation.—For the purposes of sub-sections (3) and (4), "disseminated" means making known or communicated the information to the public through notice boards, newspapers, public announcements, media broadcasts, the internet or any other means, including inspection of offices of any public authority.

[140] Section 9 in The Right To Information Act, 2005

9. Grounds for rejection to access in certain cases.—Without prejudice to the provisions of section 8, a Central Public Information Officer or State Public Information Officer, as the case may be may reject a request for information where such a request for providing access would involve an infringement of copyright subsisting in a person other than the State.

[141] Section 10 in The Right To Information Act, 2005

10. Severability.—

(1) Where a request for access to information is rejected on the ground that it is in relation to information which is exempt from disclosure, then, notwithstanding anything contained in

Court held that Looking at the object of the RTI Act, 2005 it would not have envisaged encompassing an office like that of an AGI to be covered under Section 2(h) of the RTI Act.

---

this Act, access may be provided to that part of the record which does not contain any information which is exempt from disclosure under this Act and which can reasonably be severed from any part that contains exempt information.

(2) Where access is granted to a part of the record under sub-section (1), the Central Public Information Officer or State Public Information Officer, as the case may be shall give a notice to the applicant, informing,—

(a) that only part of the record requested, after severance of the record containing information which is exempt from disclosure, is being provided;

(b) the reasons for the decision, including any findings on any material question of fact, referring to the material on which those findings were based;

(c) the name and designation of the person giving the decision;

(d) the details of the fees calculated by him or her and the amount of fee which the applicant is required to deposit; and

(e) his or her rights with respect to review of the decision regarding non-disclosure of part of the information, the amount of fee charged or the form of access provided, including the particulars of the senior officer specified under sub-section (1) of section 19 or the Central Information Commission or the State Information Commission, as the case may be, time limit, process and any other form of access.

[142] Section 11 in The Right To Information Act, 2005

11. Third party information.—

(1) Where a Central Public Information Officer or the State Public Information Officer, as the case may be, intends to disclose any information or record, or part thereof on a request made under this Act, which relates to or has been supplied by a third party and has been treated as confidential by that third party, the Central Public Information Officer or State Public Information Officer, as the case may be, shall, within five days from the receipt of the request, give a written notice to such third party of the request and of the fact that the Central Public Information Officer or State Public Information Officer, as the case may be, intends to disclose the information or record, or part thereof, and invite the third party to make a submission in writing or orally, regarding whether the information should be disclosed, and such submission of the third party shall be kept in view while taking a decision about disclosure of information: Provided that except in the case of trade or commercial secrets protected by law, disclosure may be allowed if the public interest in disclosure outweighs in importance any possible harm or injury to the interests of such third party.

(2) Where a notice is served by the Central Public Information Officer or State Public Information Officer, as the case may be, under sub-section (1) to a third party in respect of any information or record or part thereof, the third party shall, within ten days from the date of receipt of such notice, be given the opportunity to make representation against the proposed disclosure.

(3) Notwithstanding anything contained in section 7, the Central Public Information Officer or State Public Information Officer, as the case may be, shall, within forty days after receipt of the request under section 6, if the third party has been given an opportunity to make representation under sub-section (2), make a decision as to whether or not to disclose the information or record or part thereof and give in writing the notice of his decision to the third party.

(4) A notice given under sub-section (3) shall include a statement that the third party to whom the notice is given is entitled to prefer an appeal under section 19 against the decision.

Division Bench of the court was unable to agree with the conclusion of the learned Single Judge that the office of AGI falls within the description of "public authority" under RTI Act, 2005.

Chapter - 21

WHETHER PRIME MINISTER'S NATIONAL RELIEF FUND[143] IS A 'PUBLIC AUTHORITY' WITHIN THE AMBIT OF RIGHT TO INFORMATION ACT, 2005[144]

Facts in Nutshell

The respondent[145] (Aseem Takyar) in 2011, applied to the CPIO, Prime Minister's Office ("CPIO") for information pertaining to the various transactions made PMNRF during the financial year 2009-2010 and 2010-2011 ("Information Period"). The CPIO, provided some of the information sought; the CPIO however invoked the exemption under Section 8(1)(j)[146] of the RTI Act, as regards information related to amount, name and particular of each recipient, beneficiary

[143] Prime Minister's National Relief Fund (PMNRF) in India is the fund raised to provide support for people affected by natural and man made disasters. Natural disasters covered under this include flood, cyclone, earthquake etc. Man made disasters include major accidents, acid attacks, riots etc. The fund is also allotted to the people for treatment like cancer, kidney transplantation, heart surgery etc. The fund was first consolidated during the time of the first prime minister of India Jawaharlal Nehru.

[144] Appellants: Prime Minister's National Relief Fund Vs. Respondent: Aseem Takyar
Hon'ble Judges/Coram: S. Ravindra Bhat and Sunil Gaur, JJ., High Court of Delhi (Dissenting judgment by both the judges)
Decided On: 23.05.2018, MANU/DE/1960/2018
Subject: Right to Information

[145] Meaning of respondent:
The defending party in certain legal proceedings, as in a case brought by petition.

[146] Section 8 in The Right To Information Act, 2005
8. Exemption from disclosure of information.—
(1) Notwithstanding anything contained in this Act, there shall be no obligation to give any citizen,—
(a) information, disclosure of which would prejudicially affect the sovereignty and integrity of India, the security, strategic, scientific or economic interests of the State, relation with foreign State or lead to incitement of an offence;
(b) information which has been expressly forbidden to be published by any court of law or tribunal or the disclosure of which may constitute contempt of court;
(c) information, the disclosure of which would cause a breach of privilege of Parliament or the State Legislature;

and donor during the information period. Aggrieved the petitioner appealed[147] under Section 19(1)[148] of the RTI Act to the Appellate Authority. The Authority

(d) information including commercial confidence, trade secrets or intellectual property, the disclosure of which would harm the competitive position of a third party, unless the competent authority is satisfied that larger public interest warrants the disclosure of such information;

(e) information available to a person in his fiduciary relationship, unless the competent authority is satisfied that the larger public interest warrants the disclosure of such information;

(f) information received in confidence from foreign government;

(g) information, the disclosure of which would endanger the life or physical safety of any person or identify the source of information or assistance given in confidence for law enforcement or security purposes;

(h) information which would impede the process of investigation or apprehension or prosecution of offenders;

(i) cabinet papers including records of deliberations of the Council of Ministers, Secretaries and other officers: Provided that the decisions of Council of Ministers, the reasons thereof, and the material on the basis of which the decisions were taken shall be made public after the decision has been taken, and the matter is complete, or over: Provided further that those matters which come under the exemptions specified in this section shall not be disclosed;

(j) information which relates to personal information the disclosure of which has not relationship to any public activity or interest, or which would cause unwarranted invasion of the privacy of the individual unless the Central Public Information Officer or the State Public Information Officer or the appellate authority, as the case may be, is satisfied that the larger public interest justifies the disclosure of such information: Provided that the information, which cannot be denied to the Parliament or a State Legislature shall not be denied to any person.

(2) Notwithstanding anything in the Official Secrets Act, 1923 (19 of 1923) nor any of the exemptions permissible in accordance with sub-section (1), a public authority may allow access to information, if public interest in disclosure outweighs the harm to the protected interests.

(3) Subject to the provisions of clauses (a), (c) and (i) of sub-section (1), any information relating to any occurrence, event or matter which has taken place, occurred or happened twenty years before the date on which any request is made under section 6 shall be provided to any person making a request under that section: Provided that where any question arises as to the date from which the said period of twenty years has to be computed, the decision of the Central Government shall be final, subject to the usual appeals provided for in this Act.

[147] Meaning of appeal:

a. A higher court's review of the correctness of a decision by a lower court.
b. A case so reviewed.
c. A request for a higher court to review the decision of a lower court.

[148] Section 19 in The Right To Information Act, 2005

19. Appeal.—

(1) Any person who, does not receive a decision within the time specified in sub-section (1) or clause (a) of sub-section (3) of section 7, or is aggrieved by a decision of the Central Public Information Officer or the State Public Information Officer, as the case may be, may within thirty days from the expiry of such period or from the receipt of such a decision prefer an

directed the CPIO to send a fresh response to the petitioner, which was duly complied with; the petitioner, aggrieved, preferred a second appeal before the

---

appeal to such officer who is senior in rank to the Central Public Information Officer or the State Public Information Officer, as the case may be, in each public authority: Provided that such officer may admit the appeal after the expiry of the period of thirty days if he or she is satisfied that the appellant was prevented by sufficient cause from filing the appeal in time.

(2) Where an appeal is preferred against an order made by a Central Public Information Officer or a State Public Information Officer, as the case may be, under section 11 to disclose third party information, the appeal by the concerned third party shall be made within thirty days from the date of the order.

(3) A second appeal against the decision under sub-section (1) shall lie within ninety days from the date on which the decision should have been made or was actually received, with the Central Information Commission or the State Information Commission: Provided that the Central Information Commission or the State Information Commission, as the case may be, may admit the appeal after the expiry of the period of ninety days if it is satisfied that the appellant was prevented by sufficient cause from filing the appeal in time.

(4) If the decision of the Central Public Information Officer or State Public Information Officer, as the case may be, against which an appeal is preferred relates to information of a third party, the Central Information Commission or State Information Commission, as the case may be shall give a reasonable opportunity of being heard to that third party.

(5) In any appeal proceedings, the onus to prove that a denial of a request was justified shall be on the Central Public Information Officer or State Public Information Officer, as the case may be, who denied the request.

(6) An appeal under sub-section (1) or sub-section (2) shall be disposed of within thirty days of the receipt of the appeal or within such extended period not exceeding a total of forty-five days from the date of filing thereof, as the case may be, for reasons to be recorded in writing.

(7) The decision of the Central Information Commission or State Information Commission, as the case may be, shall be binding.

(8) In its decision, the Central Information Commission or State Information Commission, as the case may be, has the power to,—

   (a) require the public authority to take any such steps as may be necessary to secure compliance with the provisions of this Act, including—

      (i) by providing access to information, if so requested, in a particular form;

      (ii) by appointing a Central Public Information Officer or State Public Information Officer, as the case may be;

      (iii) by publishing certain information or categories of information;

      (iv) by making necessary changes to its practices in relation to the maintenance, management and destruction of records;

      (v) by enhancing the provision of training on the right to information for its officials;

      (vi) by providing it with an annual report in compliance with clause (b) of sub-section (1) of section 4;

   (b) require the public authority to compensate the complainant for any loss or other detriment suffered;

   (c) impose any of the penalties provided under this Act;

   (d) reject the application.

(9) The Central Information Commission or State Information Commission, as the case may be, shall give notice of its decision, including any right of appeal, to the complainant and the public authority.

Chief Information Commissioner ("CIC")[149] under Section 19(3).

Decision by CIC

The CIC then passed a final order directing the CPIO to place the details of institutional donors of the PMNRF in public domain and to disclose the information to the petitioner.

Aggrieved by the order the Fund preferred a writ petition[150] before High Court.

Decision by Single Judge of High Court

The Learned Single Judge found the CIC's order to be balanced, and dismissed the appeal. However, while passing the impugned judgment the learned Single Judge refrained from giving a conclusive finding as to whether the appellant was a public authority. Aggrieved by the decision of the Learned Single Judge, the Appellant filed the appeal before division bench[151] of High Court.

Question before the High Court Division Bench

Whether Prime Minister's National Relief Fund ("the Fund/Appellant[152]")

---

(10) The Central Information Commission or State Information Commission, as the case may be, shall decide the appeal in accordance with such procedure as may be prescribed.

149 The Central Information Commission (CIC) set up under the Right to Information Act is the authorised body, established in 2005, under the Government of India to act upon complaints from those individuals who have not been able to submit information requests to a Central Public Information Officer or State Public Information Officer due to either the officer not have been appointed, or because the respective Central Assistant Public Information Officer or State Assistant Public Information Officer refused to receive the application for information under the RTI Act.

150 A writ is a formal written order issued by a Court. Any warrant, orders, directions, and so on, issued by the Supreme Court or the High court are called writs.

A writ petition can be filed in the High Court (Article 226) or the Supreme Court (Article 32) of India when any of your fundamental rights are violated. The jurisdiction with the High Courts (Article 226) with regards to a writ petition is wider and extends to constitutional rights too.

151 A Division Bench is a term in judicial system in India in which a case is heard and judged by *at least* 2 judges. However, if the bench during the hearing of any matter feels that the matter needs to be considered by a larger bench, such a matter is referred to a larger bench.

152 Meaning of appellant:

One who appeals a court decision.

is a 'public authority' within the ambit of Section 2(h)[153] of the Right to Information Act, 2005[154] ("RTI Act").

Contention by the Learned Counsel for the Appellant

The Fund contended that PMNRF is not obliged to provide any information to the Respondent as it is not a 'public authority' under the ambit of Section 2(h) of the RTI Act. Second, the information sought by the respondent is exempt under Section 8(1)(j) of the RTI Act as it relates to personal information the disclosure of which has no relationship to any public activity and that it causes unwarranted invasion of the privacy of individuals. With regards to the first ground, the Fund contended that PMNRF is a private fund comprising of voluntary donations made by individuals and institutions and is not a business of the Central Government. Therefore no right to information can be enforced against it. The Fund further contended that PMNRF does not owe its establishment to an order of the government and does not receive any funds or finances by the government, thus, it is not a public authority under Section 2(h) of the RTI Act. It was also contended that while passing the impugned judgment the Learned Single Judge had failed to consider that the appellant finds its genesis in a personal appeal made through a press note dated 24.01.1948 by the then Prime Minister, Pt. Jawahar Lal Nehru[155]. This, according to the Fund, was a personal appeal/

[153] (h) "public authority" means any authority or body or institution of self-government established or constituted,—

(a) by or under the Constitution;
(b) by any other law made by Parliament;
(c) by any other law made by State Legislature;
(d) by notification issued or order made by the appropriate Government, and includes any—
 (i) body owned, controlled or substantially financed;
 (ii) non-Government Organisation substantially financed, directly or indirectly by funds provided by the appropriate Government

[154] Right to Information (RTI) is act of the Parliament of India to provide for setting out the practical regime of the right to information for citizens and replaces the erstwhile Freedom of information Act, 2002. Under the provisions of the Act, any citizen of India may request information from a "public authority" (a body of Government or "instrumentality of State") which is required to reply expeditiously or within thirty days. The Act also requires every public authority to computerise their records for wide dissemination and to proactively certain categories of information so that the citizens need minimum recourse to request for information formally.

[155] Pt. Jawaharlal was a freedom fighter, the first Prime Minister of India and a central figure in Indian politics before and after independence. He emerged as an eminent leader of the Indian independence movement under the tutelage of Mahatma Gandhi and served India as Prime Minister from its establishment as an independent nation in 1947 until his death in 1964.

request/decision and not an order/decision made by the Government of India. The Fund further contended that this appeal/request/decision was not a decision of the Central Government and was thus not made in the name of the Hon'ble Governor General of India, the head of Central Executive as was then required for decisions of Central Government.

The Appellant further contended that no question as regards to the operations of PMNRF are permitted to be made in the parliament in terms of Rule 47(2)(viii)1 & 47(2)(xviii)2 of the Rules of Procedure and Conduct of Business in Rajya Sabha and Rule 41(2)(viii) and 41(2)(xvii)3 of Rules of Procedure and Conduct of Business in Lok Sabha respectively. It was so because PMNRF does not owe its genesis to a decision/function of Central Executive under Sections 7, 8 or 17 of the Government of India Act, 1935 (which is in pari materia[156] to Articles 53[157], 73[158], 77[159] of Constitution of India respectively). The Fund contended

---

[156] Meaning of pari materia:

The phrase used in connection with two laws relating to the same subjectmatter that must be analyzed with each other.

[157] Article 53 in The Constitution Of India 1949

53. Executive power of the Union

(1) The executive power of the Union shall be vested in the President and shall be exercised by him either directly or through officers subordinate to him in accordance with this Constitution

(2) Without prejudice to the generality of the foregoing provision, the supreme command of the Defence Forces of the Union shall be vested in the President and the exercise thereof shall be regulated by law

(3) Nothing in this article shall

(a) be deemed to transfer to the President any functions conferred by any existing law on the Government of any State or other authority; or

(b) prevent Parliament from conferring by law functions on authorities other than the

[158] Article 73 in The Constitution Of India 1949

73. Extent of executive power of the Union

(1) Subject to the provisions of this Constitution, the executive power of the Union shall extend

(a) to the matters with respect to which Parliament has power to make laws; and

(b) to the exercise of such rights, authority and jurisdiction as are exercisable by the government of India by virtue of any treaty on agreement: Provided that the executive power referred to in sub clause (a) shall not, save as expressly provided in this constitution or in any law made by Parliament, extend in any State to matters with respect in which the Legislature of the State has also power to make laws

(2) Until otherwise provided by Parliament, a State and any officer or authority of a State may, notwithstanding anything in this article, continue to exercise in matters with respect to which Parliament has power to make laws for that State such executive power or functions as the State or officer or authority thereof could exercise immediately before the commencement of this Constitution Council of Ministers

[159] Article 77 in The Constitution Of India 1949

that PMNRF is divested of any government character as no guideline can be laid down for disbursement of amount from PMNRF, as it is not a part of any Government Scheme or business of the Central Government and also not subject to audit of Comptroller and Auditor General of India (CAG)[160]. All these points, made PMNRF fall outside the scope of 'public authority' as defined under Section 2(h) of the RTI Act.

The Fund urged that the right to privacy of specific donors is protected under Section 8(1)(j) of the RTI Act. The information sought was third party information and no public purpose would be served in making public the details of amounts given by donors. The Fund also contended that the information held by it creates a fiduciary relationship between the donors and the PMNRF, thereby exempting the information sought under Section 8(1)(e) of the RTI Act. The Appellant/Fund contended that the purpose of RTI Act is to ensure transparency and accountability in the functioning of public authorities and not of a specific donor. It further contended that disclosure without consent of the institutional donor would also be contrary to customary and traditional belief of Gupt Daan followed by many of Indian public.

Saying that the appeal lacks merit, the petitioner/appellant contended that PMNRF is headed by the Prime Minister of India and administered by a Joint Secretary to the Prime Minister as Secretary of the fund. In addition, he is assisted by the officer of the rank of a director. Thus, the fund is completely managed by

---

77. Conduct of business of the Government of India

(1) All executive action of the Government of India shall be expressed to be taken in the name of the President

(2) Orders and other instruments made and executed in the name of the President shall be authenticated in such manner as may be specified in rules to be made by the President, and the validity of an order or instrument which is so authenticated shall nor be called in question on the ground that it is not an order or instrument made or executed by the President

(3) The President shall make rules for the more convenient transaction of the business of the Government of India, and for the allocation among Ministers of the said business

[160] The Comptroller and Auditor General (CAG) of India is an authority, established by Article 148 of the Constitution of India, which audits all receipts and expenditure of the Government of India and the state governments, including those of bodies and authorities substantially financed by the government. The CAG is also the external auditor of Government-owned corporations and conducts supplementary audit of government companies, i.e., any non-banking/ non-insurance company in which Union Government has an equity share of at least 51 per cent or subsidiary companies of existing government companies.

the government officials and comes under the Prime Minister's Office. The disbursement is also for the Citizens of India to provide relied to families of those effected by the natural calamities like flood, cyclones and earthquakes etc, which is an important public function.

The petitioner/Appellant contended that the term 'public authority' as used in Section 2(h) of the RTI Act is wider in scope than the term 'Government of India' as used in the relevant Rajya Sabha and Lok Sabha Rules. It was also contended by the Fund it is not a public authority as no specific expenditure is incurred by the Consolidated Fund of India as there is no separate office of the PMNRF nor any separate staff has been allocated by the government for management of the said fund. This is substantiated by the fact that Prime Minister delegates his powers to operate the fund upon one of the officers of PMO for smooth management of the fund. The said officer takes secretarial assistance from the Funds Division of the PMO, which is established to manage other funds of the PMO. It is significant to note that all concerned in the management of the PMNRF including those providing secretarial assistance work on honorary basis while discharging their primary/ordinary assigned duties.

In the present matter, the Appellant had sought exemption from providing information under Section 8(1)(e) and (j) of the RTI Act. Section 8(1)(e) provides an exemption from furnishing of information if the, "information available to a person is in his fiduciary relationship unless the competent authority is satisfied that larger public interest warrants the disclosure of such information". Whereas Section 8(1)(j) provides that "information which relates to personal information the disclosure of which has not relationship to any public activity or interest, or which would cause unwarranted invasion of the privacy of the individual unless the Central Public Information Officer or the State Public Information Officer or the appellate authority, as the case may be, is satisfied that the larger public interest justifies the disclosure of such information: Provided that the information, which cannot be denied to the Parliament or a State Legislature shall not be denied to any person."

Contention by the Learned Counsel for the Respondent

The respondent contended that there would be no harm in disclosing the details of the donors and the beneficiaries of this fund. It was further argued that the information has been desired in larger public interest to know as to whether uniform rational criteria is followed. The disclosure of the information sought, the respondent contended will reveal whether any personal bias is shown while distribution of funds. As regards the right to privacy, it was argued that disbursement from the fund becomes a matter of 'public record'. Once the Prime Minister exercises his exclusive discretion in deciding beneficiaries, the confidential relationship which may have existed ends. Therefore, once something becomes a matter of 'public record' subsequently, the right of privacy no longer exists.

Question before the High Court

(a) Whether PMNRF is a 'public authority' as defined under Section 2(h) of the RTI Act?

(b) Whether the information sought by the Respondent, insofar as it relates to the amount, name and particular of each recipient, beneficiary and donor, could be placed in public domain?

Prime Minister National Relief Fund

The PMNRF was established pursuant to an appeal made by way of a press note dated 24/01/1948 by the then Prime Minister Jawahar Lal Nehru. He felt the need to have such a fund to make ends meet in the hard times owing to rioting and exodus from Pakistan on occasion of partition of India. In 1973, an application was filed before the Income Tax authority under Section 12A of the Income Tax Act, 1961 to register the fund as a "Trust" for the purposes of Income Tax exemption. The said application of the Fund was allowed by the Commissioner of Income Tax on 18.09.1973 and the fund was registered as a "Trust" bearing No. DLI(C)(T-25)/73-74. Subsequently, the fund was also allocated a separate Permanent Account Number (PAN)[161]. Though, no specific Trust Deed[162] was executed for the said purpose, the fund was, however, deemed

161 Permanent Account Number (PAN) is a code that acts as an identification for individuals, families and corporates (Indian and Foreign as well), especially those who pay Income Tax.

162 Meaning of deed:

a. A signed, sealed, and delivered instrument.

b. An instrument conveying an interest in real property.

to be a "Trust". Finally, in 1985, the Managing Committee of PMNRF entrusted the entire management of the said fund to the Prime Minister who was given the discretion to appoint a secretary of the fund to manage it. Since its inception, the PMNRF has been receiving voluntary donations from individuals and institutions. The funds so received by it are disbursed to provide immediate relief from natural calamities, major accidents, serious ailments, riot, etc. as per discretion and under directions of the Prime Minister.

PMNRF and RTI Act, 2005

The object of the RTI Act is to promote transparency in the working of every 'public authority' and democracy requires an informed citizenry. Transparency of information have been considered vital to the functioning of democracy, to eliminate opacity in functioning and to hold Governments and their instrumentalities accountable to the governed. Therefore, in light of the object of the RTI Act, the term 'public authority' must be subjected to a liberal interpretation.

The genesis of PMNRF reveals that it is a body which is not established by or under the Constitution or by any other law made by the Parliament or by any other law made by State Legislature. Therefore, PMNRF is not a 'public authority' as prescribed under Clauses (a) to (c) of sub-Section (h) of Section 2 of the RTI Act. What needs consideration whether PMNRF can be said to be a 'public authority' as defined under Section 2(h)(d) of the RTI Act. The Fund argues that the Press Note dated 24/01/1948 was an appeal made Pt. Nehru in his personal capacity and that it was not a decision of the Central Government at that time. Therefore, it cannot amount to a body established "by notification issued or order made by the appropriate Government" under Section 2(h)(d) of the RTI Act.

At the inception of PMNRF, a Committee comprising of the following persons was named as its "Manager", namely: -

(a) The Prime Minister.

(b) The President of the Indian National Congress party.

(c) The Deputy Prime Minister.

(d) The Finance Minister.

(e) A representative of Tata Trustees.

(f) A representative of Industry & Commerce to be chosen by FICCI[163].

The fund receives voluntary donations from individuals and institutions. No expenditure is incurred in the management of the PMNRF as it is managed on an honorary basis by all involved. Its secretary holds the position as a nominee of the Prime Minister; he is none other than a Central services officer, i.e. Joint Secretary. The fund is housed in the Prime Minister's office.

Public Authority under RTI Act, 2005

In New Tirupur Area Development Corporation Ltd. v. State of Tamil Nadu[164], where the Madras High Court, at paragraph 29 held that:

"For the purpose of interpreting the term "controlled by Government" as found in Section 2(h)(d)(i) of the RTI Act, the 'public authority' need not be a "State" within the meaning of Article 12[165] of the Constitution. That is taken care of by definition Section 2(h)(a), (b), (c) and portion of d(i). By a notification an appropriate government under Section 2(h)(d) can include any other organisations which are not "State" and even a private organisation. In order to make its intention to cover a wider range of bodies an inclusive definition is found in Section 2(h)(d)(i) and subsection (ii) covers Non-governmental organisations (NGO) with substantive funding by the Government. The only requirement for a private body or an NGO to be covered by the term 'public authority' is that either it must be a body controlled or substantially financed by the Government. Therefore, the tests applied to bring an organisation within the definition of Article 12 are unnecessary to interpret Section 2(h)(d)(i) and (ii) of the RTI Act. The tests that are to be applied must keep in mind the preamble and the object and reasons behind the RTI Act."

---

163 The Federation of Indian Chambers of Commerce and Industry (FICCI) is an association of business organisations in India. Established in 1927, on the advice of Mahatma Gandhi by GD Birla and Purushottam Das Thakurdas, it is the largest, oldest and the apex business organisation in India.

164 AIR 2010 Mad. 176

165 Article 12 in The Constitution Of India 1949

12. Definition In this part, unless the context otherwise requires, the State includes the Government and Parliament of India and the Government and the Legislature of each of the States and all local or other authorities within the territory of India or under the control of the Government of India

The RTI Act, therefore, deals with bodies which are owned, controlled or substantially financed, directly or indirectly, by funds provided by the appropriate Government and also non-government organisations substantially financed, directly or indirectly, by funds provided by the appropriate Government, in the event of which they may fall within the definition of Section 2(h)(d)(i) or (ii) respectively. A body, institution or an organisation, which is neither "State" within the meaning of Article 12 of the Constitution or instrumentalities, may still answer the definition of public authority under Section 2(h)(d)(i) or (ii).

Decision by High Court

Court held that there exists governmental control in the management of PMNRF. Therefore, the conditions in Clause (i) of Section 2(h)(d) are satisfied. Accordingly, PMNRF is held to be a 'public authority' within the scope of RTI Act. Being a public body entrusted with the task of providing immediate relief from natural calamities, major accidents, serious ailments, riot, etc, PMNRF should have disclosed the entire information about its transactions and fulfil its obligations under Section 4 of the RTI Act.

In the present matter, the Fund does not offer any service to the donors or the beneficiaries. Furthermore, the relationship between PMNRF and the donors/ beneficiaries does not take colour of a 'fiduciary relationship'[166]. The donors do not repose trust in PMNRF in conducting their business and the same holds true for the beneficiaries. On the contrary, the act of donation is an act of charity which is not sufficient to establish a fiduciary relationship. Therefore, the question of there existing a fiduciary relationship does not arise. Consequently, the defence

166 The Supreme Court in CBSE v. Aditya Bandopadhyay, MANU/SC/0932/2011 : (2011) 8 SCC 497 at paragraph 39 defined a 'fiduciary relationship' in the following words:-

"The term "fiduciary" refers to a person having a duty to act for the benefit of another, showing good faith and candour, where such other person reposes trust and special confidence in the person owing or discharging the duty. The term "fiduciary relationship" is used to describe a situation or transaction where one person (beneficiary) places complete confidence in another person (fiduciary) in regard to his affairs, business or transactions). The term also refers to a person who holds a thing in trust for another (beneficiary). The fiduciary is expected to act in confidence and for the benefit and advantage of the beneficiary, and use good faith and fairness in dealing with the beneficiary or the things belonging to the beneficiary. If the beneficiary has entrusted anything to the fiduciary, to hold the thing in trust or to execute certain acts in regard to or with reference to the entrusted thing, the fiduciary has to act in confidence and is expected not to disclose the thing or information to any third party."

of exemption sought by the Appellant under Section 8(1)(e) of the RTI Act is not sustainable.

As far as the exception in Section 8(1)(j) of the RTI Act goes, the court was of the opinion that citizens have a right to know about the management of a fund which is used for benign purposes, inter alia, like providing relief in times of natural disasters. A disclosure of such information will ensure that the voluntary donations made by the citizen body is not appropriated by any government official. In this regard, the disclosure of the information sought by the petitioner indeed serves a public purpose. Furthermore, the Court holds that disclosure of such information will not cause any unwarranted invasion of privacy of an individual. This is because once the fund is already disbursed to a beneficiary, the disbursement becomes a matter of 'public record'. Once the Prime Minister exercises his or her exclusive right to determine the beneficiaries or class of beneficiaries, the confidential relationship which may have existed comes to an end. Therefore, once something becomes a matter of 'public record', the right of privacy ceases to exist. Additionally, any violation of an individual's Right to Privacy can be contested by the concerned Third Party under the procedure prescribed under Section 11[167] of the RTI Act.

---

[167] Section 11 in The Right To Information Act, 2005

11. Third party information.—

(1) Where a Central Public Information Officer or the State Public Information Officer, as the case may be, intends to disclose any information or record, or part thereof on a request made under this Act, which relates to or has been supplied by a third party and has been treated as confidential by that third party, the Central Public Information Officer or State Public Information Officer, as the case may be, shall, within five days from the receipt of the request, give a written notice to such third party of the request and of the fact that the Central Public Information Officer or State Public Information Officer, as the case may be, intends to disclose the information or record, or part thereof, and invite the third party to make a submission in writing or orally, regarding whether the information should be disclosed, and such submission of the third party shall be kept in view while taking a decision about disclosure of information: Provided that except in the case of trade or commercial secrets protected by law, disclosure may be allowed if the public interest in disclosure outweighs in importance any possible harm or injury to the interests of such third party.

(2) Where a notice is served by the Central Public Information Officer or State Public Information Officer, as the case may be, under sub-section (1) to a third party in respect of any information or record or part thereof, the third party shall, within ten days from the date of receipt of such notice, be given the opportunity to make representation against the proposed disclosure.

(3) Notwithstanding anything contained in section 7, the Central Public Information Officer or State Public Information Officer, as the case may be, shall, within forty days after receipt of the request under section 6, if the third party has been given an opportunity to make

Court holds that whilst PMNRF does not receive funding from the Central or State Governments, yet, it is administered in the office of the Prime Minister in accordance with the policy which exists in the public domain. This is on the strength of the prestige lent by the Prime Minister, his office and the confidence that is generated that such amounts would be used for funds in the exercise of discretion for many contingencies that the donor may visualize, (or not visualize, but is confident would reach deserving beneficiaries or causes). It has to be emphasized that the appeal to generosity (in seeking donation) inherent through the nature of the fund is the confidence and trust that millions of donors repose in the Prime Minister and the office of the prime minister. All those seconded to the office of the fund are public servants; they have no personal stake or interest. Such a fund cannot but be called as a public fund. The Prime Minister has no personal stake or interest in the receipt or disbursement. The disbursement of amounts is towards deserving and noble causes, especially in unforeseen contingencies and calamities. Donations to the fund come from all kinds of sources including, sometimes, State Undertakings, both Central and State. Many such donors may even publicise about their donations in the media.

As regards the fund is not subject to audit by the CAG, court notices that Section 22[168] of the RTI Act overrides all other laws; the effect is that any impediment or bar- in any law in force- to the supply of information is overborne and has to be disregarded. Court held that disclosure of the information sought by the applicant petitioner was reasonable. The appeal was without merit and therefore, dismissed.

---

representation under sub-section (2), make a decision as to whether or not to disclose the information or record or part thereof and give in writing the notice of his decision to the third party.

(4) A notice given under sub-section (3) shall include a statement that the third party to whom the notice is given is entitled to prefer an appeal under section 19 against the decision.

[168] Section 22 in The Right To Information Act, 2005

22. Act to have overriding effect.—The provisions of this Act shall have effect notwithstanding anything inconsistent therewith contained in the Official Secrets Act, 1923 (19 of 1923), and any other law for the time being in force or in any instrument having effect by virtue of any law other than this Act.

MR. JUSTICE SUNIL GAUR (Dissenting)

PMNRF (Trust) is neither constituted by the Parliament nor by the Government and it is not managed by Government functionaries in their official capacity, but by multiple delegates. Contributions made to appellant-Trust are exempted under the Income Tax Act, 1961, but that by itself would not justify the conclusion that it is a "Public Authority". It is relevant to note that contributions flowing out of budgetary sources of Government or from the balance sheets of the public sector undertakings are not accepted. What persuades DISSENTING Judge to hold that appellant-Trust is not a "Public Authority" under the RTI Act is that Rule 47 of the Rules of Procedure and Conduct of Business in Rajya Sabha and Rule 41 of the Rules of Procedure and Conduct of Business in Lok Sabha prohibit questioning of Ministers in Parliament regarding matters which are not primarily the concern of the Government.

Afore-referred Rule 47 of the Rules of Procedure and Conduct of Business in Rajya Sabha reads as under:-

"47. Conditions of Admissibility of Questions

(1) Subject to the provisions of sub-rule (2) of this rule, a question may be asked for the purpose of obtaining information on a matter of public importance within the special cognizance of the Minister to whom it is addressed.

(2) The right to ask a question is governed by the following conditions:

(i) it shall be pointed, specific and confined to one issue only;

(ii) it shall not bring in any name or statement not strictly necessary to make the question intelligible;

(iii) if it contains a statement the member shall make himself responsible for the accuracy of the statement;

(iv) it shall not contain arguments, inferences, ironical expressions, imputations, epithets or defamatory statements;

(v) it shall not ask for an expression of opinion or the solution of an abstract legal question or of a hypothetical proposition;

(vi) it shall not ask as to the character or conduct of any person except in his official or public capacity;

(vii) it shall not exceed 100 words;

(viii) it shall not relate to a matter which is not primarily the concern of the Government of India;

(ix) it shall not ordinarily ask for information on matters which are under the consideration of a Parliamentary Committee;

(x) it shall not ask about proceedings in a Parliamentary Committee which have not been placed before the Council by a report from that Committee;

(xi) it shall not reflect on the character or conduct of any person whose conduct can only be challenged on a substantive motion;

(xii) it shall not make or imply a charge of a personal character;

(xiii) it shall not raise questions of policy too large to be dealt within the limits of an answer to a question;

(xiv) it shall not repeat in substance questions already answered or to which an answer has been refused;

(xv) it shall not ask for information on trivial matters;

(xvi) it shall not ordinarily seek information on matters of past history;

(xvii) it shall not require information set forth in accessible documents or in ordinary works of reference;

(xviii) it shall not raise matters under the control of bodies or persons not primarily responsible to the Government of India;

(xix) it shall not ask for information on a matter which is under adjudication by a court of law having jurisdiction in any part of India;

(xx) it shall not relate to a matter with which a Minister is not officially connected;

(xxi) it shall not refer discourteously to a friendly foreign country;

(xxii) it shall not seek information about matters which are in their nature secret."

(underlined to supply emphasis)

Afore-referred Rule 41 of the Rules of Procedure and Conduct of Business in Lok Sabha is as under:-

"41. Admissibility of Questions:

(1) Subject to the provisions of sub-rule (2), a question may be asked for the purpose of obtaining information on a matter of public importance within the special cognizance of the Minister to whom it is addressed.

(2) The right to ask a question is governed by the following conditions, namely:—

(i) it shall be clearly and precisely expressed and shall not be too general incapable of any specific answer or in the nature of a leading question;

(ii) it shall not bring in any name or statement not strictly necessary to make the question intelligible;

(iii) if it contains a statement the member shall make oneself responsible for the accuracy of the statement;

(iv) it shall not contain arguments, inferences, ironical expressions, imputations, epithets or defamatory statements;

(v) it shall not ask for an expression of opinion or the solution of an abstract legal question or of a hypothetical proposition;

(vi) it shall not ask as to the character or conduct of any person except in that person's official or public capacity;

(vii) it shall not ordinarily exceed 150 words;

(viii) it shall not relate to a matter which is not primarily the concern of the Government of India;

(ix) it shall not ask about proceedings in the Committee which have not been placed before the House by a report from the Committee.

(x) it shall not reflect on the character or conduct of any person whose conduct can only be challenged on a substantive motion;

(xi) it shall not make or imply a charge of a personal character;

(xii) it shall not raise questions of policy too large to be dealt with within the limits of an answer to a question;

(xiii) it shall not repeat in substance questions already answered or to which an answer has been refused;

(xiv) it shall not ask for information on trivial matters;

(xv) it shall not ordinarily ask for information on matters of past history;

(xvi) it shall not ask for information set forth in accessible documents or in ordinary works of reference;

(xvii) it shall not raise matters under the control of bodies or persons not primarily responsible to the Government of India;

(xviii) it shall not ask for information on matter which is under adjudication by a court of law having jurisdiction in any part of India;

(xix) it shall not relate to a matter with which a Minister is not officially concerned;

(xx) it shall not refer discourteously to a friendly foreign country;

(xxi) it shall not seek information about matters which are in their nature secret, such as composition of Cabinet Committees, Cabinet discussions, or advice given to the President in relation to any matter in respect of which there is a constitutional, statutory or conventional obligation not to disclose information;

(xxii) it shall not ordinarily ask for information on matters which are under consideration of a Parliamentary Committee; and

(xxiii) it shall not ordinarily ask about matters pending before any statutory tribunal or statutory authority performing any judicial or quasi-judicial functions or any commission or court of enquiry appointed to enquire into, or investigate, any matter but may refer to matters

> concerned with procedure or subject or stage of enquiry, if it is not likely to prejudice the consideration of the matter by the tribunal or commission or court of enquiry."

Decision by Dissenting Judge

The cause for which appellant-Trust was created and exists is purely charitable and neither the funds of this Trust are used for any Government projects nor is this Trust governed by any of the Government policies. So, how can this Trust be labelled as 'Public Authority'. Thus, court was of the considered view that appellant-Trust does not owe its genesis to a decision or function of Appropriate Government and Funds of appellant-Trust do not have any government character as no guidelines can be laid down for disbursement of the amount from the Funds of appellant-Trust and the contributions made to appellant-Trust enjoy exemption under Income-Tax Act like other private Trusts.

Relevantly, PMNRF cannot be deemed to be 'Public Authority' on the premise that managers of PMNRF i.e. Prime Minister, Deputy Prime Minister, Finance Ministry do not act in personal capacity. It is so said because these State Functionaries manage the PMNRF in their ex-officio capacity. If PMNRF is not non-governmental organization, then what is it? Prime Minister or any of the Managers of PMNRF does not have a legal title or basis to claim ownership of PMNRF. In fact, PMNRF is a Trust which is neither owned, controlled or financed by the Government.

Since PMNRF is not Public Authority' under the RTI Act, therefore, second issue regarding information sought being within the public domain does not survive for consideration.

Dissenting Judge hold that appellant-PMNRF is not a "Public Authority" within the definition of Section 2(h) of RTI Act and is thus, beyond its purview.

Chapter - 22

UNIFORM POLICY AND LAW ON THE SPORTS BODIES[169]

Facts in Nutshell

The Complainant sought information on following points:

(1) whether Honourable Prime Minister/PMO is aware of dissatisfaction expressed by national hockey-players winning Asian Champions Trophy on just Rs. 25,000 award-money announced by Hockey India?

(2) Is Honourable Prime Minister/PMO aware that Indian cricketers winning World Cup Final were given Rs. 2-crore award money by Board for Control of Cricket in India (BCCI) after cricketers felt dissatisfied on earlier announcement of Rs. One crore, that too in addition to bumper-awards by state-governments and others?

(3) Complete and detailed information on action taken to remove such vast disparity in award-money for national players of cricket and others;

(4) Complete and detailed information on award-money paid to sports persons by Union government in last three years;

(5) List of sports bodies (with addresses and names of office-beaters) registered with Union government;

(6) Is it true that irregularities have been reported about some sports-bodices?

(7) If yes, steps taken to action taken on such irregularities reported against sports bodies, and also to check any such probable irregularities in future.

---

[169] Appellants: Subhash Chandra Agrawal
Vs.
Respondent: PIO, Department of Sports
Hon'ble Judges/Coram:
M. Sridhar Acharyulu, Central Information Commissioner
Subhash Chandra Agrawal vs. PIO, Department of Sports (16.06.2017 - CIC), MANU/CI/0399/2017

The RTI application was made to the CPIO of PMO, who vide letter dated 5-10-2011, transferred to the Ministry of Youth Affairs and Sports. However, no response whatsoever appears to have been given to the appellant by the said Ministry. He filed complaint before Central Information Commission (CIC).

Decision by CIC

In this complaint the crux of the issue was why the BCCI and its cricket administration was not made accountable. The complainant demanded the action on bringing the BCCI under RTI Act, as suggested by the Lodha Committee and Supreme Court in recent Bihar Cricket Association case. The CPIO Mr. Patro said that Government's policy is to make every National Sports Federation a public authority under RTI Act and the BCCI is clearly declared as the National Sports Federation. Then the appellant asked why BCCI is not implementing the RTI and disclosing the information as per Section 4(1)(b) of RTI Act. He also contended that there is a huge disparity in giving reward money to the sportsman who won medals at Olympics and other prestigious international tournaments, and also disparity between Cricket and other sports. He said there is a huge competition between various governments headed by different political parties announcing reward money. If one government gives Rs. 10 lakh, the other announces Rs. 1 Crore. When cricketers winning world cup expressed dissatisfaction, their reward money was doubled to Rs. 2 Crore. The political executive government is trying to give more to gain publicity of sports-encouraging raj without any concern for public money. He also asked why the BCCI is still using the logo designed by British Raj in 1928 which resembles 90 per cent the symbol of star of India given by British Raj to his loyal princes, as mentioned in the order of CIC in CIC/MOYAS/A/2017/116693 on 9.6.2017? Why the Government of India does not change it to truly Indian Symbol with either tricolor or four lions or Ashoka's Dharm Chakra or any other logo decided by the Government of India?

Justice Mudgal Committee which was probing the IPL affairs in 2014 has highlighted in its report the need for enactment of a special legislation to declare all forms of manipulations of sports, corruption and malpractices a criminal offence. The CPIO of the Ministry of Youth and Sports Affairs represented that draft legislation was revised under the title 'The Prevention of Sports Fraud Bill, 2015' aiming at prevention of match fixing, spot fixing, manipulation of sports results, disclosure of insider information etc. The PMO has advised the department to re-examine whether sports frauds needs a standalone Act or it can be dealt with by making necessary provisions in the Indian Penal Code and to seek expert legal opinion on this. Accordingly the Ministry of Law was consulted on this issue. Beyond this the progress on this aspect is not known.

Regarding the request about National Sports Federations, Mr. Patro explained that every year the Ministry recognizes the NSFs and the list of recognized National Sports Federations all over country is available on the website of the Ministry. The list included NSFs for 47 sports but nothing about NSF on the Cricket. Because of this absence, a citizen is not in a position to know which body is the NSF for cricket and whom to ask about cricketing irregularities.

Meanwhile, it was brought to the notice of the Commission that the Minister of Youth Affairs and Sports answered an unstarred question No. 2097 raised by four MPs on 27.03.2012 in Loksabha on this issue. The question was:

(a) Whether the Government proposes to bring various sports associations/ federations including the Board of Control for Cricket in India (BCCI) under the ambit of the Right to Information Act, 2005 so as to ensure transparency in their functioning;

(b) if so, the details thereof and the response of these federations and BCCI thereon;

(c) the progress made by the Government so far in this regard;

(d) whether the BCCI gets various concessions in income tax, custom duty etc. and land at concessional rates for stadia; and

(e) if so, the details thereof during the last three years and the current year?

The answer given by the then Minister for Youth Affairs and Sports was:

(a) to (c) The need for bringing National Sports Federations (NSFs) including BCCI under ambit of Right to Information act, (RTI) 2005 has been voiced from to time to time. Accordingly Government in April, 2010 declared all the NSFs receiving grant of Rs. 10.00 lakhs or more as Public Authority under Section

2(h) of the RTI, 2005. There are major court rulings for treating the National Sports Federation as a public authorities, especially in view of the state-like function discharged by them such as selection of the national team and control and regulation of sports in the country, which also make them amenable to the writ jurisdiction of High Courts under Article 226 of the Constitution of India. Notwithstanding the above, the Government has proposed to bring all the National Sports Federations including BCCI under the RTI Act in the proposed Draft National Sports Development Bill with provision of exclusion clause protecting personal/confidential information relating to athletes.

(d) & (e) In so far as BCCI, in particular, is concerned, Government of India has been treating BCCI as a National Sports Federation and approving the proposal of BCCI for holding the events in India and participation in International events abroad. The Central Government does not extend any direct financial assistance to BCCI. But the Central Government has been granting concessions in Income tax, customs duty, etc. to BCCI. The State Governments also have provided land in many places to the Cricket Associations.

Decision by CIC

Following issues are raised:

(a) Why the Indian Cricket team even now carrying the logo of BCCI instead of sporting the Union of India symbol? Why the BCCI is still using the logo designed by British Raj in 1928 which resembles 90 per cent the symbol of star of India given by British Raj to his loyal princes, as mentioned in the order of CIC in CIC/MOYAS/A/2017/116693 on 9.6.2017? Why the Government of India does not change it to truly Indian Symbol with either tricolor or four lions or Ashoka's Dharm Chakra or any other logo decided by the Government of India?

(b) Why the Government of India, PMO or the MoYAS not taken any measures to implement its declaration that the BCCI as public authority under RTI Act, as per its answer to Loksabha referred above?

(c) Why are not they bringing a uniform policy for rewarding winning international sports persons to prevent unhealthy competition for publicity among Governments?

(d) Why the sports frauds like match fixing and betting are not prohibited and action was not being taken effectively?

(e) What is the status of action on the Bill to prevent sports frauds?

The complainant requested the Commission to consider this as his appeal and sought answers to the above questions. The Commission directs the PMO, Ministry of Law and the Ministry of Youth Affairs and Sports to explain their stand on the above questions, which are supposed to have been answered as part of their obligation under Section 4(1)(b) of RTI Act, more importantly it has to answer the Supreme Court, Lodha Committee and the appellant why RTI is not being implemented by BCCI, if it is recognized as National Sports Federation, within 30 days from the date of receipt of this order.

As suggested by the complainant, the Commission recommended that the Government of India may consider shifting the subject of sports from States List in the Constitution of India to the Concurrent List to facilitate a uniform policy and law on the sports bodies, National Sports Federations including BCCI to be accountable, answerable as public authorities under RTI Act.

Chapter - 23

RIGHT TO SPEECH AND PUBLISH DOES NOT CARRY WITH IT AN UNRESTRICTED RIGHT TO GATHER INFORMATION[170]

Facts in Nutshell

Shri. C. Ramesh (hereinafter referred to as the "appellant") submitted an appeal on 30.1.06 before Central Information Commission (CIC) seeking a direction from Commission to direct the CPIO to disclose the contents of the correspondence exchanged between the former President Late Shri K.R. Narayanan and the former Prime Minister Shri A.B. Vajpayee between the period from 28.2.02 and 15.3.02.. The appeal was received on 6.2.06. The comments from the CPIO were received on 10.5.06. Initially the appeal was heard on 24.5.06 by a Bench consisting of Shri M.M. Ansari acting as the Principal Information Commissioner and Shri A. Tiwari acting as the Companion Commissioner. The Bench took into account the significance of the issues involved and decided to refer it to the Full Bench. The matter was discussed in the Full Bench on 27th June 2006 and it was decided to re-hear the matter. In view of the fact that the appellant is a resident of Vellore it was decided to arrange the hearing through video conferencing. The matter was finally heard on 21.7.06.

The appellant submitted an application under the Right to Information Act (hereinafter referred to as "Act") on 7.11.05, seeking copies of all documents/ correspondence exchanged between the former President Late Shri K.R. Narayanan and the former Prime Minister Shri. A.B. Vajpayee between the period

---

[170] Appellants: C. Ramesh
Vs.
Respondent: Ministry of Personnel, Public Grievances and Pensions
Hon'ble Judges/Coram:
Wajahat Habibullah, C.I.C., Padma Balasubramaniam, M.M. Ansari and O.P. Kejariwal, I.Cs.
C. Ramesh vs. Ministry of Personnel, Public Grievances and Pensions (08.08.2006 - CIC), MANU/CI/0429/2006

from 28.2.02 and 15.3.02. The application was considered by Ms. Harjot Kaur, Deputy Secretary and CPIO of the Department of Personnel and Training, Ministry of Personnel, Public Grievances and Pensions (hereinafter referred to as the CPIO).

Decision by CPIO

The disclosure of the information was denied by the CPIO on the following grounds:

(i) That Justice Nanavati/ Justice Shah Commission of Enquiry also asked for the correspondence between the President, late Shri K. R. Narayanan and the former Prime Minister on Gujarat riots and the Government of India claimed privilege under Section 123 and 124 of the Indian Evidence Act, 1872 and Article 74(2) read with Article 78 and Article 361 of the Constitution.

(ii) That in terms of Section 8(1)(a) of the Right to Information Act, 2005, the disclosure of the requested information would prejudicially affect the sovereignty and integrity of India, the security, strategic, scientific or economic interests of the State.

Aggrieved by the order of the CPIO, the appellant preferred an appeal on 3.12.05 before Sri Brahm Dutt, Additional Secretary (S & V), Department of Personnel & Training) the designated appellate authority under the Right to Information Act. In his appeal petition, the appellant contended:

(i) That the Right to Information Act has an over-riding effect over the Indian Evidence Act and as such the requisite information cannot be denied to him in view of the clear provisions of Section 22 of the said Act.

(ii) The information/correspondence between the President and the Prime Minister cannot be denied under the Right to Information Act as such information/ correspondence is not covered under the exemptions provided for under Section 8 of the Act.

(iii) The correspondence between the former Prime Minister and the former President is most important to the people of the country and they have a right to know as to how their interests were protected by the

Government during the Gujarat riots.

(iv) Article 74(2), 78 and 361 nowhere states that the information/correspondence between the President and the Prime Minister should not be disclosed.

(v) That the former President himself at one point of time revealed to the press the brief of what he wrote to the Prime Minister. As such, it cannot be argued that the disclosure of full content of the correspondence will in any way prejudicially affect the sovereignty and integrity of India, the security, strategic, scientific, economic interests of the State.

(vi) The CPIO should have applied Section 10 of the Act and should have at least provided that part of the information, which can reasonably be severed from any part that, contains prejudicial information.

Decision by Appellate Authority

The Appellate Authority assertively averred that the relationship between the Right to Information Act and the Constitution of India would be just the opposite. The correspondence in question would fall within the purview of Article 74(2), 78 and 361 of the Constitution and would be entitled to be treated as privileged communication. The Appellate Authority also concluded that publication of such information or furnishing of such information under the Right to Information Act would cause damage to the public interest and accordingly he upheld the order of the CPIO denying the information to the appellant.

Decision by CIC

The first question that needs to be determined in this case is as to whether the provisions of the Indian Evidence Act stands over-ridden by the Right to Information Act, 2005? In this connection it is pertinent to refer to provisions of Section 22 of the Act, which reads as under:

The provisions of this Act shall have effect notwithstanding anything inconsistent therewith contained in the Official Secrets Act, 1923, and any other law for the time being in force or in any instrument having effect by virtue of any law other than this Act.

A plain reading of Section 22 makes it clear that it not only over-rides the Official Secrets Act, but also all other laws and that ipso facto include the Indian Evidence Act. In view of this no public authority can claim to deny any information on the ground that it happens to be a "privileged" one under the Indian Evidence Act. Section 3 of the Right to Information Act confers a right on all citizens to obtain information and it casts an obligation on all public authorities to provide the information so demanded. The right thus conferred is only subject to the other provisions of the Act and to no other law.

The second question that needs to be determined is as to whether the Government or for that matter a public authority can deny or refuse to give an information to a citizen on the ground that the information so demanded is covered by Article 74 (2), 78 or Article 361 of the Constitution of India and as such it cannot be furnished. In this case the CPIO and the Appellate Authority have argued that the Right to Information Act does not and cannot override the Constitutional provisions. On the other hand the Appellant has submitted that there is no repugnancy between the Right to Information conferred by the Act and the constitutional provisions taken recourse to by the CPIO and by the Appellate Authority for denying the requested information. The Appellant has submitted that none of these Articles anywhere state that the information/correspondence between the President and the Prime Minister should not be disclosed. As observed by the Hon'ble Apex Court in Bommai's case, Article 361 is the manifestation of the theory prevalent in English law that 'King can do no wrong' and, for that reason, his actions are beyond the process of the court. Any and every action taken by the President is really the action of his ministers and subordinates. It is they, who have to answer for, defend and justify any and every action taken by them in the name of the President, if such action is questioned in a Court of law. The President cannot be called upon to answer for or justify the action. It is for the Council of Ministers to do so. Where the President acts through his subordinates, it is for the subordinate to defend the action.

Before deciding the issue of applicability of Article 74(2) to the instant case, it is pertinent to refer again to the provisions of Article 74(2), which clearly stipulates that the court shall not inquire into whether any advice was at all tendered and even if there was any such advice, the court shall not inquire as to what advice was tendered. In this connection the following observations of Justice Sawant and Justice Kuldip Singh in S. R. Bommai v. Union of India (MANU/SC/0444/1994 : AIR 1994 SC 1918) regarding the scope and ambit of Article 74(2) are quite relevant:

The object of Article 74(2) was not to exclude any material or documents from the scrutiny of the Courts but to provide that an order issued by or in the name of the President could not be questioned on the ground that it was either contrary to the advice tendered by the Ministers or was issued without obtaining any advice from the Ministers. Its object was only to make the question whether the President had followed the advice of the Ministers or acted contrary thereto, non-justiciable.

Justice Ahmadi also agreed that Article 74(2) is no bar to the production of all the material on which the ministerial advice was based. This issue has been further clarified in a recent case by the Hon'ble Supreme Court (Rameshwar Prasad and Ors.vs. Union of India and Anr.MANU/SC/0399/2006 : AIR2006SC980):

A plain reading of Article 74(2) stating that the question whether any, and if so what, advice was tendered by Ministers to the President shall not be inquired into in any Court, may seem to convey that the Court is debarred from inquiring into such advice but Bommai has held that Article 74(2) is not a bar against scrutiny of the material.

In S.P Gupta's case[171] the question arose as to whether the views expressed by the Chief Justice of the High Court and the Chief Justice of India on consultation form part of the advice. In this case the two Chief Justices were consulted on "full and identical facts" and their views were obtained and it is after considering those views that the Council of Ministers tendered its advice to the President. The views expressed by the two Chief Justices preceded the formation of the advice. The Hon'ble Supreme Court clearly held that merely because their views are referred to in the advice that is ultimately tendered by the Council of Ministers, they do not necessarily become part of the advice. The Court further ruled that what is protected against disclosure under Clause (2) of

---

[171] S.P. Gupta v. Union of India, 1981 SCC Supp. 87

Article 74 is only the advice tendered by the Council of Ministers. The reasons that have weighed with the Council of Ministers in giving the advice would certainly form part of the advice. But the material on which the reasoning of the Council of Ministers is based and advice given cannot be said to form part of the advice. The Hon'ble Apex Court illustrating the point with the example of a judgment clearly laid down the law as follows:

The judgment would undoubtedly be based on the evidence led before the Court and it would refer to such evidence and discuss it but on that account can it be said that the evidence forms part of the judgment? The judgment would consist only of the decision and the reasons in support of it and the evidence on which the reasoning and the decision are based would not be part of the judgment. Similarly the material on which the advice tendered by the Council of Ministers is based cannot be said to be part of the advice and the correspondence exchanged between the Law Minister, the Chief Justice of Delhi and the Chief Justice of India which constituted the material forming the basis of the decision of the Central Government must accordingly be held to be outside the exclusionary rule enacted in Clause (2) of Article 74.

The CPIO cannot deny information sought under the Right to Information Act by taking recourse to either the Law of Evidence or Article 74(2), of the Constitution of India. It is legally permissible for the public authority to deny the information on grounds of national security under Section 8(1)(a). However, a public authority may still allow access to such information if public interest in disclosure outweighs the harm to the protected interests. Prima facie the correspondence involves a sensitive matter of public interest. The sensitivity of the matter and involvement of a larger public interest has also been admitted by all concerned including the appellant.

The Commission after careful consideration has, therefore, decided to call for the correspondence in question and it will examine as to whether its disclosure will serve or harm the public interest. After examining the documents the Commission will first consider whether it would be in public interest to order disclosure or not, and only then it will issue appropriate directions to the public authority.

Chapter - 24

WHETHER THERE IS ANY IMMUNITY TO THE REPORT OF HON. LT. GOVERNOR SUBMITTED TO UNION GOVERNMENT[172]

Facts in Nutshell

Appellant filed RTI application for certified copies of the request/ recommendation to dissolve the Delhi Legislative Assembly sent by Hon. Lt. Governor to the Union Government or the President and certified copy of all the documents/records, based on which decision to dissolve the Delhi Legislative Assembly was taken. The CPIO denied on 25.11.2014 claiming exemption under section 8(1)(c) of the RTI Act. His first appeal was disposed on 13.01.2015 without further action.

Two Main Questions Before the CIC are

a) whether there is any immunity to the report of Hon. Lt. Governor submitted to Union government under Constitution? b) Whether information sought will cause breach of privilege of Parliament or State Legislature, which is barred by Section 8(1)(c)?

Information

Whether the information sought by appellant was 'information'? The definition of information under Section 2(f) of the RTI Act is:

"information" means any material in any form, including records, documents,

---

[172] Appellants: Aditya Jain

Vs.

Respondent: Lieutenant Governor Secretariat

Hon'ble Judges/Coram:

M. Sridhar Acharyulu, Information Commissioner

Aditya Jain vs. Lieutenant Governor Secretariat (25.05.2016 - CIC), MANU/CI/0102/2016

memos, e-mails, opinions, advices, press releases, circulars, orders, logbooks, contracts, reports, papers, samples, models, data material held in any electronic form and information relating to any private body which can be accessed by a public authority under any other law for the time being in force;

Appellant sought the report sent by the LG Office under Article 239AB of the Constitution and other related papers. The Commission holds that the report of the LG, etc., is the "information" under Section-2(f) of RTI Act. Subject to Section-8, every citizen has right to information about report and that the report is held by the Office of LG and the Ministry of Home Affairs.

Constitutional Position of Governor and Lt Governor

The Constitution has provided protection to advice given by President & Governor from inquiry in court, under Article 74(2) & Art 163(3) respectively, Article 163(3) Constitution says:

The question whether any, and if so what, advice was tendered by Ministers to the Governor shall not be inquired into in any court.

This provision protects the advice given by the Council of Ministers, immunity from being probed into, but there is no prohibition against the disclosure. Following articles provided administration of Delhi Union Territory. Article 239(1) says:

Save as otherwise provided by Parliament by law, every Union territory shall be administered by the President acting, to such extent as he thinks fit, through an administrator to be appointed by him with such designation as he may specify. (2) Notwithstanding anything contained in Part VI, the President may appoint the Governor of a State as the administrator of an adjoining Union territory, and where a Governor is so appointed, he shall exercise his functions as such administrator independently of his Council of Ministers.

Office of Hon. Lt Governor

Article 239 of the Constitution provides that every Union Territory shall be administered by the President, to such extent as he thinks fit, through an administrator to be appointed by him with such designation as he may specify.

Articles 239A, 239AA 239AB and 239B provide for local legislature or Council of Ministers in those Union Territories and deal with several aspects of administration in relation to the National Capital Territory, the Lieutenant Governor and Legislative Assembly. The office of LG, being a constitutional authority, should be a 'public authority'. All the privileges and immunities that are associated with high office of LG are provided and protected under RTI Act through various exceptions.

Article 239AA Provides for Lt Governor, it Says

Article 239AA(1) As from the date of commencement of the Constitution (Sixty-ninth Amendment) Act, 1991, the Union territory of Delhi shall be called the National Capital Territory of Delhi (hereafter in this Part referred to as the National Capital Territory) and the administrator thereof appointed under Article 239 shall be designated as the Lieutenant Governor.

Article 239AA(4) There shall be a Council of Ministers consisting of not more than ten per cent of the total number of members in the Legislative Assembly, with the Chief Minister at the head to aid and advise the Lieutenant Governor in the exercise of his functions in relation to matters with respect to which the Legislative Assembly has power to make laws, except in so far as he is, by or under any law, required to act in his discretion.....

Immunity available only to advice tendered to Governor or President by the Council of Ministers and that is not available to the Lt Governor of New Delhi UT.

Lt. Governor as Public Authority under RTI

The Office of Governor is a Public authority had been held to be public authority by the Hon'ble High Court of Bombay at Goa in Public Information Officer, Joint Secretary to the Governor Vs Manoj Parrikar [Writ Petition No. 478 OF 2008].

Undoubtedly, the post of President and that of the Governor is created by the Constitution......... The President and the Governor owe their existence to the Constitution. Being so, the President and the Governor are clearly covered by clause (h) of the definition of the "public authority" (15).

....the mere fact that the President and the Governor are authorities mentioned in sub-clauses (iv) of section 2(e) of the RTI Act, would not exclude them from the definition of "public authority".

Bombay High Court fortified their view by a decision of the Special Bench (of Three Judges) of Delhi High Court, rendered in Secretary General, Supreme Court of India vs. Subhash Chandra Agarwal, (L.P.A. No. 501/2009 decided on 12th January, 2010). In that case, the Chief Justice of India (who is the "competent authority" under section 2(e)(ii) of the RTI Act) was also held to be the "public authority". (Para 17)

Immunity from Probing into Advise of the Governor

The Office of Hon. Lt Governor is contending that the information sought is protected under Article 163 (3) of the Constitution, which says:

The question whether any, and if so what advice was tendered by Ministers to the Governor shall not be inquired into in any court.

Under this Article, the Governor has independent discretionary power and hence his decision could not be questioned. Does it mean that the advice tendered by the Council of Ministers to the Governor is secret or privileged or should not be disclosed? Such an inference is baseless. The advise tendered by the Council of Ministers to the Governor and the material based on which such advice was given need to be disclosed and debated. The Supreme Court in S.R. Bommai laid down a landmark principle that though advice cannot be probed into, the material based on which such advice was tendered can be reviewed by Judiciary as that formed basic structure of the Constitution. Thus, the Cabinet's advice to Governor or President is neither a secret nor privileged. The RTI Act under Section-8(1)(i) makes it mandatory that the decisions of Council of Ministers, the reasons thereof, and the material on the basis of which the decisions were taken shall be made public after the decision has been taken, and the matter is complete, or over. The information referred to in this proviso is the decision by the Executive, which is similar to the decision of the LG to advice the Union government to dissolve Delhi Legislative Assembly. This cannot be considered as a Secret document which cannot be disclosed.

As stated in proviso of Section-8(1)(i) or RTI Act, the Executive has to disclose the decision, the reasons thereof and the material on the basis of which the decision was taken, after the decision has been taken, the matter is complete, or over. The advice of the LG to the Union Government was already acted upon when the Delhi Legislative Assembly was dissolved, fresh elections were held and a new Cabinet was installed. Thus, the matter is complete and over. The Executive should publish this information voluntarily as per S. 8(1)(i) proviso. At this stage, there should not be any problem in disclosing the report sought.

The Supreme Court in Bommai, SR vs. Union of India, MANU/SC/0444/1994 : (1994) 3 SCC 1) stated that notwithstanding Art. 74(2), it is open to the Court to inquire [para 2, 167(II), 453]:

Commission finds that it is clarified that the material 'information' can be reviewed by the Judiciary. The review is possible only when information is disclosed. The Constitution nowhere accorded immunity from disclosure.

Decision by CIC

Information sought has to be shared, because a) the immunity under Article 163(3) will not apply to Lt. G., b) such immunity is from probing but not from disclosure, c) request for information is not probe into advice, d) not exempted by any provision of RTI Act, e) there is no stay operating on disclosure, f) the information sought is already known, g) there is need for transparency in decision making process regarding dissolving and elected house in public interest, h) there is neither executive privilege nor legislative privilege and i) there is nothing to show that disclosure would case breach of parliamentary privilege.

Chapter - 25

INFORMATION REGARDING UNDER TRAIL PRISONERS[173]

Facts in Nutshell

Appellant by her RTI application had sought information regarding steps taken by the Home Department, Government of India towards the implementation of the Central Directive No. V-13013/70/2012-IS (VI) dated 17.01.2013 issued by Government of India Ministry of Home Affairs to the Home Secretaries to all States. PIO replied on 09.02.2015 providing para-wise reply. She stated to have received only part information, and there was no information from Central Jails of Tihar and District Jail of Rohini. She filed first appeal and thereafter, approached the Commission.

Information sought was concerning a very important matter of public interest, which engaged the Supreme Court, Legislature, Executive and the Law Commission since a long time. The Home Ministry requested the State Governments and Union Territories to adopt various measures to reduce overcrowding of prisons. The Parliament by Act 25 of 2005 amended Code of Criminal Procedure, 1973 providing for maximum period for which an under-trial prisoner can be detained under any law not being an offence for which the punishment of death has been specified one of the punishments. Section 436A says:

"436-A. Maximum period for which an under-trial prisoner can be detained where a person has, during the period of investigation, inquiry or trial under this Code of an offence under any law (not being an offence for which the punishment of death has been specified as one of the punishments under that law) undergone

---

173 Appellants: Divya Iyer
Vs.
Respondent: Tihar Jail
Hon'ble Judges/Coram:
M. Sridhar Acharyulu, Information Commissioner
Divya Iyer vs. Tihar Jail (13.08.2015 - CIC), MANU/CI/0203/2015

detention for a period extending up to one-half of the maximum period of imprisonment specified for that offence under that law, he shall be released by the Court on his personal bond with or without sureties: Provided that the Court may, after hearing the Public Prosecutor and for reasons to be recorded by it in writing, order the continued detention of such person for a period longer than one-half of the said period or release him on bail instead of the personal bond with or without sureties: Provided further that no such person shall in any case be detained during the period of investigation inquiry or trial for more than the maximum period of imprisonment provided for the said offence under that law. Explanation.—In Computing the period of detention under this section for granting bail the period of detention passed due to delay in proceeding caused by the accused shall be excluded.]"

This circular mentioned data collected by NCRB in 2011 that 67% of inmates are under-trials, though percentage of overcrowding was steadily going down. Invariably it has been found that only the poor and indigent who have not been able to put up the surety are those who have continued to languish as under-trials for very long periods and that too for minor offences. The lack of adequate legal aid and a general lack of awareness about rights of arrestees are principal reasons for the continued detention of individuals accused of bailable offences, where bail is a matter of right and where an order of detention is supposed to be an aberration. Thus a disproportionate amount of our prison-space and resources for prison maintenance are being invested on UTPs which is not sustainable.

States/UTs may hence consider taking the following actions: 1. Constitute a Review Committee in every district with the District Judge as Chairman, and the District Magistrate and District SP as members to meet every three months and review the cases. 2. Jail Superintendent should conduct a survey of all cases where the UTPs have completed more than one-fourth of the maximum sentence. He should prepare a survey list and send the same to the District Legal Service Authority (DLSA) as well as the UT Review Committee. 3. Prison authorities may educate under-trial prisoners on their rights to bail. 4. Provide legal aid - may be provided through empanelled lawyers of DLSA to cases presented for release on bail and reduction of bail amount. 5. The list should be made available to the non-official visitors as well as District Magistrates/Judges who conduct periodic inspections of the jails. 6. Home Department may also develop management information system to ascertain the progress made jail-wise in this regard. Action taken to implement the suggestions in all the jails may kindly be intimated within one month.

Appellant Wanted to Know

"(a) whether Review Committee has been set up in the District? If so, names, contact numbers and designations of all members of the committee, if not constituted, reasons for the same.

(b) Whether jail superintendent has completed the survey of cases where the UTPs have completed more than one-fourth of the maximum sentence and sent it to District Legal Services Authority and UT Review Committee, details thereof,

(c) Whether UT prisoners were duty informed about their rights to bail, details thereof,

(d) Whether Legal Aid was provided to them for getting released on bail and reduction of bail amount,

(e) Whether list was made available to the non-official visitors as well as District Magistrates/Judges

(f) Whether Management Information System has been developed?"

Reply by PIO

PIO stated on 9.2.2015 that RTI request has been forwarded to PIO Central Jail Tihar and District Jail Rohini. Information pertaining to Prison Head Quarters was as under:

"A (1 & 2). A proposal for constitution of a District under trial prisoner review committee has been sent to Dy. Secretary(Home) GNCTD vide letter 23-12-14 and response in this regard is still awaited.

E. Board of Visitors has already been notified but the same is challenged before Delhi High Court and is not fully functioning.

F. (1) Prisoner Management System and Visitor Management System developed by National Informatics Centre Run in Central Jail Tihar in all the jails for keeping prisoners information and their visitors record respectively.

(2) The said Management Information system is used to store all details of prisoners and their visitors. This is web based software run on internet.

(3) As per information received from all jails, two UTPs were found eligible under section 436 A of Cr.P.C. during 1-10-2014 to 30-11-14 and out of them one UTP was released and other UTP was released in this case but detained in other multiple cases

(4) N/A"

Superintendent from Jail No. 5 said that, being a convict jail, their jail does not have the information about under trial prisoners.

Directions Relating to Under-Trial Prisoners

The Hon'ble Supreme Court in Vijay Aggarwal v. Union of India & Ors. W.P. (Crl) No. 32/2013 on 05 September, 2014 issued several directions relating to under-trial prisoners vis-à-vis. Section 436-A of the Code of Criminal Procedure, 1973.

"(i) Jurisdictional Magistrate/Chief judicial Magistrates/Sessions Judge shall hold one sitting in a week in each jail/prison for two months commencing from 1st October, 2014 for the purposes of effective implementation of Section 436-A of the Code of Criminal Procedure.

(ii) In its sitting in jail, the above judicial officers shall identify the under-trial prisoners who have completed half period of the maximum period or maximum period of imprisonment provided for the said offence under the law and

(iii) After complying with the procedure prescribed under Section 436-A pass an appropriate order in jail itself for release of such under-trial prisoners who fulfill the requirement of Section 436-A for their release immediately.

(iv) Such jurisdictional Magistrate/Chief Judicial Magistrate/Sessions Judge shall submit the report of each of such sitting to the Registrar General of the High Court and

(v) At the end of two months, the Registrar General of each High Court shall submit the report to the Secretary General of this Court without any delay. To facilitate the compliance of the above order, we direct the jail Superintendent of each jail/prison to provide all necessary facilities for holding the court sitting by the above judicial officers. A Copy of this Order shall be sent to the Registrar General of each High Court, who in turn will communicate the copy of the order to all Sessions Judges within his State for necessary compliance."

Supreme Court also directed that jurisdictional Magistrate/Chief judicial Magistrates/Sessions Judge shall hold one sitting in a week in each jail/prison for two months commencing from 1st October, 2014 for the purposes of effective implementation of Section 436-A of the Code of Criminal Procedure. In its sitting in jail, the above judicial officers shall identify the under-trial prisoners who have completed half period of the maximum period or maximum period of imprisonment provided for the said offence under the law and after complying with the procedure prescribed under Section 436-A pass an appropriate order in jail itself for release of such under-trial prisoners who fulfill the requirement of Section 436-A for their release immediately. Such jurisdictional Magistrate/Chief Judicial Magistrate/ Sessions Judge shall submit the report of each of such sitting to the Registrar General of the High Court and at the end of two months, the Registrar General of each High Court shall submit the report to the Secretary General of this Court without any delay. To facilitate the compliance of the above order, we direct the jail Superintendent of each jail/prison to provide all necessary facilities for holding the court sitting by the above judicial officers.

In Hussainara Khatoon & Ors v. Home Secretary, State of Bihar (MANU/ SC/0123/1979 : AIR 1979 SC 1819), the Supreme Court it was held "Ordinarily when a person is accused of more than one offence, the sentences of imprisonment imposed are directed to run concurrently but assuming the sentences of imprisonment be consecutive, the under-trial prisoners here have suffered incarceration for the maximum period for which they could be sent to jail on conviction for multiple offences. There is absolutely no reason why the under trials be allowed to continue in jail for a moment longer since such continuance of detention would be violative not only of human dignity but also of their fundamental right under Art. 21. The Supreme Court had interpreted that the right to life and personal liberty under Article 21 of the Constitution of India includes the right to speedy justice, which includes the right to free legal aid. The NHRC has drawn the attention of the Chief Justices of the High Courts to the delays in the grant of bails to under-trial prisoners and has suggested a number of remedial measures. One of them is that, as the prisoners are in judicial custody, the district judges should regularly visit the prisons within their jurisdiction and identify cases of long-staying under-trials that need special attention.

Decision by CIC

It is the constitutional responsibility and statutory obligation of the Governments to review each case of under-trial prisoner and take appropriate action including release of the prisoners and inform the prisoners concerned and the concerned authorities.

The Commission would like to add another duty, the duty to inform also to the authorities, which will facilitate the release, or enable prisoner or any other person to demand release based on the information made available. The Commission finds it necessary and appropriate for the Under-trial Review Committee to issue necessary instructions to provide the release-related-information to the concerned from time to time for effective implementation of Section 436A and directions of the Supreme Court.

Even a single day delay in release of under-trial prisoners, who are entitled to that release as per Section 436A, will amount to serious violation of their right to life under Article 21 of Constitution. For this violation no amount of compensation would be sufficient. Hence the authorities must prevent the breach of Article 21 of Constitution by implementation of Section 436A.

The Commission directed the authorities of Tihar Jail and Rohini Jail, to provide a) latest status on the implementation of the Central directive dated 17-

1-2015, and b) proposed list of prisoners to be released and other possible consequences like review committee meetings, etc within 20 days from the date of receipt of this order to the appellant, which shall also be disclosed under Section 4(1)(b) of RTI Act in their official website.

The Commission also directed the Home Department to issue directives to all Jail authorities to prepare the list of under-trials supposed to be released from time to time at least for every quarter informing the fact of their release. Any such release of under-trial prisoner cannot be delayed for the sake of report or publication of information.

Chapter - 26

COPIES OF COURT DOCUMENTS CAN BE OBTAINED ONLY BY APPLYING UNDER COURT RULES AND NOT RTI[174]

Facts in Nutshell

The point falling for determination in the appeal was with regard to the right of a third party to apply for certified copies to be obtained from the High Court by invoking the provisions of Right to Information Act without resorting to Gujarat High Court Rules prescribed by the High Court.

Brief Facts Which Led to Filing of This Appeal Are As Follows:

An RTI application dated 05.04.2010 was filed by Respondent No. 2 seeking information pertaining to the following cases-Civil Application No. 5517 of 2003 and Civil Application No. 8072 of 1989 along with all relevant documents and certified copies. In reply, by letter dated 29.04.2010, Public Information Officer, Gujarat High Court informed Respondent No. 2 that for obtaining required copies, he should make an application personally or through his advocate on affixing court fees stamp of Rs. 3/- with requisite fee to the "Deputy Registrar". It was further stated that as Respondent No. 2 is not a party to the said proceedings, as per Rule 151 of the Gujarat High Court Rules, 1993, his application should be accompanied by an affidavit stating the grounds for which the certified copies are required and on making such application, he will be

---

174 Appellants: Chief Information Commissioner
Vs.
Respondent: High Court of Gujarat and Ors.
Hon'ble Judges/Coram:
R. Banumathi, A.S. Bopanna and Hrishikesh Roy, JJ., Supreme Court of India
Chief Information Commissioner vs. High Court of Gujarat and Ors. (04.03.2020 - SC) : MANU/SC/0275/2020,
AIR2020SC4333
2020(I)CLR(SC)810

supplied the certified copies of the documents as per Rules 149 to 154 of the Gujarat High Court Rules, 1993.

Being aggrieved, Respondent No. 2 preferred Appeal No. 84 of 2010 before the Appellate Authority-Registrar Administration Under Section 19 of the Right to Information Act, 2005 (for short "RTI Act"). The appeal was dismissed vide order dated 04.08.2010 on the ground that for obtaining certified copies, the alternative efficacious remedy is already available under the Gujarat High Court Rules, 1993 and that under the provisions of RTI Act, no certified copies can be provided.

Respondent No. 2 then filed Second Appeal No. 1437 of 2010-11 before the Appellant-Chief Information Commissioner and notice was sent to Respondent No. 1. Respondent No. 1-High Court filed its response reiterating the position that there are provisions Under Rules 149 to 154 of the Gujarat High Court Rules for anybody who wants to obtain the certified copies as per which, application/affidavit should be filed stating the grounds for which the documents are required and with requisite court fee stamps. Respondent No. 1 stated that despite the letter dated 02.07.2010 by the Deputy Registrar (CC Section), Decree Department, Gujarat High Court to Respondent No. 2 informing him of the procedure for getting certified copies, Respondent No. 2 has not made application as per the Rules of the High Court and that the Public Information Officer cannot be compelled to breach the High Court Rules and hence, the appeal filed before the Chief Information Commissioner (CIC) is liable to be dismissed. Relying upon Sections 6(2) and 22 of the RTI Act, the Appellant-Chief Information Commissioner vide its order dated 04.04.2013 directed Public Information Officer of the Gujarat High Court to provide the information sought by Respondent No. 2 within twenty days.

Challenging the order of Chief Information Commissioner, Respondent No. 1 filed Special Civil Application No. 7880 of 2013 before the High Court. The learned Single Judge, while admitting the petition, passed an interim order dated 11.10.2013 directing Respondent No. 1 to provide the information sought by Respondent No. 2 within four weeks. The learned Single Judge held that the legality and validity of the direction given by the Appellant and the right of

Respondent No. 2 to receive the copies under RTI Act will be considered at the stage of final hearing. It was however clarified that supply of information by Respondent No. 1 shall not be construed as acceptance of applicability of RTI Act to the High Court.

Being aggrieved by the interim order, Respondent No. 1-High Court preferred Letters Patent Appeal No. 1348 of 2013 before the Division Bench contending that the party who seeks certified copies has to make an application along with the copying charges and requisite court fees stamp as per Rules 149 to 154 of the Gujarat High Court Rules. As per the Rules, if the certified copy is sought by a person who is not a party to the litigation, his application has to be accompanied by an affidavit stating therein the purpose for which he requires the certified copies. Vide impugned order, the High Court allowed the Letters Patent Appeal holding that when a particular field is governed by the Rules which are not declared ultra-vires, then there is no question of applying the fresh Rules and make the situation confusing. The High Court held that in the light of the High Court Rules, certified copies may be given on payment of charges as per the Rules and also the applicant (Respondent No. 2) has to file an affidavit disclosing the purpose for which the certified copies are required and there is no question of making an application under the RTI Act. The Division Bench set aside the order of the Chief Information Commissioner by observing that when a copy is demanded by any person, the same has to be in accordance with the Rules of the High Court on the subject.

RTI Act, 2005

Section 8(1) of the RTI Act provides for exemption from disclosure of information. Right to information is subject to exceptions or exemptions stated in Section 8(1)(a) to 8(1)(j) of the RTI Act. There are ten clauses of Section 8(1) of the RTI Act. Clause (a) of Sub-section (1) of Section 8 deals with information that would compromise the sovereignty or integrity of the country and like matter; Clause (b) covers any information which has been expressly forbidden to be published by any court of law or tribunal or the disclosure of which may constitute contempt of court; Clause (c) covers such matters which would cause a breach of privilege of the Parliament or the State Legislatures; Clause (d) protects information of commercial nature and trade secrets and intellectual property; Clause (e) exempts the disclosure of any information available to a person in his fiduciary relationship, unless the competent authority is satisfied that the larger public interest warrants the disclosure of such information; Clause (f) prevents information being disseminated, if it is received in confidence from any foreign Government; Clause (g) exempts the disclosure of any information which endanger the life or physical safety of any person or identify the source of information or assistance given in confidence for law enforcement or security purposes; Clause (h) bars access to such information which would impede the process of investigation or apprehension or prosecution of offenders; Clause (i) forbids records and papers relating to deliberations of ministers and officers of the executive being made available, subject to a proviso; and, Clause (j) prohibits disclosure of personal information unless there is an element of public interest involved.

In Central Public Information Officer, Supreme Court of India v. Subhash Chandra Agrawal MANU/SC/1561/2019 : 2019 (16) SCALE 40, the Supreme Court upheld the order passed by the Central Information Commissioner directing the CPIO, Supreme Court of India to furnish information as to the assets declared by the Hon'ble Judges of the Supreme Court. The Constitution Bench held that such disclosure would not, in any way, impinge upon the personal information and right to privacy of the Judges. The fiduciary relationship Rule in terms of Section 8(1)(e) of the RTI Act was held inapplicable. Learned Counsel appearing for the parties extensively relied upon the observations of the Supreme Court in Subhash Chandra Agarwal. Since the issue before us is the High Court Rules vis-a-vis., the RTI Act, we do not propose to refer the various observations copiously relied upon by the learned Counsel appearing for the parties.

Decision by Supreme Court of India

The preamble to the RTI Act suggests that the Act was enacted "to promote transparency and accountability in the working of every public authority.......". The Act was enacted by keeping in view the right of "an informed citizenry and transparency of information which are vital to its functioning and also to contain corruption and to hold Governments and their instrumentalities accountable to the governed.....". The preamble opens with a reference to the Constitution having established a democratic republic and the need therefore, for an informed citizenry. The preamble reveals that legislature was conscious of the likely conflict with other public interest including efficient operations of the Governments and optimum use of limited fiscal resources and the preservation of confidentiality of sensitive information and the necessity to harmonise these conflicting interests. A citizen of India has every right to ask for any information subject to the limitation prescribed under the Act. The right to seek information is only to fulfill the objectives of the Act laid down in the preamble, that is, to promote transparency of information.

The information held by the High Court on the judicial side are the personal information of the parties to the litigation or information furnished by the Government in relation to a particular case. There may be information held by the High Court relating to the cases which have been obtained from the various tribunals in exercise of the supervisory jurisdiction of the High Court Under Article 227 of the Constitution of India. For instance, the matters arising out of the orders by the Income Tax Appellate Tribunal, Customs Excise and Service Tax Appellate Tribunal and other tribunals over which the High Court exercises the supervisory jurisdiction. The orders/judgments passed by the High Court though are the documents which are concerned to the rights and liabilities of the parties to the litigation. Under Section 8(1)(j) of the RTI Act, the Central Public Information Officer or the appellate authority may order disclosure of personal information if they are satisfied that the larger public interest justifies disclosure. Insofar as the High Court Rules are concerned, if the information or certified copies of the documents/record of proceedings/orders on the judicial side of the Court is required, all that the third party is required to do is to file an application/affidavit stating the reasons for seeking such information. On being satisfied about the reasons for requirement of the certified copy/disclosure of information, the Court or the concerned Officer would order for grant of certified copies.

Court held that:

(i) Rule 151 of the Gujarat High Court Rules stipulating a third party to have access to the information/obtaining the certified copies of the documents or orders requires to file an application/affidavit stating the reasons for seeking the information, is not inconsistent with the provisions of the RTI Act; but merely lays down a different procedure as the practice or payment of fees, etc. for obtaining information. In the absence of inherent inconsistency between the provisions of the RTI Act and other law, overriding effect of RTI Act would not apply.

(ii) The information to be accessed/certified copies on the judicial side to be obtained through the mechanism provided under the High Court Rules, the provisions of the RTI Act shall not be resorted to.

Chapter - 27

INFORMATION REGARDING EXCLUSION OF NAME FROM THE VOTERS LIST[175]

Facts in Nutshell

The Complainant by his RTI application had sought information regarding exclusion of his name in the voters list. He wanted to know the procedure by which the name can be excluded, can a person be excluded from the voter list even when he has resided in the same address previously when he voted etc. Claiming non-furnishing of information, complainant approached the Commission.

Contentions by Complainant

The complainant submitted that he was a valid voter duly registered and listed in the voters' list. He had exercised his franchise during the elections for 2013 Delhi Assembly Elections, 2014-Lok Sabha Elections, as his name was figuring in the voters list of the Assembly Constituency No. 11-Nangloi, Delhi. To his surprise he could not find his name in the list, when he went to polling booth to cast his vote in the recent Delhi Assembly Elections in February, 2015. He, therefore, filed an RTI applications seeking the reasons for deleting his name from the voters' list, even though he was residing at the same address. But he was not provided with any reply so far and hence he approached the Commission. The complainant alleged that his name was deliberately deleted from the voters' list by the vested interests, leading to denial of his right to vote. There is none from

---

[175] Appellants: Sumit
Vs.
Respondent: Chief Election Officer
Hon'ble Judges/Coram:
M. Sridhar Acharyulu, Information Commissioner
Sumit vs. Chief Election Officer (29.07.2015 - CIC) : MANU/CI/0193/2015

the Chief Election Officer to explain their case about the deletion of name of appellant from voter's list.

Indian Constitution

Part XV-Elections, under Article 325 says: No person to be ineligible for inclusion in, or to claim to be included in a special, electoral roll on grounds of religion, race, caste or sex. This Article supports the preparation of one general electoral roll for each constituency, for election to both the houses of Parliament.

Article 326 says: Elections to the House of the People and to the Legislative Assemblies of States to be on the basis of Adult Suffrage.

Every citizen who is above 18 years of age has a right to vote. This is called Adult Suffrage. This provision is made with the vision of maximum participation and providing an opportunity to the youth to select their leaders. When a citizen casts his vote, he is expressing his opinion or consent in favour of one candidate among several, to represent him and act on his behalf. Hence this right also falls under the scope of right to freedom of speech and expression in Article 19(1)(a) of Indian Constitution and Article 19(1) and (2) of the International Covenant on Civil and Political Rights can be made in his regard.

Thus Article 326 guarantees the right to vote to every citizen above the age of 18. In addition Section 62 of the Representation of Peoples Act (RoPA), 1951 states that every person who is in the electoral roll of that constituency will be entitled to vote. Thus, the Constitution and the RoPA make it clear that every individual above the age of 18, whose name is in the electoral rolls, and does not attract any of the disqualifications under the Act, may cast his vote. This is a non discriminatory, voluntary system of voting.

The word "elector" has been defined in Section 2(e) of the RP Act, 1951 which reads as under:

" 'elector' in relation to a constituency means a person whose name is entered in the electoral roll of that constituency for the time being in force and who is not subject to any of the disqualifications mentioned in section 16 of the Representation of the People Act, 1950 (43 of 1950)."

The applicant in this case is the 'elector' as he was duly included in voter's list.

Section 16 of the RP Act, 1950, which has been referred to in the above-quoted definition of the word "elector" reads as under:

"16. Disqualifications for registration in an electoral roll. (1) A person shall be disqualified for registration in an electoral roll if he is not a citizen of India; or is of unsound mind and stands so declared by a competent court; or is for the time being disqualified from voting under the provisions of any law relating to corrupt practices and other offences in connection with elections.

(2) The name of any person who becomes so disqualified after registration shall forthwith be struck off the electoral roll in which it is included:

Provided that the name of any person struck off the electoral roll of a constituency by reason of a disqualification under clause (c) of Sub-section (1) shall forthwith be reinstated in that roll if such disqualification is, during the period such roll is in force, removed under any law authorizing such removal."

Section 19 of the RP Act, 1950 relates to the "conditions of registration". It provides as under:

"19. Conditions of registration. Subject to the foregoing provisions of this Part, every person who-is not less than [eighteen years] of age on the qualifying date, and is ordinarily resident in a constituency, shall be entitled to be registered in the electoral roll for that constituency."

"20. Meaning of 'ordinarily resident'.

(1) A person shall not be deemed to be ordinarily resident in a constituency on the ground only that he owns; or is in possession of, a dwelling house therein.

(1A) A person absenting himself temporarily from his place of ordinary residence shall not by reason thereof cease to be ordinarily resident therein.

(1B) A member of Parliament or of the Legislature of a State shall not during the term of his office cease to be ordinarily resident in the constituency in the electoral roll of which he is registered as an elector at the time of his election as such member, by reason of his absence from that constituency in connection with his duties as such member.

(2) A person who is a patient in any establishment maintained wholly or mainly for the reception and treatment of persons suffering from mental illness or mental defectiveness, or who is detained in prison or other legal custody at any place, shall not by reason thereof be deemed to be ordinarily resident therein.

(3) Any person having a service qualification shall be deemed to be ordinarily resident on any date in the constituency in which, but for his having such service qualification, he would have been ordinarily resident on that date.

(4) Any person holding any office in India declared by the President in consultation with the Election Commission to be an office to which the provisions of this sub-section apply, shall be deemed to be ordinarily resident on any date in the constituency in which, but for the holding of any such office, he would have been ordinarily resident on that date.

(5) The statement of any such person as is referred to in sub-section (3) or Sub-section (4) made in the prescribed form and verified in the prescribed manner, that [but for his having the service qualification] or but for his holding any such office as is referred to in sub-section (4) he would have been ordinarily resident in a specified place on any date, shall, in the absence of evidence to the contrary, be accepted as correct.

(6) The wife of any such person as is referred to in sub-section (3) or Sub-section (4) shall if she be ordinarily residing with such person be deemed to be ordinarily resident on in the constituency specified by such person under sub-section (5).

(7) If in any case a question arises as to where a person is ordinarily resident at any relevant time, the question shall be determined with reference to all the facts of the case and to such rules as may be made in this behalf by the Central Government in consultation with the Election Commission.

(8) In sub-sections (3) and (5) "service qualification" means-being a member of the armed forces of the Union; or being a member of a force to which

the provisions of the Army Act, 1950 (46 of 1950), have been made applicable whether with or without modifications; or being a member of an armed police force of a State, who is serving outside that State; or being a person who is employed under the Government of India, in a post outside India."

All the above provisions of law have to be read together and the conjoint effect thereof is that a person in order to qualify to be registered as an elector in relation to a constituency, besides fulfilling other qualifications, must be a citizen of India, not less than 18 years of age on the qualifying date (which by virtue of Section 14 of RoP Act, 1950, means the first day of January of the year in which the electoral list of the constituency is prepared or revised), and, what is significant here, be "ordinarily resident" in that constituency.

Right to Elect

The Hon'ble Supreme Court said in Jyoti Basu v. Debi Ghosal, [MANU/SC/0144/1982 : (1982) 1 SCC 691]:

"A right to elect, fundamental though it is to democracy, is, anomalously enough, neither a fundamental right nor a common law right. It is pure and simple, a statutory right."

The Hon'ble Supreme Court, in PUCL v. Union of India, in a landmark judgment in September, 2013 upheld the constitutional right of citizens to cast a negative vote in elections. And in Paragraph 52 said:

"No doubt, the right to vote is a statutory right but it is equally vital to recollect that this statutory right is the essence of democracy. Without this, democracy will fail to thrive. Therefore, even if the right to vote is statutory, the significance attached with the right is massive. Thus, it is necessary to keep in mind these facets while deciding the issue at hand."

In Ashby v White, (1703) 92 ER 126, Mr. Ashby was prevented from voting at an election by the misfeasance of a constable, Mr. White, on the apparent pretext that he was not a settled inhabitant. At the time, the case attracted considerable national interest, and debates in Parliament. It was later known as the Aylesbury election case. In the House of Lords, it attracted the interest of Peter King, 1st Baron King who spoke and maintained the right of electors to have a remedy at common law for denial of their votes, against Tory insistence on the privileges of the House of Commons. Sir Thomas Powys defended William White in the House of Lords. The argument submitted was that the Commons alone had the power to determine election cases, not the courts. Lord Holt Chief Justice was dissenting from the judgment in the Court of King's Bench, but his dissent was upheld by the House of Lords by a vote of fifty to sixteen. Classic statement that emerged is:

"If the plaintiff has a right, he must of necessity have a means to vindicate and maintain it, and a remedy if he is injured in the exercise or enjoyment of it, and, indeed it is a vain thing to imagine a right without a remedy; for want of right and want of remedy are reciprocal. (https://en.wikipedia.org/wiki/Ashby_v_White)."

Right to vote

This right to vote has been provided in India by Section 62 of RP Act, saying, he will get right to vote only if his name is found in voter's list. Representation of People Act, 1951, Section 62 dealing with Right to vote says:

"(1) No person who is not, and except as expressly provided by this Act, every person who is, for the time being entered in the electoral roll of any constituency shall be entitled to vote in that constituency.

(2) No person shall vote at an election in any constituency if he is subject to any of the disqualifications referred to in section 16 of the Representation of the People Act, 1950 (43 of 1950).

(3) No person shall vote at a general election in more than one constituency of the same class, and if a person votes in more than one such constituency, his votes in all such constituencies shall be void.

(4) No person shall at any election vote in the same constituency more than once, notwithstanding that his name may have been registered in the electoral roll for that constituency more than once, and if he does so vote, all his votes in that constituency shall be void."

Issue before Central Information Commission (CIC)

The issue before the Commission is: what is the duty of the public authority regarding deletion from voter's list and whether a deleted voter can demand compensation if the name of eligible voter is deleted from the list wrongfully?

Fight for Right to Vote

Here is the case of complainant, a young boy, who cast his vote in Assembly elections in 2013 and Parliament Elections 2014, could not exercise the same in 2015 Assembly Elections in Delhi, due to deletion of his name from the list without notice though he was residing in same address. He was not even informed that his name was deleted from the list. There was no communication from the Election Office to appellant explaining the reasons for deletion, because of this non-communication the complainant lost his pre-existing statutory right to vote, which is fundamental in democracy. Thus he was denied his right.

The Public Authority of Chief Election Office has two kinds of duties under two different capacities. First duty: Under Principles of Natural Justice, the office or officer which intend to delete the name of a valid voter from the voter's list has to inform such voter their intended action, reasons for the same and provide a reasonable opportunity to defend his voting right. Any order without following these principles of natural justice, cannot be considered as valid order. Thus CEO had a duty to justify the deletion even before the voter approached through RTI Act.

Second duty: The Public Authority has to respond to an applicant who filed RTI request to know the reasons for deletion of his name. As the CPIO was not present and RTI application was not responded, the version of public authority about any communication to the complainant before deleting his name is not available. From the record made available to the Commission it is clear that there was no response to RTI request. Thus two duties appears to have been breached.

Deletion from Voter's List

The Representation of the People Act, 1950 and the Rules made there under prescribe a detailed procedure for preparation and revision of voters' list. A valid voters' list constitutes the actual basis for the democratic process. That is the reason why the RoP Act provides for effective machinery at various stages for proper verification of the claims of the persons for inclusion in or deletion from the voters' list. While Section 21 of the Act provides for preparation and revision of electoral rolls in general, Section 22 prescribes the procedure for deletion of names, which are already present in the list. Section 23 of the Act provides for inclusion of names in the existing electoral rolls. Section 22 of Representation of People Act 1950 clearly stated that giving reasonable opportunity is mandatory.

"Section 22. Correction of entries in electoral rolls.-If the electoral registration officer for a constituency, on application made to him or on his own motion, is satisfied after such inquiry as he thinks fit, that any entry in the electoral roll of the constituency-

(a) is erroneous or defective in any particular,

(b) should be transposed to another place in the roll on the ground that the person concerned has changed his place of ordinary residence within the constituency, or

(c) should be deleted on the ground that the person concerned is dead or has ceased to be ordinarily resident in the constituency or is otherwise not entitled to be registered in that roll, the electoral registration officer shall, subject to such general or special directions, if any, as may be given by the Election Commission in this behalf, amend, transpose or delete the entry:

Provided that before taking any action on any ground under clause (a) or clause (b) or any action under clause (c) on the ground that the person concerned has ceased to be ordinarily resident in the constituency or that he is otherwise not entitled to be registered in the electoral roll of that constituency, the electoral registration officer shall give the person concerned a reasonable opportunity of being heard in respect of the action proposed to be taken in relation to him."

The Registration of Electors Rules, 1960, Section 21A which was added in 1987, more specifically reiterated the duty to provide reasonable opportunity to the affected voter before the deletion. It says:

"Rule 21A, Deletion of names.-If it appears to the registration officer at any time before the final publication of the roll that owing to inadvertence or error or otherwise, the names of dead persons or of persons who have ceased to be, or are not, ordinarily residents in the constituency or of persons who are otherwise not entitled to be registered in that roll, have been included in the roll and that remedial action should be taken under this rule, the registration officer, shall-

(a) prepare a list of the names and other details of such electors;

(b) exhibit on the notice board of his office a copy of the list together with a notice as to the time and place at which the question of deletion of these names from the roll will be considered, and also publish the list and the notice in such other manner as he may think fit; and

(c) after considering any verbal or written objections that may be preferred, decide whether all or any of the names should be deleted from the roll: Provided that before taking any action under this rule in respect of any person on the ground that he has ceased to be, or is not, ordinarily resident in the constituency, or is otherwise not entitled to be registered in that roll, the registration officer shall make every endeavour to give him a reasonable opportunity to show cause why the action proposed should not be taken in relation to him."

Through this rule CEO is entrusted with duty to prepare and publish a list of deletions proposed, notice about inquiry and to give reasonable opportunity to defend, before ordering deletion.

Decision by CIC

The Commission found the merit in the contention of the complainant, that his right to vote was violated. He prayed the Commission to direct the PIO to a) provide reasons for deletion, b) restore right to vote, c) to cause inquiry into such deletion, d) inform action taken against the responsible officer and e) provide remedy for breach of right (i.e., compensation). These are legally valid claims. Such deletion of voter from list without informing the reasons would seriously affect the democratic operation prescribed by the Constitution and Representation of People Act, 1950 which is the foundation of governance as per rule of law. Appellant is surely entitled to compensation under law for reasons discussed above. Not only the appellant, each voter who's valid voting right is violated by arbitrary decision of the officer without communicating reasons and giving an opportunity to represent why his name should not be removed, is entitled to such compensation if he was not allowed to vote on that ground, and restoration of voting rights within reasonable time. Principles of Natural Justice, Section 22 of Representation of People Act 1950, Section 21A of the Registration of Electors Rules, 1960 and the ratio in 2009 judgment of Andhra Pradesh High Court demand that a valid voter is expected to be get adequate opportunity of being heard by the authority before deletion of name of voter. The Commission records its appreciation for appellant, the young boy for his anguish at the unjust denial of opportunity to cast his vote in recent Assembly elections in Delhi, showing greater concern for the right to vote and choosing the path of RTI to seek the reasons and restoration of right lost. In fact, he was performing his duty as alert citizen of this democratic country to secure his most valuable right, i.e., right to vote.

The Commission directed CPIO of Public Authority (Chief Election Officer)

"(a) to show cause why penalty should not be imposed for not furnishing the information to the complainant within the prescribed period,

(b) to inform appellant the reasons for deletion of his name from the voter's list,

(c) to inform if any inquiry was conducted into such deletion after deletion, if not

(d) to conduct an inquiry into arbitrary deletion of his name,

(e) to inform what action was proposed to be taken against officer responsible for deleting his name,

(f) to inform when his name will be included in the list and right to vote will be restored,

(g) to prepare a set of guidelines to follow before deleting names, to inform fact of proposed deletion, grounds for such action of deletion, and provision of adequate opportunity to affected voter to represent his case etc, and post the same on official website, along with FAQs on the subject, and

(h) to pay compensation of Rs. 10,000/- on the grounds that appellant was not informed about deletion, not informed about the grounds/reasons for deletion which amounted to violation of right, and he was not given any response to his RTI application within 30 days as stipulated by RTI Act."

Chapter - 28

CONCILIATION PROCEEDING CONFIDENTIALITY NEEDS TO BE PROTECTED[176]

Facts in Nutshell

Appellant through his RTI application sought information with regard to case of Rama Agarwal before Delhi Legal Aid, copy of detail proceeding, copy of complaint, copy of hearing on 29.6.2010 etc. CPIO replied that information sought on point No. 1 & 3 is confidential. First appellate authority upheld PIO reply. Appellant approached the Commission. Appellant claimed that her story was a prolonged struggle knocking the doors of almost every forum of justice. She married to Anil Aggarwal in 1983 and two children were born out of this wedlock. She alleged that she was confined in a private mental asylum forcibly, and released after her daughter's complaint, and again she was forcibly taken to IHBAS institute and kept on strong medicines. She was referred to counselling under Delhi State Legal Services Authority. She is seeking copy of details of the proceedings of the case under DSLSA. Appellant says those details are most required in her Domestic Violence and Divorce cases pending at Patiala House Courts.

Proceedings Before the Central Information Commission

Appellant sought to have details of the proceedings about conciliation of dispute involving her. Respondent officer stated that according to Rule 20

---

[176] Appellants: Rama Aggarwal
Vs.
Respondent: PIO, Delhi State Legal Service Authority
Hon'ble Judges/Coram:
M. Sridhar Acharyulu, Information Commissioner
Rama Aggarwal vs. PIO, Delhi State Legal Service Authority (13.08.2015 - CIC) : MANU/CI/0204/2015

Mediation & Conciliation Rules, proceedings of mediation and conciliation cannot be obtained and cannot be used for any purpose other than achieving conciliation.

Relevance of Conciliation in Marital Disputes

Conciliation is a process that attempts to resolve disputes by compromise or voluntary agreement. In contrast with arbitration, the mediator/conciliator does not bring in a 'binding award', and the parties are free to accept or reject the recommendation of the conciliator.

If a third party is asked to involve informally, the process can be called mediation. Whether there is any law or not, mediation can be resorted if both the sides of disputants agree on to resolve with the assistance of mediator. Final conclusion of mediation could be enforced or not enforced based on the consent of parties. Generally the mediator will not hear or decide any case or give any judgment. He only facilitates the settlement between disputing parties by helping them in understanding the issues involved. Conciliation and mediation are generally interchangeable expressions.

Conciliation is recognized by law as one of the methods of dispute resolution and provides for it under various statues. The Code of Civil Procedure (CPC) in Order 32A provides for conciliation between the parties. After amendment, Section 89 of CPC provided a strong base for court sponsoring the conciliation process with the support of a pro-active judge, who finds the conciliators and directs the parties to them, as a matter of statutory obligation.

This method was recognized and practically found useful as quite appropriate process to tackle marital problems, where legal, procedural, evidentiary and technical issues of rights of parties take a secondary seat and possible welfare of children, peace of the parties or the need to protect the relationship in 'marriage' is given priority unless there are compelling reasons to dissolve the marriage. Even for a peaceful separation, conciliation, as a precondition for mutual consent divorce application, is considered as a practical problem-solving-approach.

The process of conciliation received statutory recognition in the CPC (O-XXXIIA Rule 3), in Industrial Disputes Act (s 12) and the Hindu Marriage Act 1955 (s 23).

Hindu Marriage Act and Conciliation

Under amended Hindu Marriage Act 1955 (HM Act), the approach of the courts towards family disputes is different from that of other ordinary civil proceedings. Conciliation is preferred as the first resort by the courts. Another important feature is that speedy trial is prescribed as a preferred mode of resolution of disputes.

Section 23(2) says that before proceeding to grant any relief under HM Act, it shall be the duty of the court, in the first instance, in every case where it is possible to do so, consistently with the nature and circumstances of the case to make every endeavour to bring about reconciliation between the parties. However, reconciliation cannot be resorted to when the relief of divorce is claimed, based on grounds of conversion, unsound mind, virulent disease, venereal disease, renouncing the world by entering religious order, missing for seven years, [s. 13(ii) to (vi)]. These grounds are irreconcilable as per proviso under s. 23(2) of the HM Act.

There is a prohibition on publication of proceedings in family cases. The HM Act 1955 was amended in 1976 wherein provided for in camera proceedings, under s. 22, if desired by the parties and imposed a prohibition on publication of family proceedings except the judgment of the high court or Supreme Court printed or published with the previous permission of the court. If any person prints or publishes any matter in contravention of the provisions of s. 22(1) he shall be punishable with fine, which may extend to 1000 rupees. Section 21B is added to facilitate day-to-day hearing, of marriage disputes, for quick disposition.

Confidentiality of Conciliation Proceeding

As per the UNCITRAL Conciliation Rules, the Conciliator and the parties must keep confidential all matters relating to the conciliation proceedings. Article 14 of Rules says: 'Subject to agreement of the parties or mandatory law, the provisions prohibit disclosure to outsiders of any matters relating to the conciliation proceedings. Such guarantee of confidentiality is conducive to reaching an amicable settlement in informal proceedings'. Confidentiality extends also to the settlement agreement, except where its disclosure is necessary for purposes of implementation and enforcement. Confidentiality is a merit of mediation. It is also considered as ethics of this dispute resolution process which achieved a status of the 'best alternative' to litigation. Those who fear the undue publicity, possibility of invasion of privacy and defamation, avoid litigation in court of law, complaint to police station and prefer a confidential, closed door discussion to sort out the differences and resolving the misunderstandings that threaten the relationship in either business or marriage.

The Arbitration and Conciliation Act, 1996

The Arbitration and Conciliation Act 1996, has provided for confidentiality norm for conciliation/mediation proceedings and also made the evidence of mediation not admissible in other court proceedings.

"70. Disclosure of information: When the conciliator receives factual information concerning the dispute from a party, he shall disclose the substance of that information to the other party in order that the other party may have the opportunity to present any explanation which he considers appropriate: Provided that when a party gives any information to the conciliator, subject to a specific condition that it be kept confidential, the conciliator shall not disclose that information to the other party.

75. Confidentiality: Notwithstanding anything contained in any other law for the time bring in force, the conciliator and the parties shall keep confidential all matters relating to the conciliation proceedings. Confidentiality shall extend also to the settlement agreement, except where its disclosure is necessary for purposes of implementation and enforcement.

81. Admissibility of evidence in other proceedings: The parties shall not rely on or introduce as evidence in arbitral or judicial proceedings, whether or not such proceedings relate to the dispute that is the subject of the conciliation proceedings,-

a. views expressed or suggestions made by the other party in respect of a possible settlement of the dispute;
b. admissions made by the other party in the course-, of the conciliation proceedings;

c. proposals made by the conciliator;

d. the fact that the other party had indicated his willingness to accept a proposal for settlement made by the conciliator.

Mediation and Conciliation Rules, 2004

14. Rule 20 : Confidentiality, disclosure and inadmissibility of information.

"(a) When a mediator/conciliator receives factual information concerning the dispute(s) from any party, he shall disclose the substance of that information to the other party, so that the other party may have an opportunity to present such explanation as it may consider appropriate.

Provided that, when a party gives information to the mediator/conciliator subject to a specific condition that it be kept confidential, the mediator/conciliator shall not disclose that information to the other party.

(b) Receipt or perusal, or preparation of records, reports or other documents by the mediator/conciliator, while serving in that capacity shall be confidential and the mediator/conciliator shall not be compelled to divulge information regarding those documents nor as to what transpired during the mediation/conciliation before any court of tribunal or any other authority or any person or group of persons.

(c) Parties shall maintain confidentiality in respect of events that transpired during the mediation/conciliation and shall not rely on or introduce the said information in other proceedings as to:

i. views expressed by a party in the course of the mediation/conciliation proceedings;

ii. documents obtained during the mediation/conciliation which were expressly required to be treated as confidential or other notes, drafts or information given by the parties or the mediator/conciliator;

iii. proposals made or views expressed by the mediator/conciliator.

iv. admission made by a party in the course of mediation/conciliation proceedings;

v. the fact that a party had or had not indicated willingness to accept a proposal;

(d) There shall be no audio or video recording of the mediation/conciliation proceedings.

(e) No statement of parties or the witnesses shall be recorded by the mediator/conciliator."

Rule 21 : Privacy.

"The Mediation/conciliation sessions or meetings would be conducted in privacy where the persons as mentioned in Rule 12 shall be entitled to represent parties. However, other persons may attend only with the permission of the parties and with the consent of the mediator/conciliator."

Confidentiality is at the heart of a mediation proceedings and is critical to a successful resolution. The parties must be assured that they can share sensitive information at the mediation session, where it is necessary to see that their true needs and interests may be met, without fear of subsequent disclosure to their detriment. Such confidentiality plays an important role both in the joint sessions involving all of the disputants at the mediation session as well as in private caucuses which the mediator may have with one or more of the parties during the course of the session. This is the rule worldwide.

Supreme Court Assures Confidentiality

The Supreme Court assured the confidentiality of the process in two judgments. In Moti Ram(D) Thr. L.Rs. and Anr. v. Ashok Kumar and Anr., Markandey Katju, Gyan Sudha Misra, JJ., MANU/SC/1077/2010 : [2010] 14 (ADDL) SCR 809 decided on 20.7.2010 explained:

"In this connection, we would like to state that mediation proceedings are totally confidential proceedings. This is unlike proceedings in Court which are conducted openly in the public gaze. If the mediation succeeds, then the mediator should send the agreement signed by both the parties to the Court without mentioning what transpired during the mediation proceedings. If the mediation is unsuccessful, then the mediator should only write one sentence in his report and send it to the Court stating that the 'Mediation has been unsuccessful'. Beyond that, the mediator should not write anything which was discussed, proposed or done during the mediation proceedings. This is because in mediation, very often, offers, counter offers and proposals are made by the parties but until and unless the parties reach to an agreement signed by them, it will not amount to any concluded contract. If the happenings in the mediation proceedings are disclosed, it will destroy the confidentiality of the mediation process."

The Supreme Court said in yet another case of Haresh Dayaram Thakur v. State of Maharashtra and Others, MANU/SC/0363/2000 : AIR 2000 SC 2281, D.P. Mohapatra and RP Sethi, JJ. said:

"Section 67 which makes provision regarding role of conciliator provides in Sub-section (I) that the conciliator shall assist the parties in an independent and impartial manner in their attempt to reach an amicable settlement of their dispute. In Sub-section (2) thereof, it is provided that the conciliator shall be guided by principles of objectivity, fairness and justice, giving consideration to, among other things, the rights and obligations of the parties, the usages of the trade concerned and the circumstances surrounding the dispute including any previous business practices between the parties. In Sub-section (4) of Section 67 it is laid down that the conciliator may, at any stage of the conciliation proceedings, make proposals for a settlement of the dispute. Such proposals need not be in writing and need not be accompanied by a statement of the reasons therefore. Section 69 contains the provision regarding communication between conciliator and parties whether orally or in writing and about the place of meeting etc. In Section 70 provision is made regarding disclosure of information. Therein it is provided, inter alia, that when the conciliator receives factual information concerning the dispute from a party, he shall disclose the substance of that information to the other party in order that the other party may have the opportunity to present any explanation which he considers appropriate. In the proviso to the section it is stated that when a party gives any information to the conciliator subject to a specific condition that it be kept confidential, the conciliator shall not disclose that information to the other party. Under Section 72 it is laid down that each party may, on his own initiative or at the invitation of the conciliator, submit to the conciliator suggestions for the settlement of the dispute."

Section 75 which incorporates in the status the confidentiality clause provides that notwithstanding anything contained in any other law for the time being in force, the conciliator and the parties shall keep confidential all matters relating to the conciliation proceedings. Confidentiality shall extend also to the settlement agreement, except where its disclosure is necessary for purposes of implementation and enforcement.

RTI Act v A&C Act

The RTI Act will definitely override the Arbitration & Conciliation Act 1996 and information has to be disclosed subject to Section 8 of RTI Act. We need to examine the application and provisios to exceptions under Section (8) that enlists some special instances where the authorities need not disclose. Section 8(1)(e) of the RTI Act, 2005 exempts from disclosure-

"information available to a person in his fiduciary relationship, unless the competent authority is satisfied that the larger public interest warrants the disclosure of such information;"

As per the traditional definition, a 'fiduciary' is a person who occupies a position of trust in relation to someone else, therefore requiring him to act for the latter's benefit within the scope of that relationship. Anything given and taken in confidence expecting confidentiality to be maintained will be information available to a person in fiduciary capacity. Therefore communication made during conciliation proceeding between the parties and also communication between mediator and other parties, qualifies to be made in fiduciary capacity.

The proceedings of Mediation are supposed to be protected under Section 8(1)(j) also, which says:

"information which relates to personal information the disclosure of which has not relationship to any public activity or interest, or which would cause unwarranted invasion of the privacy of the individual unless the Central Public Information Officer or the State Public Information Officer or the appellate authority, as the case may be, is satisfied that the larger public interest justifies the disclosure of such information: Provided that the information, which cannot be denied to the Parliament or a State Legislature shall not be denied to any person."

Larger public interest is an exception for these two exemptions. But in the interest of conciliation in general as an alternative dispute proceedings there is a need to protect the confidentiality. The moment the proceedings of the mediation are allowed to be disclosed in the form of certified copies under RTI Act, or evidence in other proceedings or publicized openly, the parties will not prefer mediation or conciliation, which will increase pendency, stress and burden on the courts besides delaying the marital dispute resolutions affecting several families. Even the parties would lose possibility of resolving.

Mediation is best alternative dispute resolution process for domestic disputes, only because the parties cannot use this proceeding for obtaining the material to use in litigation. Mediation process cannot be used by parties as pre-litigation step to collect material. If RTI is allowed to be exercised in securing information about mediation, cantankerous spouse will exploit mediation as a source to get information with which they can harass the other spouse and use it in courts of law also. Thus the public interest in disclosure of the information, if any, is not higher than that in protection of mediation proceedings as per Section 8(2). Comparatively there is a higher public interest in protecting the confidentiality and privacy of the proceedings of mediation and there is no public interest in disclosure. Hence under Section 8(2) information about mediation proceedings cannot be given. As there is no larger public interest, the mediation information attracts provisions of exemptions under Section 8(1)(e) and (j). Hence cannot be disclosed.

Decision by CIC

The Commission having perused the file found that the it is a proceeding for counselling, a prelude to or part of conciliation. The conciliation in general will include the counselling also. Appellant being a party to mediation/counselling proceedings cannot seek the information about the other party as it attracts exemptions under Section 8(1)(e) and (j) of RTI Act, 2005. The mediator or conciliator will advise or guide or apprise the parties of the issues or steps that help resolving the dispute, he will neither adjudicate not award any decision. When there is a counselling between a person and counsellor, there emerges fiduciary relationship. Appellant has already filed a case for domestic violence. Wife claimed that proceeding before legal service authority was in the nature of a divorce proceeding. From the nature of proceedings it is apparently clear that it was not a divorce proceeding, but a counselling and conciliation proceeding, confidentiality of which need to be protected as per the law and in public interest. Information regarding negotiation, mediation, conciliation and counselling will fall under exempted clause of information of other spouse, being personal and given in fiduciary capacity and, no public interest is established in disclosure, while there is larger public interest in protecting that information as that would help mediation to flourish, hence such information shall not be disclosed. Hence the appeal is rejected.

Chapter - 29

RULE OF CONFIDENTIALITY AND MEDICAL INFORMATION[177]

Facts in Nutshell

Appellant by his RTI application dated 15.9.2014 had sought copy of the OPD slip and all the prescriptions given by the doctors to his ex-wife namely Razia for her medical aliment during the year 2007 to 2009. PIO replied that the information asked by the applicant is related to the psychiatric medical information of the person and hence are exempted under section 8(1)(e) of the RTI Act. Being unsatisfied, appellant has filed first appeal. First Appellate Authority upheld the decision of the CPIO, while Director told appellant that he was seeking information belonging to third party which cannot be given. Thereafter, has approached this Commission.

Contentions

Both the parties made their submissions. The appellant claimed that he was paying Rs. 22000 a month to his estranged wife for maintenance of her and three children, out of his monthly salary of Rs 50,000 under an order of a court. He said that he needs this information to justify his claim for the custody of three minor children. Because she was suffering from the mental disorder, leaving children under her custody will endanger the life of the children. He wants the

---

[177] Appellants: Viqar Ahmad

Vs.

Respondent: Institute of Human Behaviour and Allied Sciences

Hon'ble Judges/Coram:

M. Sridhar Acharyulu, Information Commissioner

Viqar Ahmad vs. Institute of Human Behaviour and Allied Sciences (13.07.2015 - CIC) : MANU/CI/0173/2015

custody of the children on the ground of her psychiatric ailment, for which he is seeking her medical record for the relevant period from the respondent authority.

The respondent authority submitted that they will not maintain any record for the patients of Out-Patient Department (OPD), except one register. The slips containing prescription of medicines will be in the custody of the patients as they were given to them. The contents of prescription are part of the slip given to out- patients. That alone can reveal the seriousness or otherwise of patient's ailments. There is no need to doubt that the public authority does not have it.

Ordinary medical case record is different from the psychiatric case record. Ordinary patient has right to his medical record, but who has the right to receive records regarding psychiatric patients? Guardian of the patient can have it only in the best interest of the patient. If not, the hospital, that is expected to play a role of trust and decide in the best interest of mentally ill persons. They have to examine who is seeking their information, whether that would be in the interest of the patient or not. Though PIO could not explain properly, perhaps that was the purpose of claiming the defence of information being received in fiduciary capacity. Here the interest of woman patient and interests of children are clashing with each other. The CPIO has a tough job to discriminate good and bad of two interests and decide. If the woman is proved to be seriously suffering from psychiatric problem, the interests of children get jeopardized. If her ailment is minor, separating children from her may not be in the interest of both the mother and children. The purpose of husband behind demanding the ailment record of his wife, should be proved to be sincere and truthful. If he wanted this information to be used strategically to inflict suffering on complaining wife, the CPIO cannot straight away give all information.

Following aspects cannot be ignored regarding the psychiatric case records. These details were presented by the CPIO.

"(a) Psychiatric Case Records contain information about emotional disorders, history of suffering of patient.

(b) Psychiatrist has to maintain Neutrality & Confidentiality with patient and family members. He owes duty of confidentiality as he received information in fiduciary capacity. Disclosure of information shared by them with psychiatrist should not be disclosed which would invade the right to privacy as explained by Supreme Court in Kharak Singh v State of U.P. (MANU/SC/0085/1962 : AIR 1963 SC 1295).

(c) Psychiatric case records cannot be equated with ordinary medical records. Access to full records might provoke serious reactions, including attempt to suicide.

(d) India does not have statute like one in UK Access to Health Records Act 1990. According to 'Geriatric Psychiatric Outpatient Care: The Private Practice Model in the USA' authored by Eliott M. Stein and Gary S. Moak in the text book "Principles and Practice of Geriatric Psychiatry, 3rd Edition, the family, relatives or friends are important source of information. If access to information is provided they may refuse to be involved and thus disrupt treatment.

(e) The Principles of Medical Ethics in the US have gone to the extent of protecting information from disclosure even when the patient informs the doctor that he might kill someone.

(f) According to Claire Zilber MD in his article "Ethics and the Doctor Patient Relationship", it is prescribed that in the principles of medical ethics that the doctor can inform of the intended target, but even in such situations one must disclose only relevant information about the threat and that the privacy of the patient should be protected.

(g) As per Health Insurance Portability and Accountability Act HIPAA of 1996, psychotherapy notes prepared by mental health professional, requires proper authorization then only it can be disclosed to any third party.

(h) The Indian Psychiatric Society formulated Clinical Practice Guidelines for Psychiatrists in India, 2004, section relating to Human Rights and Privileges of Mentally Ill Persons, revealing medical records can put the safety of others from whom information is obtained at risk. The professionals are required to maintain confidentiality to all verbal, recorded or computer stored material.

RTI Act, 2005

Section 11 deals with third party information. Where an Appropriate Information Officer intends to disclose any information or record or part thereof on a request, which relates to or has been supplied by a third party and has been treated as confidential by that third party, the concerned Public Information Officer shall give a written notice to such third party of the request, informing that he intends to disclose the information on record, or part thereof, and invite the third party to make a submission in writing or orally, regarding whether the information should be disclosed, and such submission of the third party shall be kept in mind while taking a decision about disclosure of information.

Ordinarily the information sought for by a person must be made available and such person need not give reasons for the information he seeks. Another important aspect of the matter is that in respect of information relating to a third party the concerned Public Information Officer must give notice to the third party and if such third party makes submissions then to consider the said submissions.

Medical Ethics

The medical records of a person are generally confidential, considering the Indian Medical Council (Professional Conduct, Etiquette and Ethics) Regulations 2002 framed under the provisions of the Indian Medical Council Act, 1956, which hereinafter are referred to as the Regulations.

"Regulation 2.2 which is relevant, reads as under:

2.2. Patience, Delicacy and Secrecy. Patience and delicacy should characterize the physician. Confidences concerning individual or domestic life entrusted by patients to a physician and defects in the disposition or character of patients observed during medical attendance should never be revealed unless their revelation is required by the law of the State. Sometimes, however, a physician must determine whether his duty to society requires him to employ knowledge, obtained through confidence as a physician, to protect a healthy person against a communicable disease to which he is about to be exposed. In such instance, the physician should act as he would wish another to act toward one of his own family in like circumstances.

It appears from this Regulation, that the information as sought should not be revealed unless the revelation is required by the law of the State."

The next relevant is Regulation 7.14 which reads as under:

"7.14. The registered medical practitioner shall not disclose the secrets of a patient that have been learnt in the exercise of his/her profession except:

(i) in a court of law under orders of the Presiding Judge;

(ii) in circumstances where there is a serious and identified risk to a specific person and/or community; and

(iii) notifiable diseases. In case of communicable/notifiable diseases, concerned public health authorities should be informed immediately."

The Declaration of Geneva, adopted by the 2nd General Assembly of the World Medical Association, Geneva, Switzerland, September, 1948 and as amended thereafter, in which there is a provision pertaining to right to confidentiality of information about the patients health status, medical condition, diagnosis, prognosis and treatment and all other information of a personal kind with the exception, that descendants may have a right of access to information that would inform them of their health risk.

Right to Privacy

In R. Rajagopal @ R.R. Gopal & Anr. v. State of Tamil Nadu & Ors., MANU/SC/0056/1995 : [1994] 6 SCC 632, the Supreme Court held: A citizen has a right "to safeguard the privacy of his own, his family, marriage, procreation, motherhood, childbearing and education among other matters."

In Mr. "X" v. Hospital "Z", MANU/SC/0733/1998 : (1998 Supp(1) SCR 723, (1998) 8 SCC 296) case the issue was disclosure of information of a patient affected by HIV. The person, whose information was disclosed, sought an action in damages, by moving the National Consumer Disputes Redressal Commission which was rejected and then he appealed to the Supreme Court. In considering the duty to maintain confidentially, the Court observed that in doctor patient relationship, the most important aspect is the doctor's duty of maintaining secrecy and the doctor cannot disclose to a person any information regarding his patient, which he has gathered in the course of treatment nor can the doctor disclose to anyone else the mode of treatment or the advice given by him to the patient.

In this case the Supreme Court said: The Code of Medical Ethics, carves out an exception to the Rule of confidentiality and permits the disclosure in the circumstances enumerated in the judgment under which public interest would override the duty of confidentiality particularly where there is an immediate or future health risk to others. Truth also may not be an exception in cases of privacy. Dealing with the aspect of privacy, the Supreme Court observed in para 27:

"Disclosure of even true private facts has the tendency to disturb a person's tranquility. It may generate many complexes in him and may even lead to psychological problems. He may, thereafter, have a disturbed life all through. In the face of these potentialities, and as already held by this Court in its various decisions referred to above, the Right of Privacy is an essential component of right to life envisaged by Article 21. The right however, is not absolute and may be lawfully restricted for the prevention of crime, disorder or protection of health or morals or protection of rights and freedom of others."

The confidentiality required to be maintained of the medical records of a patient including a convict considering the Regulations framed by the Medical Council of India cannot override the provisions of the Right to Information Act. If there be inconsistency between the Regulations and the Right to Information Act, the provisions of the Act would prevail over the Regulations and the information will have to be made available in terms of the Act. The Act, however, carves out some exceptions, including the release of personal information, the disclosure of which has no relationship to any public activity or interest or which would cause unwarranted invasion of the right to privacy. In such cases discretion has been conferred on the concerned Public Information Officer to make available the information, if satisfied, that the larger public interest justifies the disclosure. This discretion must be exercised, bearing in mind the facts of each case and the larger public interest. Normally records of a person sentenced or convicted or remanded to police or judicial custody, if during that period such person is admitted in hospital and nursing home, should be made available to the person asking the information provided such hospital nursing home is maintained by the State or

Public Authority or any other Public Body. It is only in rare and in exceptional cases and for good and valid reasons recorded in writing can the information may be denied.

Hippocratic Oath

The Hippocratic Oath consists of two parts. The first, or covenant; is the solemn agreement concerning the relationship of apprentice to teacher and the obligations enjoined on the pupil. The second part constitutes the ethical code. It is on the basis of the above that International Code of Medical Ethics has laid down as under:

"A physician shall preserve absolute confidentiality on all he knows about his patient even after his patient has died."

The Indian Medical Council Act controls the medical education and regulates the professional conduct. Section 20A which was inserted by the Indian Medical Council (Amendment) Act 1964 provides as under:

"Professional Conduct: (1) The Council may prescribe the standards of professional conduct and etiquette and a code of ethics for medical practitioners, (2) Regulations made by the Council under sub-section (1) may specify which violations thereof shall constitute infamous conduct in any professional respect, that it is to say, professional misconduct, and such provision shall have effect notwithstanding anything Contained in any law for the time being in force."

Decision by Central Information Commission (CIC)

There are three aspects to be decided. 1) Whether information sought is personal information of third person (in this case Mrs. Razia). 2) Whether there is any public interest that facilitate disclosure of information? 3) Is it third party information and that the views of that person should necessarily be obtained as per section 11 of the RTI Act?

Outpatient register contains the information about the number of visits of the patient. It is a public register and may not contain any information about the disease of the patient. If the verification of register and related documents available with the OPD, also reveal the disease, it could be the personal information of the patient. In such a case the public interest has to be examined and views of third party should be obtained.

Though the information about disease and treatment is personal under certain circumstances the public interest justifies the disclosure and that could be exception to the rule of confidentiality medical information. Based on the possibility of public interest out-weighing the protected interests as prescribed under section 8(2) of the RTI Act, the Commission finds that there is justification for disclosure.

However the number of visits, nature of treatment, and information available in the register and other related records if any, is personal or private information or not has to be ascertained by the concerned doctors having necessary skill in specialization. If that information has to be protected normally, the CPIO has to consult the third party, in this case Ms Razia.

All this process can be done only by the doctors of public authority who can also consult the experts having special knowledge. If the register reveals number of visits of the patient to 'Out Patient Department' that could be disclosed to the appellant, as that cannot be considered as the personal information. If the records also reveal the nature of her ailment, the public interest explained above demands the disclosure. Still the views of the patient need to be ascertained. Hence the Commission remands the RTI application to the PIO, to be decided afresh by the CPIO within 30 days.

ANNEXURE

THE RIGHT TO INFORMATION ACT, 2005

No. 22 of 2005
[15th June, 2005]

An Act to provide for setting out the practical regime of right to information for citizens to secure access to information under the control of public authorities, in order to promote transparency and accountability in the working of every public authority, the constitution of a Central Information Commission and State Information Commissions and for matters connected therewith or incidental thereto.

WHEREAS the Constitution of India has established democratic Republic;

AND WHEREAS democracy requires an informed citizenry and transparency of information which are vital to its functioning and also to contain corruption and to hold Governments and their instrumentalities accountable to the governed;

AND WHEREAS revelation of information in actual practice is likely to conflict with other public interests including efficient operations of the Governments, optimum use of limited fiscal resources and the preservation of confidentiality of sensitive information;

AND WHEREAS it is necessary to harmonise these conflicting interests while preserving the paramountcy of the democratic ideal;

NOW, THEREFORE, it is expedient to provide for furnishing certain information to citizens who desire to have it.

BE it enacted by Parliament in the Fifty-sixth Year of the Republic of India as follows:—

CHAPTER I

Preliminary

1. Short title, extent and commencement

(1) This Act may be called the Right to Information Act, 2005.

(2) It extends to the whole of India except the State of Jammu and Kashmir.

(3) The provisions of sub-section (1) of section 4, sub-sections (1) and (2) of section 5, sections 12, 13, 15,16, 24, 27 and 28 shall come into force at once, and the remaining provisions of this Act shall come into force on the one hundred and twentieth day of its enactment.

2. Definitions

In this Act, unless the context otherwise requires,—

(a) "appropriate Government" means in relation to a public authority which is established, constituted, owned, controlled or substantially financed by funds provided directly or indirectly—

(i) by the Central Government or the Union territory administration, the Central Government;

(ii) by the State Government, the State Government;

(b) "Central Information Commission" means the Central Information Commission constituted under sub-section (1) of section 12;

(c) "Central Public Information Officer" means the Central Public Information Officer designated under sub-section (1) and includes a Central Assistant Public Information Officer designated as such under sub-section (2) of section 5;

(d) "Chief Information Commissioner" and "Information Commissioner" mean the Chief Information Commissioner and Information Commissioner appointed under sub-section (3) of section 12;

(e) "competent authority" means—

(i) the Speaker in the case of the House of the People or the Legislative Assembly of a State or a Union territory having such Assembly and the Chairman in the case of the Council of States or Legislative Council of a State;

(ii) the Chief Justice of India in the case of the Supreme Court;

(iii) the Chief Justice of the High Court in the case of a High Court;

(iv) the President or the Governor, as the case may be, in the case of other authorities established or constituted by or under the Constitution;

(v) the administrator appointed under article 239 of the Constitution;

(f) "information" means any material in any form, including records, documents, memos, e-mails, opinions, advices, press releases, circulars, orders, logbooks, contracts, reports, papers, samples, models, data material held in any electronic form and information relating to any private body which can be accessed by a public authority under any other law for the time being in force;

(g) "prescribed" means prescribed by rules made under this Act by the appropriate Government or the competent authority, as the case may be;

(h) "public authority" means any authority or body or institution of selfgovernment established or constituted—

(a) by or under the Constitution;

(b) by any other law made by Parliament;

(c) by any other law made by State Legislature;

(d) by notification issued or order made by the appropriate Government, and includes any—

(i) body owned, controlled or substantially financed;

(ii) non-Government organisation substantially financed,

directly or indirectly by funds provided by the appropriate Government;

(i) "record" includes—

(a) any document, manuscript and file;

(b) any microfilm, microfiche and facsimile copy of a document;

(c) any reproduction of image or images embodied in such microfilm (whether enlarged or not); and

(d) any other material produced by a computer or any other device;

(j) "right to information" means the right to information accessible under this Act which is held by or under the control of any public authority and includes the right to—

(i) inspection of work, documents, records;

(ii) taking notes, extracts or certified copies of documents or records;

(iii) taking certified samples of material;

(iv) obtaining information in the form of diskettes, floppies, tapes, video cassettes or in any other electronic mode or through printouts where such information is stored in a computer or in any other device;

(k) "State Information Commission" means the State Information Commission constituted under sub-section (1) of section 15;

(l) "State Chief Information Commissioner" and "State Information Commissioner" mean the State Chief Information Commissioner and the State Information Commissioner appointed under sub-section (3) of section 15;

(m) "State Public Information Officer" means the State Public Information Officer designated under sub-section (1) and includes a State Assistant Public Information Officer designated as such under sub-section (2) of section 5;

(n) "third party" means a person other than the citizen making a request for information and includes a public authority.

Chapter-II

3. Right to information

3. Subject to the provisions of this Act, all citizens shall have the right to information.

4. Obligations of public authorities

(1) Every public authority shall—

(a) maintain all its records duly catalogued and indexed in a manner and the form which facilitates the right to information under this Act and ensure that all records that are appropriate to be computerised are, within a reasonable time and subject to availability of resources, computerised and connected through a network all over the country on different systems so that access to such records is facilitated;

(b) publish within one hundred and twenty days from the enactment of this Act,—

(i) the par ticulars of its organisation, functions and duties;

(ii) the powers and duties of its officers and employees;

(iii) the procedure followed in the decision making process, including channels of supervision and accountability;

(iv) the norms set by it for the discharge of its functions;

(v) the rules, regulations, instructions, manuals and records, held by it or under its control or used by its employees for discharging its functions;

(vi) a statement of the categories of documents that are held by it or under its control;

(vii) the particulars of any arrangement that exists for consultation with, or representation by, the members of the public in relation to the formulation of its policy or implementation thereof;

(viii) a statement of the boards, councils, committees and other bodies consisting of two or more persons constituted as its part or for the purpose of its advice, and as to whether meetings of those boards, councils, committees and other bodies are open to the public, or the minutes of such meetings are accessible for public;

(ix) a directory of its officers and employees;

(x) the monthly remuneration received by each of its officers and employees, including the system of compensation as provided in its regulations;

(xi) the budget allocated to each of its agency, indicating the particulars of all plans, proposed expenditures and reports on disbursements made;

(xii) the manner of execution of subsidy programmes, including the amounts allocated and the details of beneficiaries of such programmes;

(xiii) particulars of recipients of concessions, permits or authorisations granted by it;

(xiv) details in respect of the information, available to or held by it, reduced in an electronic form;

(xv) the particulars of facilities available to citizens for obtaining information, including the working hours of a library or reading room, if maintained for public use;

(xvi) the names, designations and other particulars of the Public Information Officers;

(xvii) such other information as may be prescribed; and thereafter update these publications every year;

(c) publish all relevant facts while formulating important policies or announcing the decisions which affect public;

(d) provide reasons for its administrative or quasi-judicial

(2) It shall be a constant endeavour of every public authority to take steps in accordance with the requirements of clause (b) of sub-section (1) to provide as much information suo motu to the public at regular intervals through various means of communications, including internet, so that the public have minimum resort to the use of this Act to obtain information.

(3) For the purposes of sub-section (1), every information shall be

disseminated widely and in such form and manner which is easily accessible to the public.

(4) All materials shall be disseminated taking into consideration the cost effectiveness, local language and the most effective method of communication in that local area and the information should be easily accessible, to the extent possible in electronic format with the Central Public Information Officer or State Public Information Officer, as the case may be, available free or at such cost of the medium or the print cost price as may be prescribed.

Explanation.—For the purposes of sub-sections (3) and (4), "disseminated" means making known or communicated the information to the public through notice boards, newspapers, public announcements, media broadcasts, the internet or any other means, including inspection of offices of any public authority.

5. Designation of Public Information Officers.

(1) Every public authority shall, within one hundred days of the enactment of this Act, designate as many officers as the Central Public Information Officers or State Public Information Officers, as the case may be, in all administrative units or offices under it as may be necessary to provide information to persons requesting for the information under this Act.

(2) Without prejudice to the provisions of sub-section (1), every public authority shall designate an officer, within one hundred days of the enactment of this Act, at each sub-divisional level or other sub-district level as a Central Assistant Public Information Officer or a State Assistant Public Information Officer, as the case may be, to receive the applications for information or appeals under this Act for forwarding the same forthwith to the Central Public Information Officer or the State Public Information Officer or senior officer specified under sub-section (1) of section 19 or the Central Information Commission or the State Information Commission, as the case may be:

Provided that where an application for information or appeal is given to a Central Assistant Public Information Officer or a State Assistant Public

Information Officer, as the case may be, a period of five days shall be added in computing the period for response specified under sub-section (1) of section 7.

(3) Every Central Public Information Officer or State Public Information Officer, as the case may be, shall deal with requests from persons seeking information and render reasonable assistance to the persons seeking such information.

(4) The Central Public Information Officer or State Public Information Officer, as the case may be, may seek the assistance of any other officer as he or she considers it necessary for the proper discharge of his or her duties.

(5) Any officer, whose assistance has been sought under sub-section (4), shall render all assistance to the Central Public Information Officer or State Public Information Officer, as the case may be, seeking his or her assistance and for the purposes of any contravention of the provisions of this Act, such other officer shall be treated as a Central Public Information Officer or State Public Information Officer, as the case may be.

6. Request for obtaining information.

(1) A person, who desires to obtain any information under this Act, shall make a request in writing or through electronic means in English or Hindi or in the official language of the area in which the application is being made, accompanying such fee as may be prescribed, to—

(a) the Central Public Information Officer or State Public Information Officer, as the case may be, of the concerned public authority;

(b) the Central Assistant Public Information Officer or State Assistant Public Information Officer, as the case may be, specifying the particulars of the information sought by him or her:

Provided that where such request cannot be made in writing, the Central Public Information Officer or State Public Information Officer, as the case may be, shall render all reasonable assistance to the person making the request orally to reduce the same in writing.

(2) An applicant making request for information shall not be required to give any reason for requesting the information or any other personal details except those that may be necessary for contacting him.

(3) Where an application is made to a public authority requesting for an information,—

(i) which is held by another public authority; or

(ii) the subject matter of which is more closely connected with the functions of another public authority,

the public authority, to which such application is made, shall transfer the application or such part of it as may be appropriate to that other public authority and inform the applicant immediately about such transfer:

Provided that the transfer of an application pursuant to this sub-section shall be made as soon as practicable but in no case later than five days from the date of receipt of the application.

7. Disposal of request.

(1) Subject to the proviso to sub-section (2) of section 5 or the proviso to subsection (3) of section 6, the Central Public Information Officer or State Public Information Officer, as the case may be, on receipt of a request undersection 6 shall, as expeditiously as possible, and in any case within thirty days of the receipt of the request, either provide the information on payment of such fee as may be prescribed or reject the request for any of the reasons specified in sections 8 and 9: Provided that where the information sought for concerns the life or liberty of a person, the same shall be provided within forty-eight hours of the receipt of the request.

(2) If the Central Public Information Officer or State Public Information Officer, as the case may be, fails to give decision on the request for information within the period specified under sub-section (1), the Central Public Information Officer or State Public Information Officer, as the case may be, shall be deemed to have refused the request.

(3) Where a decision is taken to provide the information on payment of any further fee representing the cost of providing the information, the Central

Public Information Officer or State Public Information Officer, as the case may be, shall send an intimation to the person making the request, giving—

(a) the details of further fees representing the cost of providing the information as determined by him, together with the calculations made to arrive at the amount in accordance with fee prescribed under subsection (1), requesting him to deposit that fees, and the period intervening between the despatch of the said intimation and payment of fees shall be excluded for the purpose of calculating the period of thirty days referred to in that sub-section;

(b) information concerning his or her right with respect to review the decision as to the amount of fees charged or the form of access provided, including the particulars of the appellate authority, time limit, process and any other forms.

(4) Where access to the record or a part thereof is required to be provided under this Act and the person to whom access is to be provided is sensorily disabled, the Central Public Information Officer or State Public Information Officer, as the case may be, shall provide assistance to enable access to the information, including providing such assistance as may be appropriate for the inspection.

(5) Where access to information is to be provided in the printed or in any electronic format, the applicant shall, subject to the provisions of sub-section (6), pay such fee as may be prescribed:

Provided that the fee prescribed under sub-section (1) of section 6 and sub-sections (1) and (5) of section 7 shall be reasonable and no such fee shall be charged from the persons who are of below poverty line as may be determined by the appropriate Government.

(6) Notwithstanding anything contained in sub-section (5), the person making request for the information shall be provided the information free of charge where a public authority fails to comply with the time limits specified in sub-section (1).

(7) Before taking any decision under sub-section (1), the Central Public

Information Officer or State Public Information Officer, as the case may be, shall take into consideration the representation made by a third party under section 11.

(8) Where a request has been rejected under sub-section (1), the Central Public Information Officer or State Public Information Officer, as the case may be, shall communicate to the person making the request,—

(i) the reasons for such rejection;

(ii) the period within which an appeal against such rejection may be preferred; and

(iii) the particulars of the appellate authority.

(9) An information shall ordinarily be provided in the form in which it is sought unless it would disproportionately divert the resources of the public authority or would be detrimental to the safety or preservation of the record in question.

8. Exemption from disclosure of information.

(1) Notwithstanding anything contained in this Act, there shall be no obligation to give any citizen,—

(a) information, disclosure of which would prejudicially affect the sovereignty and integrity of India, the security, strategic, scientific or economic interests of the State, relation with foreign State or lead to incitement of an offence;

(b) information which has been expressly forbidden to be published by any court of law or tribunal or the disclosure of which may constitute contempt of court;

(c) information, the disclosure of which would cause a breach of privilege of Parliament or the State Legislature;

(d) information including commercial confidence, trade secrets or intellectual property, the disclosure of which would harm the competitive position of a third party, unless the competent authority is satisfied that larger public interest warrants the disclosure of such information;

(e) information available to a person in his fiduciary relationship, unless the competent authority is satisfied that the larger public interest warrants the disclosure of such information;

(f) information received in confidence from foreign Government;

(g) information, the disclosure of which would endanger the life or physical safety of any person or identify the source of information or assistance given in confidence for law enforcement or security purposes;

(h) information which would impede the process of investigation or apprehension or prosecution of offenders;

(i) cabinet papers including records of deliberations of the Council of Ministers, Secretaries and other officers:

Provided that the decisions of Council of Ministers, the reasons thereof, and the material on the basis of which the decisions were taken shall be made public after the decision has been taken, and the matter is complete, or over: Provided further that those matters which come under the exemptions specified in this section shall not be disclosed;

(j) information which relates to personal information the disclosure of which has no relationship to any public activity or interest, or which would cause unwarranted invasion of the privacy of the individual unless the Central Public Information Officer or the State Public Information Officer or the appellate authority, as the case may be, is satisfied that the larger public interest justifies the disclosure of such information:

Provided that the information which cannot be denied to the Parliament or a State Legislature shall not be denied to any person.

(2) Notwithstanding anything in the Official Secrets Act, 1923 nor any of the exemptions permissible in accordance with sub-section (1), a public authority may allow access to information, if public interest in disclosure outweighs the harm to the protected interests.

(3) Subject to the provisions of clauses (a), (c) and (i) of sub-section (1), any information relating to any occurrence, event or matter which has taken place, occurred or happened twenty years before the date on which any request is made under secton 6 shall be provided to any person making a request under that section:

Provided that where any question arises as to the date from which the said period of twenty years has to be computed, the decision of the Central Government shall be final, subject to the usual appeals provided for in this Act.

9. Grounds for rejection to access in certain cases

Without prejudice to the provisions of section 8, a Central Public Information Officer or a State Public Information Officer, as the case may be, may reject a request for information where such a request for providing access would involve an infringement of copyright subsisting in a person other than the State.

10. Severability

(1) Where a request for access to information is rejected on the ground that it is in relation to information which is exempt from disclosure, then, notwithstanding anything contained in this Act, access may be provided to that part of the record which does not contain any information which is exempt from disclosure under this Act and which can reasonably be severed from any part that contains exempt information.

(2) Where access is granted to a part of the record under sub-section (1), the Central Public Information Officer or State Public Information Officer, as the case may be, shall give a notice to the applicant, informing—

(a) that only part of the record requested, after severance of the record containing information which is exempt from disclosure, is being provided;

(b) the reasons for the decision, including any findings on any material question of fact, referring to the material on which those findings were based;

(c) the name and designation of the person giving the decision;

(d) the details of the fees calculated by him or her and the amount of fee which the applicant is required to deposit; and

(e) his or her rights with respect to review of the decision regarding non-disclosure of part of the information, the amount of fee charged or the form of access provided, including the particulars of the senior officer specified under sub-section (1) of section 19 or the Central Information Commission or the State Information Commission, as the case may be, time limit, process and any other form of access.

11. Third party information.

(1) Where a Central Public Information Officer or a State Public Information Officer, as the case may be, intends to disclose any information or record, or part thereof on a request made under this Act, which relates to or has been supplied by a third party and has been treated as confidential by that third party, the Central Public Information Officer or State Public Information Officer, as the case may be, shall, within five days from the receipt of the request, give a written notice to such third party of the request and of the fact that the Central Public Information Officer or State Public Information Officer, as the case may be, intends to disclose the information or record, or part thereof, and invite the third party to make a submission in writing or orally, regarding whether the information should be disclosed, and such submission of the third party shall be kept in view while taking a decision about disclosure of information:

Provided that except in the case of trade or commercial secrets protected by law, disclosure may be allowed if the public interest in disclosure outweighs in importance any possible harm or injury to the interests of such third party.

(2) Where a notice is served by the Central Public Information Officer or State Public Information Officer, as the case may be, under sub-section (1) to a third party in respect of any information or record or part thereof, the third party shall, within ten days from the date of receipt of such notice, be given the opportunity to make representation against the proposed disclosure.

(3) Notwithstanding anything contained in section 7, the Central Public Information Officer or State Public Information Officer, as the case may be, shall, within forty days after receipt of the request under section 6, if the third party has been given an opportunity to make representation under sub-section (2), make a decision as to whether or not to disclose the information or record or part thereof and give in writing the notice of his decision to the third party.

(4) A notice given under sub-section (3) shall include a statement that the third party to whom the notice is given is entitled to prefer an appeal under section 19 against the decision.

CHAPTER III

The Central Information Commission

12. Constitution of Central Information Commission

(1) The Central Government shall, by notification in the Official Gazette, constitute a body to be known as the Central Information Commission to exercise the powers conferred on, and to perform the functions assigned to, it under this Act.

(2) The Central Information Commission shall consist of—

(a) the Chief Information Commissioner; and

(b) such number of Central Information Commissioners, not exceeding ten, as may be deemed necessary.

(3) The Chief Information Commissioner and Information Commissioners shall be appointed by the President on the recommendation of a committee consisting of—

(i) the Prime Minister, who shall be the Chairperson of the committee;

(ii) the Leader of Opposition in the Lok Sabha; and

(iii) a Union Cabinet Minister to be nominated by the Prime Minister.

Explanation.—For the purposes of removal of doubts, it is hereby declared that where the Leader of Opposition in the House of the People has not been recognised as such, the Leader of the single largest group in opposition of the Government in the House of the People shall be deemed to be the Leader of Opposition.

(4) The general superintendence, direction and management of the affairs of the Central Information Commission shall vest in the Chief Information Commissioner who shall be assisted by the Information Commissioners and may exercise all such powers and do all such acts and things which may be exercised or done by the Central Information Commission autonomously without being subjected to directions by any other authority under this Act.

(5) The Chief Information Commissioner and Information Commissioners shall be persons of eminence in public life with wide knowledge and experience in law, science and technology, social service, management, journalism, mass media or administration and governance.

(6) The Chief Information Commissioner or an Information Commissioner shall not be a Member of Parliament or Member of the Legislature of any State or Union territory, as the case may be, or hold any other office of profit or connected with any political party or carrying on any business or pursuing any profession.

(7) The headquarters of the Central Information Commission shall be at Delhi and the Central Information Commission may, with the previous approval of the Central Government, establish offices at other places in India.

13. Term of office and conditions of service.

(1) The Chief Information Commissioner shall hold office for a term of five years from the date on which he enters upon his office and shall not be eligible for reappointment:

Provided that no Chief Information Commissioner shall hold office as such after he has attained the age of sixty-five years.

(2) Every Information Commissioner shall hold office for a term of five years from the date on which he enters upon his office or till he attains the age of sixty-five years, whichever is earlier, and shall not be eligible for reappointment as such Information Commissioner:

Provided that every Information Commissioner shall, on vacating his office under this sub-section be eligible for appointment as the Chief Information Commissioner in the manner specified in sub-section (3) of section 12:

Provided further that where the Information Commissioner is appointed as the Chief Information Commissioner, his term of office shall not be more than five years in aggregate as the Information Commissioner and the Chief Information Commissioner.

(3) The Chief Information Commissioner or an Information Commissioner shall before he enters upon his office make and subscribe before the President or some other person appointed by him in that behalf, an oath or affirmation according to the form set out for the purpose in the First Schedule.

(4) The Chief Information Commissioner or an Information Commissioner may, at any time, by writing under his hand addressed to the President, resign from his office:

Provided that the Chief Information Commissioner or an Information Commissioner may be removed in the manner specified under section 14.

(5) The salaries and allowances payable to and other terms and conditions of service of—

(a) the Chief Information Commissioner shall be the same as that of the Chief Election Commissioner;

(b) an Information Commissioner shall be the same as that of an Election Commissioner:

Provided that if the Chief Information Commissioner or an Information Commissioner, at the time of his appointment is, in receipt of a pension, other than a disability or wound pension, in respect of any previous service under the Government of India or under the Government of a State, his salary in respect of the service as the Chief Information Commissioner or an Information Commissioner shall be reduced by the amount of that pension including any portion of pension which was commuted and pension equivalent of other forms of retirement benefits excluding pension equivalent of retirement gratuity:

Provided further that if the Chief Information Commissioner or an Information Commissioner if, at the time of his appointment is, in receipt of retirement benefits in respect of any previous service rendered in a Corporation established by or under any Central Act or State Act or a Government company owned or controlled by the Central Government or the State Government, his salary in respect of the service as the Chief Information Commissioner or an Information Commissioner shall be reduced by the amount of pension equivalent to the retirement benefits:

Provided also that the salaries, allowances and other conditions of service of the Chief Information Commissioner and the Information Commissioners shall not be varied to their disadvantage after their appointment.

(6) The Central Government shall provide the Chief Information Commissioner and the Information Commissioners with such officers and employees as may be necessary for the efficient performance of their functions under this Act, and the salaries and allowances payable to and the terms and conditions of service of the officers and other employees appointed for the purpose of this Act shall be such as may be prescribed.

14. Removalof Chief Information Commissioner or Information Commissioner.

(1) Subject to the provisions of sub-section (3), the Chief Information Commissioner or any Information Commissioner shall be removed from his office only by order of the President on the ground of proved misbehaviour or incapacity after the Supreme Court, on a reference made to it by the President, has, on inquiry, reported that the Chief Information Commissioner or any Information Commissioner, as the case may be, ought on such ground be removed.

(2) The President may suspend from office, and if deem necessary prohibit also from attending the office during inquiry, the Chief Information

Commissioner or Information Commissioner in respect of whom a reference has been made to the Supreme Court under sub-section (1) until the President has passed orders on receipt of the report of the Supreme Court on such reference.

(3) Notwithstanding anything contained in sub-section (1), the President may by order remove from office the Chief Information Commissioner or any Information Commissioner if the Chief Information Commissioner or a Information Commissioner, as the case may be,—

(a) is adjudged an insolvent; or

(b) has been convicted of an offence which, in the opinion of the President, involves moral turpitude; or

(c) engages during his term of office in any paid employment outside the duties of his office; or

(d) is, in the opinion of the President, unfit to continue in office by reason of infirmity of mind or body; or

(e) has acquired such financial or other interest as is likely to affect prejudicially his functions as the Chief Information Commissioner or a Information Commissioner.

(4) If the Chief Information Commissioner or a Information Commissioner in any way, concerned or interested in any contract or agreement made by or on behalf of the Government of India or participates in any way in the profit thereof or in any benefit or emolument arising therefrom otherwise than as a member and in common with the other members of an incorporated company, he shall, for the purposes of sub-section (1), be deemed to be guilty of misbehavior.

CHAPTER IV

The State Information Commission

15. Constitution of State Information Commission.

(1) Every State Government shall, by notification in the Official Gazette, constitute a body to be known as the .... (name of the State)

Information Commission to exercise the powers conferred on, and to perform the functions assigned to, it under this Act.

(2) The State Information Commission shall consist of—

(a) the State Chief Information Commissioner, and

(b) such number of State Information Commissioners, not exceeding ten, as may be deemed necessary.

(3) The State Chief Information Commissioner and the State Information Commissioners shall be appointed by the Governor on the recommendation of a committee consisting of—

(i) the Chief Minister, who shall be the Chairperson of the committee;

(ii) the Leader of Opposition in the Legislative Assembly; and

(iii) a Cabinet Minister to be nominated by the Chief Minister

Explanation.—For the purposes of removal of doubts, it is hereby declared that where the Leader of Opposition in the Legislative Assembly has not been recognised as such, the Leader of the single largest group in opposition of the Government in the Legislative Assembly shall be deemed to be the Leader of Opposition.

(4) The general superintendence, direction and management of the affairs of the State Information Commission shall vest in the State Chief Information Commissioner who shall be assisted by the State Information Commissioners and may exercise all such powers and do all such acts and things which may be exercised or done by the State Information Commission autonomously without being subjected to directions by any other authority under this Act.

(5) The State Chief Information Commissioner and the State Information Commissioners shall be persons of eminence in public life with wide knowledge and experience in law, science and technology, social service, management, journalism, mass media or administration and governance.

(6) The State Chief Information Commissioner or a State Information Commissioner shall not be a Member of Parliament or Member of the Legislature of any State or Union territory, as the case may be, or hold

any other office of profit or connected with any political party or carrying on any business or pursuing any profession.

(7) The headquarters of the State Information Commission shall be at such place in the State as the State Government may, by notification in the Official Gazette, specify and the State Information Commission may, with the previous approval of the State Government, establish offices at other places in the State.

16. Term of office and conditions of service.

(1) The State Chief Information Commissioner shall hold office for a term of five years from the date on which he enters upon his office and shall not be eligible for reappointment:

Provided that no State Chief Information Commissioner shall hold office as such after he has attained the age of sixty-five years.

(2) Every State Information Commissioner shall hold office for a term of five years from the date on which he enters upon his office or till he attains the age of sixty-five years, whichever is earlier, and shall not be eligible for reappointment as such State Information Commissioner:

Provided that every State Information Commissioner shall, on vacating his office under this sub-section, be eligible for appointment as the State Chief Information Commissioner in the manner specified in sub-section (3) of section 15:

Provided further that where the State Information Commissioner is appointed as the State Chief Information Commissioner, his term of office shall not be more than five years in aggregate as the State Information Commissioner and the State Chief Information Commissioner.

(3) The State Chief Information Commissioner or a State Information Commissioner shall before he enters upon his office make and subscribe before the Governor or some other person appointed by him in that behalf, an oath or affirmation according to the form set out for the purpose in the First Schedule.

(4) The State Chief Information Commissioner or a State Information Commissioner may, at any time, by writing under his hand addressed to

the Governor, resign from his office:

Provided that the State Chief Information Commissioner or a State Information Commissioner may be removed in the manner specified under section 17.

(5) The salaries and allowances payable to and other terms and conditions of service of—

(a) the State Chief Information Commissioner shall be the same as that of an Election Commissioner;

(b) the State Information Commissioner shall be the same as that of the Chief Secretary to the State Government:

Provided that if the State Chief Information Commissioner or a State Information Commissioner, at the time of his appointment is, in receipt of a pension, other than a disability or wound pension, in respect of any previous service under the Government of India or under the Government of a State, his salary in respect of the service as the State Chief Information Commissioner or a State Information Commissioner shall be reduced by the amount of that pension including any portion of pension which was commuted and pension equivalent of other forms of retirement benefits excluding pension equivalent of retirement gratuity:

Provided further that where the State Chief Information Commissioner or a State Information Commissioner if, at the time of his appointment is, in receipt of retirement benefits in respect of any previous service rendered in a Corporation established by or under any Central Act or State Act or a Government company owned or controlled by the Central Government or the State Government, his salary in respect of the service as the State Chief Information Commissioner or the State Information Commissioner shall be reduced by the amount of pension equivalent to the retirement benefits:

Provided also that the salaries, allowances and other conditions of service of the State Chief Information Commissioner and the State

Information Commissioners shall not be varied to their disadvantage after their appointment.

(6) The State Government shall provide the State Chief Information Commissioner and the State Information Commissioners with such officers and employees as may be necessary for the efficient performance of their functions under this Act, and the salaries and allowances payable to and the terms and conditions of service of the officers and other employees appointed for the purpose of this Act shall be such as may be prescribed.

17. Removal of State Chief Information Commissioner or State Information Commissioner

(1) Subject to the provisions of sub-section (3), the State Chief Information Commissioner or a State Information Commissioner shall be removed from his office only by order of the Governor on the ground of proved misbehaviour or incapacity after the Supreme Court, on a reference made to it by the Governor, has on inquiry, reported that the State Chief Information Commissioner or a State Information Commissioner, as the case may be, ought on such ground be removed.

(2) The Governor may suspend from office, and if deem necessary prohibit also from attending the office during inquiry, the State Chief Information Commissioner or a State Information Commissioner in respect of whom a reference has been made to the Supreme Court under sub-section (1) until the Governor has passed orders on receipt of the report of the Supreme Court on such reference.

(3) Notwithstanding anything contained in sub-section (1), the Governor may by order remove from office the State Chief Information Commissioner or a State Information Commissioner if a State Chief Information Commissioner or a State Information Commissioner, as the case may be,—

(a) is adjudged an insolvent; or

(b) has been convicted of an offence which, in the opinion of the Governor, involves moral turpitude; or

(c) engages during his term of office in any paid employment outside the duties of his office; or

(d) is, in the opinion of the Governor, unfit to continue in office by reason of infirmity of mind or body; or

(e) has acquired such financial or other interest as is likely to affect prejudicially his functions as the State Chief Information Commissioner or a State Information Commissioner.

(4) If the State Chief Information Commissioner or a State Information Commissioner in any way, concerned or interested in any contract or agreement made by or on behalf of the Government of the State or participates in any way in the profit thereof or in any benefit or emoluments arising therefrom otherwise than as a member and in common with the other members of an incorporated company, he shall, for the purposes of sub-section (1), be deemed to be guilty of misbehaviour.

CHAPTER V

18. Powers and functions of Information Commissions.

(1) Subject to the provisions of this Act, it shall be the duty of the Central Information Commission or State Information Commission, as the case may be, to receive and inquire into a complaint from any person,—

(a) who has been unable to submit a request to a Central Public Information Officer or State Public Information Officer, as the case may be, either by reason that no such officer has been appointed under this Act, or because the Central Assistant Public Information Officer or State Assistant Public Information Officer, as the case may be, has refused to accept his or her application for information or appeal under this Act for forwarding the same to the Central Public Information Officer or State Public Information Officer or senior officer specified in subsection (1) of section 19 or the Central Information Commission or the State Information Commission, as the case may be;

(b) who has been refused access to any information requested under this Act;

(c) who has not been given a response to a request for information or access to information within the time limit specified under this Act;

(d) who has been required to pay an amount of fee which he or she considers unreasonable;

(e) who believes that he or she has been given incomplete, misleading or false information under this Act; and

(f) in respect of any other matter relating to requesting or obtaining access to records under this Act.

(2) Where the Central Information Commission or State Information Commission, as the case may be, is satisfied that there are reasonable grounds to inquire into the matter, it may initiate an inquiry in respect thereof.

(3) The Central Information Commission or State Information Commission, as the case may be, shall, while inquiring into any matter under this section, have the same powers as are vested in a civil court while trying a suit under the Code of Civil Procedure, 1908, in respect of the following matters, namely:— 5 of 1908

(a) summoning and enforcing the attendance of persons and compel them to give oral or written evidence on oath and to produce the documents or things;

(b) requiring the discovery and inspection of documents;

(c) receiving evidence on affidavit;

(d) requisitioning any public record or copies thereof from any court or office;

(e) issuing summons for examination of witnesses or documents; and

(f) any other matter which may be prescribed.

(4) Notwithstanding anything inconsistent contained in any other Act of Parliament or State Legislature, as the case may be, the Central Information Commission or the State Information Commission, as the case may be, may, during the inquiry of any complaint under this Act, examine any record to which this Act applies which is under the control

of the public authority, and no such record may be withheld from it on any grounds.

19. Appeals

(1) Any person who, does not receive a decision within the time specified in subsection (1) or clause (a) of sub-section (3) of section 7, or is aggrieved by a decision of the Central Public Information Officer or State Public Information Officer, as the case may be, may within thirty days from the expiry of such period or from the receipt of such a decision prefer an appeal to such officer who is senior in rank to the Central Public Information Officer or State Public Information Officer as the case may be, in each public authority:

Provided that such officer may admit the appeal after the expiry of the period of thirty days if he or she is satisfied that the appellant was prevented by sufficient cause from filing the appeal in time.

(2) Where an appeal is preferred against an order made by a Central Public Information Officer or a State Public Information Officer, as the case may be, under section 11 to disclose third party information, the appeal by the concerned third party shall be made within thirty days from the date of the order.

(3) A second appeal against the decision under sub-section (1) shall lie within ninety days from the date on which the decision should have been made or was actually received, with the Central Information Commission or the State Information Commission:

Provided that the Central Information Commission or the State Information Commission, as the case may be, may admit the appeal after the expiry of the period of ninety days if it is satisfied that the appellant was prevented by sufficient cause from filing the appeal in time.

(4) If the decision of the Central Public Information Officer or State Public Information Officer, as the case may be, against which an appeal is preferred relates to information of a third party, the Central Information Commission or State Information Commission, as the case may be, shall give a reasonable opportunity of being heard to that third party.

(5) In any appeal proceedings, the onus to prove that a denial of a request was justified shall be on the Central Public Information Officer or State Public Information Officer, as the case may be, who denied the request.

(6) An appeal under sub-section (1) or sub-section (2) shall be disposed of within thirty days of the receipt of the appeal or within such extended period not exceeding a total of forty-five days from the date of filing thereof, as the case may be, for reasons to be recorded in writing.

(7) The decision of the Central Information Commission or State Information Commission, as the case may be, shall be binding.

(8) In its decision, the Central Information Commission or State Information Commission, as the case may be, has the power to—

(a) require the public authority to take any such steps as may be necessary to secure compliance with the provisions of this Act, including—

(i) by providing access to information, if so requested, in a particular form;

(ii) by appointing a Central Public Information Officer or State Public Information Officer, as the case may be;

(iii) by publishing certain information or categories of information;

(iv) by making necessary changes to its practices in relation to the maintenance, management and destruction of records;

(v) by enhancing the provision of training on the right to information for its officials;

(vi) by providing it with an annual report in compliance with clause (b) of subsection (1) of section 4;

(b) require the public authority to compensate the complainant for any loss or other detriment suffered;

(c) impose any of the penalties provided under this Act;

(d) reject the application.

(9) The Central Information Commission or State Information Commission, as the case may be, shall give notice of its decision, including any right of appeal, to the complainant and the public authority.

(10) The Central Information Commission or State Information Commission, as the case may be, shall decide the appeal in accordance with such procedure as may be prescribed.

20. Penalties

(1) Where the Central Information Commission or the State Information Commission, as the case may be, at the time of deciding any complaint or appeal is of the opinion that the Central Public Information Officer or the State Public Information Officer, as the case may be, has, without any reasonable cause, refused to receive an application for information or has not furnished information within the time specified under sub-section (1) of section 7 or malafidely denied the request for information or knowingly given incorrect, incomplete or misleading information or destroyed information which was the subject of the request or obstructed in any manner in furnishing the information, it shall impose a penalty of two hundred and fifty rupees each day till application is received or information is furnished, so however, the total amount of such penalty shall not exceed twenty-five thousand rupees:

Provided that the Central Public Information Officer or the State Public Information Officer, as the case may be, shall be given a reasonable opportunity of being heard before any penalty is imposed on him:

Provided further that the burden of proving that he acted reasonably and diligently shall be on the Central Public Information Officer or the State Public Information Officer, as the case may be.

(2) Where the Central Information Commission or the State Information Commission, as the case may be, at the time of deciding any complaint or appeal is of the opinion that the Central Public Information Officer or the State Public Information Officer, as the case may be, has, without any reasonable cause and persistently, failed to receive an application for information or has not furnished information within the time specified under subsection (1) of section 7 or malafidely denied the request for information or knowingly given incorrect, incomplete or misleading information or destroyed information which was the subject of the request

or obstructed in any manner in furnishing the information, it shall recommend for disciplinary action against the Central Public Information Officer or the State Public Information Officer, as the case may be, under the service rules applicable to him.

CHAPTER VI

Miscellaneous

21. Protection of action taken in good faith.

No suit, prosecution or other legal proceeding shall lie against any person for anything which is in good faith done or intended to be done under this Act or any rule made thereunder.

22. Act to have overriding effect

The provisions of this Act shall have effect notwithstanding anything inconsistent therewith contained in the Official Secrets Act, 1923, and any other law for the time being in force or in any instrument having effect by virtue of any law other than this Act.

23. Bar of jurisdiction of courts

No court shall entertain any suit, application or other proceeding in respect of any order made under this Act and no such order shall be called in question otherwise than by way of an appeal under this Act.

24. Act not to apply to certain organizations

(1) Nothing contained in this Act shall apply to the intelligence and security organisations specified in the Second Schedule, being organisations established by the Central Government or any information furnished by such organisations to that Government:

Provided that the information pertaining to the allegations of corruption and human rights violations shall not be excluded under this sub-section:

Provided further that in the case of information sought for is in respect of allegations of violation of human rights, the information shall only be provided after the approval of the Central Information Commission, and notwithstanding anything contained in section 7, such information shall be provided within forty-five days from the date of the receipt of request.

(2) The Central Government may, by notification in the Official Gazette, amend the Schedule by including therein any other intelligence or security organisation established by that Government or omitting therefrom any organisation already specified therein and on the publication of such notification, such organisation shall be deemed to be included in or, as the case may be, omitted from the Schedule.

(3) Every notification issued under sub-section (2) shall be laid before each House of Parliament.

(4) Nothing contained in this Act shall apply to such intelligence and security organisation being organisations established by the State Government, as that Government may, from time to time, by notification in the Official Gazette, specify: Provided that the information pertaining to the allegations of corruption and human rights violations shall not be excluded under this sub-section:

Provided further that in the case of information sought for is in respect of allegations of violation of human rights, the information shall only be provided after the approval of the State Information Commission and, notwithstanding anything contained in section 7, such information shall be provided within forty-five days from the date of the receipt of request.

(5) Every notification issued under sub-section (4) shall be laid before the State Legislature.

25. Monitoring and Reporting

(1) The Central Information Commission or State Information Commission, as the case may be, shall, as soon as practicable after the end of each year, prepare a report on the implementation of the provisions of this Act during that year and forward a copy thereof to the appropriate Government.

(2) Each Ministry or Department shall, in relation to the public authorities within their jurisdiction, collect and provide such information to the Central Information Commission or State Information Commission, as the case

may be, as is required to prepare the report under this section and comply with the requirements concerning the furnishing of that information and keeping of records for the purposes of this section.

(3) Each report shall state in respect of the year to which the report relates,—

(a) the number of requests made to each public authority;

(b) the number of decisions where applicants were not entitled to access to the documents pursuant to the requests, the provisions of this Act under which these decisions were made and the number of times such provisions were invoked;

(c) the number of appeals referred to the Central Information Commission or State Information Commission, as the case may be, for review, the nature of the appeals and the outcome of the appeals;

(d) particulars of any disciplinary action taken against any officer in respect of the administration of this Act;

(e) the amount of charges collected by each public authority under this Act;

(f) any facts which indicate an effort by the public authorities to administer and implement the spirit and intention of this Act;

(g) recommendations for reform, including recommendations in respect of the particular public authorities, for the development, improvement, modernisation, reform or amendment to this Act or other legislation or common law or any other matter relevant for operationalising the right to access information.

(4) The Central Government or the State Government, as the case may be, may, as soon as practicable after the end of each year, cause a copy of the report of the Central Information Commission or the State Information Commission, as the case may be, referred to in sub-section (1) to be laid before each House of Parliament or, as the case may be, before each House of the State Legislature, where there are two Houses, and where there is one House of the State Legislature before that House.

(5) If it appears to the Central Information Commission or State Information Commission, as the case may be, that the practice of a public authority in relation to the exercise of its functions under this Act does not conform with the provisions or spirit of this Act, it may give to the authority a recommendation specifying the steps which ought in its opinion to be taken for promoting such conformity.

26. Appropriate Government to prepare programmes

(1) The appropriate Government may, to the extent of availability of financial and other resources,—

(a) develop and organise educational programmes to advance the understanding of the public, in particular of disadvantaged communities as to how to exercise the rights contemplated under this Act;

(b) encourage public authorities to participate in the development and organisation of programmes referred to in clause (a) and to undertake such programmes themselves;

(c) promote timely and effective dissemination of accurate information by public authorities about their activities; and

(d) train Central Public Information Officers or State Public Information Officers, as the case may be, of public authorities and produce relevant training materials for use by the public authorities themselves.

(2) The appropriate Government shall, within eighteen months from the commencement of this Act, compile in its official language a guide containing such information, in an easily comprehensible form and manner, as may reasonably be required by a person who wishes to exercise any right specified in this Act.

(3) The appropriate Government shall, if necessary, update and publish the guidelines referred to in sub-section (2) at regular intervals which shall, in particular and without prejudice to the generality of sub-section (2), include—

(a) the objects of this Act;

(b) the postal and street address, the phone and fax number and, if available, electronic mail address of the Central Public Information Officer or State Public Information Officer, as the case may be, of every public authority appointed under sub-section (1) of section 5;

(c) the manner and the form in which request for access to an information shall be made to a Central Public Information Officer or State Public Information Officer, as the case may be;

(d) the assistance available from and the duties of the Central Public Information Officer or State Public Information Officer, as the case may be, of a public authority under this Act;

(e) the assistance available from the Central Information Commission or State Information Commission, as the case may be;

(f) all remedies in law available regarding an act or failure to act in respect of a right or duty conferred or imposed by this Act including the manner of filing an appeal to the Commission;

(g) the provisions providing for the voluntary disclosure of categories of records in accordance with section 4;

(h) the notices regarding fees to be paid in relation to requests for access to an information; and

(i) any additional regulations or circulars made or issued in relation to obtaining access to an information in accordance with this Act.

(4) The appropriate Government must, if necessary, update and publish the guidelines at regular intervals.

27. Power to make rules by appropriate Government

(1) The appropriate Government may, by notification in the Official Gazette, make rules to carry out the provisions of this Act.

(2) In particular, and without prejudice to the generality of the foregoing power, such rules may provide for all or any of the following matters, namely:—

(a) the cost of the medium or print cost price of the materials to be disseminated under sub-section (4) of section 4;

(b) the fee payable under sub-section (1) of section 6;

(c) the fee payable under sub-sections (1) and (5) of section 7;

(d) the salaries and allowances payable to and the terms and conditions of service of the officers and other employees under sub-section (6) of section 13 and sub-section (6) of section 16;

(e) the procedure to be adopted by the Central Information Commission or State Information Commission, as the case may be, in deciding the appeals under sub-section (10) of section 19; and

(f) any other matter which is required to be, or may be, prescribed.

28. Power to make rules by competent authority.

(1) The competent authority may, by notification in the Official Gazette, make rules to carry out the provisions of this Act.

(2) In particular, and without prejudice to the generality of the foregoing power, such rules may provide for all or any of the following matters, namely:—

(i) the cost of the medium or print cost price of the materials to be disseminated under sub-section (4) of section 4;

(ii) the fee payable under sub-section (1) of section 6;

(iii) the fee payable under sub-section (1) of section 7; and

(iv) any other matter which is required to be, or may be, prescribed

29. Laying of rules.

(1) Every rule made by the Central Government under this Act shall be laid, as soon as may be after it is made, before each House of Parliament, while it is in session, for a total period of thirty days which may be comprised in one session or in two or more successive sessions, and if, before the expiry of the session immediately following the session or the successive sessions aforesaid, both Houses agree in making any modification in the rule or both Houses agree that the rule should not be made, the rule shall thereafter have effect only in such modified form or

be of no effect, as the case may be; so, however, that any such modification or annulment shall be without prejudice to the validity of anything previously done under that rule.

(2) Every rule made under this Act by a State Government shall be laid, as soon as may be after it is notified, before the State Legislature.

30. Power to remove difficulties.

(1) If any difficulty arises in giving effect to the provisions of this Act, the Central Government may, by order published in the Official Gazette, make such provisions not inconsistent with the provisions of this Act as appear to it to be necessary or expedient for removal of the difficulty:

Provided that no such order shall be made after the expiry of a period of two years from the date of the commencement of this Act.

(2) Every order made under this section shall, as soon as may be after it is made, be laid before each House of Parliament.

31. Repeal

The Freedom of Information Act, 2002 is hereby repealed

THE FIRST SCHEDULE

[See sections 13 (3) and 16(3)]

Form of oath or affirmation to be made by the Chief Information Commissioner/the Information Commissioner/the State Chief Information Commissioner/the State Information Commissioner

"I, ..., having been appointed Chief Information Commissioner /Information Commissioner / State Chief Information Commissioner / State Information Commissioner swear in the name of God solemnly affirm that I will bear true faith and allegiance to the Constitution of India as by law established, that I will uphold the sovereignty and integrity of India, that I will duly and faithfully and to the best of my ability, knowledge and judgment perform the duties of my office without fear or favour, affection or ill-will and that I will uphold the Constitution and the laws.".

THE SECOND SCHEDULE

(See section 24)

Intelligence and security organisation established by the Central Government

1. Intelligence Bureau.
2. Research and Analysis Wing of the Cabinet Secretariat.
3. Directorate of Revenue Intelligence.
4. Central Economic Intelligence Bureau.
5. Directorate of Enforcement.
6. Narcotics Control Bureau.
7. Aviation Research Centre.
8. Special Prontier Force.
9. Border Security Force.
10. Central Reserve Police Force.
11. Indo-Tibetan Border Police.
12. Central Industrial Security Force.
13. National Security Guards.
14. Assam Rifles.
15. Special Service Bureau
16. Special Branch (CID), Andaman and Nicobar.
17. The Crime Branch-C.I.D.-CB, Dadra and Nagar Haveli.
18. Special Branch, Lakshadweep Police.

INDEX